A HISTORY OF BIRKBECK COLLEGE
UNIVERSITY OF LONDON
DURING THE SECOND WORLD-WAR
1939-1945

A HISTORY OF BIRKBECK COLLEGE UNIVERSITY OF LONDON DURING THE SECOND WORLD-WAR 1939-1945

Ex Pace Per Bellum In Pacem

BY

E. H. WARMINGTON

M.A. (CANTAB.), F.R.HIST.S.

PROFESSOR OF CLASSICS

(UNIVERSITY OF LONDON)

BIRKBECK COLLEGE

PUBLISHED BY

BIRKBECK COLLEGE, MALET STREET, LONDON, W.C.1

PRINTED IN ENGLAND
BY
J. W. RUDDOCK & SONS LTD, LINCOLN

Harold Gordon Jackson

IN MEMORIAM

HAROLD GORDON JACKSON

MDCCCLXXXVIII — MCML

FVIT ILLE

COLLEGII HVIVS MAGISTER

AB ANNO DOMINI MCMXLIII AD ANNVM MCML

SCIENTIAE STVDIOSVS

IDEM

ARTIVM AMATOR

SALVE ET VALE

AMICE

Contents

Illustrations

Preface

In this book will be found the story of Birkbeck College in the University of London during six years of modern warfare; the object is to afford, first to persons connected in one way or another with the college, and next to a wider range of readers, a true, if incomplete, picture of events, and thus to put on record a piece of academic history ; and the motive for the work was a feeling among people that the fortunes of Birkbeck College, throughout that dreadful time of struggle between nations, were in some ways unlike those of any other school of learning. My decision to tackle such a task was made one day after I had spoken our thoughts to our late Master of the College, Professor Harold Gordon Jackson. In reply to me, first he said that he had long wished such a record to be written; and that a beginning already made had come to nothing because of more pressing needs. Then, with serious intent behind his twinkling eyes and smiling mouth, he asked me whether I would undertake the labour myself. After a short silence, for I had been caught unawares, I gave the answer " Yes " ; and hence rose and grew this history. In the hope that, if I had been able to ask his leave to dedicate it to him, he would not have given the reply " No," I now dedicate it to his memory.

C. Delisle Burns, in *A Short History of Birkbeck College*, sketched his story to the end of the year 1923 ; but of all that befell the college between that year and the present time of writing the tale has not yet been told. Told it must be some time, because the years between 1920 and the summer of 1951 form a well marked period in the growth of the college. Meanwhile the fortunes of one part—the years 1939-1945—of this period need recording without delay, while many memories are still fresh and sound, and in some detail, because no portion of the college's history is worthier of telling than is the stirring theme of this book. In any continuation of Burns' narrative the present work will have no place as it stands now, for it is written in much greater fullness than the "Short History" is ; my narrative is thus not a piece of sequel brought out before its proper time ; it is a special record of the war-years, and, in my opinion, stands in its own right a unity and separate ; although a time should come when its substance may be embodied in a wider history of the college.

Readers of this book will be mostly people who have a deep personal interest in our college ; but very many even of these will not have shared in its life for any great length of time ; further, conditions change with the passing of years ; moreover, there will be other readers whose connection with the college has been little or none. For these, and all people whose relations with us are not regular or long lasting, have been written sentences, paragraphs, and footnotes which state facts about the college but will seem needless to sharers in the life of the college during the time of the war, and to others. Some of the happenings may have been overstressed ; some may have been unduly slighted. Yet, to my mind, men and women who in London partook in the fears and hopes, the worry and relief, the toil and rest, the pains and pleasures—unforgettable to people who lived through them—of those six strange years of hard war, will feel that, of all the contents of this book, most is rightly recalled to mind now, and rescued from the dim half-light of things already partly forgotten, or from the blank darkness of the wholly unknown.

This leads to two things in the shape of this history which call for comment by me if not criticism by my readers. First, the scale of the story brings it into a class of academic narrative in which the recital of events term-by-term is coherent and justifiable through the whole, with some exceptions in the parts. These exceptions, and certain dangers always lurking in a method very like that which we find in such wider histories as present their subject year by year, have led me to leave now and again, without forsaking, any strict order of events. Second, there will be those people having little knowledge and no personal experience of the war, which has made this history what it is ; and further I have some hope that the book will find readers when all who lived during the period of the war are gone. For this reason I have brought in some mention of the main happenings of the war, even when they cannot be said to have had any visible effect, instant or later, on the life of Birkbeck College. Such insertions of this sort as I have made recall the mind to the setting and background of the story at points when these are best not ignored ; they also indicate shortly certain feelings of partakers in the whole story.

This work is based on two kinds of evidence—documents belonging to the college and to persons ; and memories of persons, myself among them, who were inmates of it during the war. Therefore I thank first those members past and present of the college's administrative staff who let me at all times use written material preserved at the college, especially Minutes of its Governors and their Committees, of its Academic Board, of its Students' Union and their Council ; and copies of official letters[1] written by the Secretary. These officers of the college are : the late Professor H. G. Jackson, Master 1943-1950 ; the late G. F. Troup Horne, Secretary of the College and Clerk to the Governors, 1919-1952—Horne also gave me personal details of his experiences and rendered much help, whereas Jackson met his death before he could do either— ; Dr. J. F. Lockwood, successor to Jackson in the Mastership ; and A. J. Caraffi, successor to Horne in the Secretaryship ; I thank also Sir John Maud, Jackson's predecessor, 1939-1943, in the Mastership. Second, I am grateful further to other members of our staffs, especially Heads of Departments, and to past students, and indeed to all persons whose records and memories and, in parts of the narrative, even quoted words, add substance and life to bare facts. Next, with regard to my descriptions, culled from the college's records and others, of the dangers which beset and the harm which was done to the college's area, through attacks by the enemy, I acknowledge most courteous help from our neighbours of Geraldine House, *The Daily Mirror Newspapers Limited*, whose Editorial Manager, H. E. Barkworth, kindly sent me on loan a copy of the booklet *The Call*—

[1] During the war was lost only one set of these, belonging to the period the 1st of May to the 31st of July, 1940.

and the Answer, presented by *The Mirror* to their people who returned from the war. From it I gathered several pieces of useful information ; these and other points of detail were confirmed by P. A. Hicks who was in charge of the Air Raid Precautions at *The Mirror*. I have also added a few things from the work of John Ross, to whom I am obliged for the kindness he showed in allowing me to use a manuscript of his, from which was edited, in an abridged form, by Leonard Dudeney, a booklet on experiences of Wyman and Sons Ltd., during the raids, and bearing the title *War came to New Street Square*. One or two details come from *Fleet Street Blitzkrieg Diary* by Gordon Robbins (Ernest Benn Ltd.). For the map of the college's area given at the end, I owe much help to Professor W. G. East, Head of our Department of Geography after Professor S. W. Wooldridge went to King's College, and to Miss M. Black of the same Department. Of the various material published on the history of the war and used by me, I would mention here the Supplement to the *London Gazette* (38437, 20th Oct.) of 19th October 1948, "Air Operations by Air Defence of Great Britain and Fighter Command in connection with the German Flying Bomb and Rocket Offensives, 1944-45," by Air Chief Marshal Sir Roderic Hill, Vice-Chancellor of London University at the time of the completion of the present work (he died 6th October 1954) ; *The Royal Air Force* 1939-1945, Vol. I, by D. Richards, and Vol. III, by H. St. G. Saunders; and *The Second World War*, by Sir Winston S. Churchill. Again, I record here my thanks to people who gave me clerical help in the construction of this book : Mrs. Howard Mills, of Totteridge ; Miss Enid Ellis, who died not long after she had finished her task ; and her sister, Miss Gwen Ellis, who belongs to our General Office ; and I am grateful to Messrs. J. W. Ruddock and Sons Limited, of Lincoln, who undertook the printing of the volume and bestowed on it their usual skill and care. Last, I thank the Governors of Birkbeck College for their support in providing the costs of production.

E. H. WARMINGTON, M.A., F.R.HIST.SOC.
Professor of Classics
Birkbeck College, Malet Street, London, W.C. 1 1954

CHAPTER ONE

WAITING AND SUSPENSE

SESSION 1938-1939

Foreword

THE fortunes of Birkbeck College, a School in the University of London, during the war of 1939-1945 were but very small movements in a great and deadly struggle of whole peoples ; indeed anyone who puts the picture of the troubles and toils of the college within the background of the war mingles, with something immense, something which in comparison is minute. None the less, any mention of the vastly greater subject with the vastly smaller should never be taken as an unworthy heightening of the smaller part toward the level of the greater whole ; the deeds of even one man or woman are thought worthy of record in the story of an almost world-wide turmoil. The history here to be related, describing a portion of Britain in action during a violent contest, will be found to justify itself.

During the years 1939-1945, Birkbeck College could have gone from its place in London to some other near abode in Britain ; it could have closed its doors altogether. It remained in London, and was closed down for a very short time only ; so that its record over those years is part of London in action. Again, at any time the college's cramped, crowded and shabby buildings might have been wholly destroyed, its inmates mutilated or killed, its busy life brought to a stop ; but none of these things happened. Studious work was indeed hindered and the drab structures with their contents were partly wrecked and ruined ; but the theme of all that follows in this history is the manner in which a college of London's University, having chosen for well considered reasons to face in its own home a period of stress and strain, passed through all its dangers, and survived.

* * * * *

The function of Birkbeck College

The main task of the college, which is not residential, is the provision in the evenings of classes and University life, in two Faculties[1], Arts and Science, of the University of London : (a) for undergraduates engaged on full-time paid work during the day, but desiring to obtain, by working at the college also, a Degree of Bachelor of Arts or Bachelor of Science of the University of London ; and (b) for post-graduates, who, whether occupied (as many are) or not, in other work during the day, are intent on pursuing research for its own sake or with a view to obtaining a Higher Degree of the University. Most of the students at the college are Internal, but a few are External.

The neighbourhood of Birkbeck College before 1941

The area of London in which the college lay can be described as a parallelogram[2] with somewhat twisted sides formed by several highways : Holborn, well to the north of the college, and running west-north-west and east-south-east ; Fleet Street, well to the south and running east and west and west-south-west ; Chancery Lane, to the west and running nearly north-west and south-south-east ; and, to the east, Shoe Lane, running almost from due south to north, and then joining St. Andrew Street running north-west. The area is midsplit by Fetter Lane running roughly north and south ; and by the street Breams Buildings with Nevill's Court, Middle New Street, and Little New Street, running roughly east and west. Birkbeck College was nearly in the centre of this area, and almost at the meeting of the street Breams Buildings with Fetter Lane. Until May, 1941, the college was packed in with other full-sized buildings not only to the north, south and west, but also to the east along both sides of Fetter Lane.

[1] Continuance of a third Faculty, of Laws, ceased after Session 1937-1938, as also of a Department of Music. Instruction in first-year courses in the University's Faculty of Medicine ceased at the college to be separate from its teaching in the Faculty of Science. The college may add instruction in any other Faculty or Faculties into which the college may be admitted by the University.

[2] See map at the end.

There were to be had from the college no views of St. Paul's Cathedral or of the Old Bailey, or of other structures such as became familiar to us in the period from May 1941 and the transfer of the college to Bloomsbury in 1951.

The premises of Birkbeck College

The college had since 1885 occupied premises a little north of the Public Record Office which lies between the highways Holborn and Fleet Street. In its own main building at No. 20 Breams[1] Buildings, were the offices of the Administration, most of the Faculty of Science, the Common and Committee and Council rooms, the Students' Office, the College's Theatre,[2] and the Kitchen and Refectory ; and, in Greystoke Place[3] on the opposite side of the street Breams Buildings, the General Library, the Faculty of Arts (except the Department of Geography, which is common to both Faculties and occupied four rooms rented by the College in Field House,[4] where also the Department of Mathematics used one room), and parts of the Zoology and Botany Departments. Much was closely packed and overthronged, especially in the Faculty of Science, but there were great hopes for the future, because as planned, according to decisions of the college, by Charles Holden, architect of the University, a new building, authorised several years earlier, was about to rise for the college on the University's site at Malet Street in Bloomsbury.

Foreboding and Forethought

During the first part of the year 1938, the world had seen the so-called " Rome-Berlin Axis " become stronger and stronger. Austria had become in March part of Hitler's Reich, and Germany's " Siegfried Line " had been made nearly ready along her western borders. In all Great Britain's millions

[1] I follow the common habit. Strict accuracy would demand Bream's.

[2] A real theatre with stage, arena and lower and upper balconies.

[3] Property of the London County Council, to whom the college paid a nominal rent. To it were transferred the furniture from Buchanan Buildings when these were given up by the college in September 1938.

[4] Owned by the Field Press (1930) Ltd., until April 1944, then by the Hulton Press Ltd.

of people not many persons yet believed that a frightful conflict might well be near ; but there were some in authority who had wisdom to take thought of such a thing. In June a notice from the Corporation of the City of London was sent to Birkbeck College about use of our buildings in the event of war, with reference to Air Raid Precautions ; and about voluntary sharing by members of our staff in the civic services which were then being planned. The college arranged for an Air Raid Precautions Officer to inspect its buildings, but postponed the question about the staff until further knowledge could be obtained ; meanwhile the Corporation was told that, if war came, the normal work of the college would without doubt be suspended ; that all the teaching staff had been invited by the University to offer their services in the various State activities for which they were specially fitted ; and that it was doubtful whether any member of the college would be present in the buildings[1] ; the laboratories would be at the service of the British Government if that were feasible, which was unlikely in view of their central position in London.

The International Crisis of the year 1938. *Preparations*

Not long before the opening of a new Academic Session—that of 1938-1939—on the 26th of September, came the dread danger of war over the demands made by Germany on Czechoslovakia. In the University of London, the Vice-Chancellor informed the Senate, at an extraordinary meeting held on the 28th, that, after a special meeting of the Collegiate Council and others, he had advised the University's Schools and Institutions, except the Medical Schools and Birkbeck College, that they should delay their opening for a week after the advertised day. Teachers who had asked whether their agreements with the University would be prejudiced by their taking service under the Crown, were informed that they would not. On the

[1] The attitude here expressed by the college has two points of interest:—

(i) it illustrates the universal predominance of the idea of air-power in future war ; and

(ii) the actual events after war came were far different from what people had expected.

29th, George Senter, Principal of Birkbeck College, met informally the Heads of the College's Departments of Science, its Dean of the Faculty of Arts, and its Librarian ; and they discussed the position of the staff, graduates and under-graduates of the college and of the University, and measures for protecting the windows of the Library and for other safeguarding of valuable apparatus, books and records. The college resolved to make inventories of valuable property in the different Departments, deposit them in safe keeping, and keep them up to date; if war broke out, arrangements would be made to transfer the property to places freer from danger. It was felt that undergraduate classes must be discontinued, but a College Recruiting Board (consisting of the Principal; the two Deans of Faculties; Professor H. G. Jackson; and Dr. D. Dakin) was resolved on to help the University about graduates (other than such as were teachers of the college) and undergraduates in case of sudden need. For shelter during any air-raids, it was clear that nearby Field House was the largest available building, if the Field Press would allow the college to put it to such use by members of the students and staff. But shortly afterwards followed, on the 30th, the hollow agreement at Munich, between sly Hitler and honest Chamberlain, whereby war was averted but the treatment meted out to Czechoslovakia brought enormous gain to Germany.

Respite. Session 1938-1939

In our mixed feelings of relief and disgust, we hoped, with Chamberlain, that the agreement would bring lasting peace ; but not only had the session 1938-1939 begun in the shadow of the crisis, but also there was a general belief that our Empire had gained merely a respite in which to make preparations for a later outbreak of war; and the work[1] of this whole academic year, including all the usual examinations, was done under an ever stronger feeling of tension. But throughout the session the College performed in normal fashion its usual function.

[1] I omit details since they are not relevant to a history of the college at war.

Growing tension. Plans for dispersal of University Institutions

In the early part of the session, the growing uneasiness all over Europe led to the pursuit of far-reaching policy by the chief authorities of the Universities in Britain. After the dire threat to peace in September 1938, plans were considered for dispersal, should the country be forced into war, of those University institutions which were situated in places believed by the British Government to be open to danger. A single thought above all others dominated the minds of the British ; it was felt that, should war break out, heavy attacks would be made straightway, by day and by night, on London, by German aeroplanes coming from the east and south-east and bringing bombs filled with high explosives and possibly poisonous gas, which would cause fearful loss of life among the civilian people; almost any other part of the country would be safer than London. Early in the year 1939 a deputation of the Committee of Vice-Chancellors and Principals of the Universities in the United Kingdom asked the advice of the Lord Privy Seal as to whether, in the opinion of the British Government, education in Universities should in fact be continued in time of war ; and what Universities, if the Government believed that education should so continue, ought to make special arrangements. The Lord Privy Seal replied that University education should go on ; but that the University of London should arrange to disperse its schools to other parts of Britain, because of the belief that severe air-raids would take place. On receipt of this advice in confidence, the Senate of the University of London decided that, should war break out, the staff of its central administration must leave London, and that Birkbeck College must close[1]. Most of the colleges, schools, institutes and institutions which formed part of the University each now planned to leave in whole or part on the outbreak of war for places[2] decided on by the Committee of Vice-Chancellors and

[1] Because the great majority of its students were engaged in full-time paid work in or near London during the day, and so could not be sent elsewhere in Britain. See pp. 14, 26.

[2] Where a college or colleges of a University, or similar institutions, existed already.

Principals, avoiding thus many a concentration of large groups of people in any one place in an area deemed to be very dangerous.

Germany threatens ; Europe makes ready

The new year 1939 brought nothing to ease dire forebodings except in people who could believe that the best would come. While Hitler hoped to split somewhat listless France from Britain, Chamberlain visited Rome in January in the hope of detaching Italy from Germany, where Hitler now opened a "diplomatic attack" on Poland. In March came the entry of the Germans into Prague, the dissolution of the Czechoslovakian Republic, and the establishment instead of a German "satellite" state on the frontier of Poland, to whom Britain, promptly stiffening in attitude, gave a guarantee. Then Germany seized Memel ; the Russian proposal for a six-power conference was not taken up ; April saw Mussolini's attack on Albania ; the declaration of a German Protectorate over Bohemia and Moravia ; fruitless attempts to achieve a pact of Britain, France and Russia against Germany ; a useless appeal by Roosevelt, President of the United States of America, to both dictators ; British guarantees to Greece and Roumania ; denouncement by Hitler of the Anglo-German naval agreement and of Germany's non-aggression pact with Poland ; and the introduction of conscription in Britain. As spring changed to summer, preparations for war went on over most of Europe ; Germany and Italy were in formal alliance ; further attempts by Britain and France to make some agreement with Russia came to nothing. The general fear, which lay heavy on the mind, lest cities and towns be battered and destroyed by bombs dropped from aeroplanes, was heightened by the effects of dismal rumours about new explosives of frightful power which might be made. Our part of the world was very small, but it lay in London and London is large ; London is our capital city ; London is a sort of heart of Britain. What might happen to London?

Further plans of London University. Action of Birkbeck College and of its Staff

Through the spring and early summer the University of London was planning in detail the organisation and policy of the University in time of war. Early in May, the Academic Board[1] of Birkbeck College was again considering possible activities of the academic staff if the college closed.[2] In view of advice from the University of London stating that, if war came soon, there was a possibility of granting, to such students as were in the final year of their course, a degree without examination ; and, to students preparing for the Intermediate examination, exemption from requirements of this examination, should none be held : lists of candidates with probable decisions were prepared by the college and held in readiness. We wondered whether this summer term at college was to be our last one at least in some sense. Since the college's premises in Breams Buildings were not at this time deemed fit for adaptation for air-raid shelters, and it was felt that, if any persons were present during an air raid, they could best use shelter in Field House, it had been arranged that members of the college could take refuge there. During this summer term, after active negotiations, the tenders for the College's new building from various contractors were considered. When the assets available were seen to be insufficient, severe economies and new financial arrangements were made; estimates proffered by Prestige and Company were approved; and the contract was in July sealed at £155,839[3]. Yet grim forebodings of imminent disaster in the form of war were a growing sickness in the minds of all. In the ordinary run of life this malady was hidden except when it was given outlet in speech or writing ; but ominous signs more striking in character than mere words were not wanting. For example, by February, the students of the college, largely through its branch of the Student

[1] See p. 36.

[2] When war came, teaching in Universities was a reserved occupation ; but this had no effect on the policy of Birkbeck College, as will be seen. We had 938 students at the end of the session.

[3] In comparison with prices of the time of writing (1952-1953), this sum of course seems very small. Moreover, the intended building did not include the fourth floor, which was later added to the building, nor what is now its north-east wing.

Christian Movement, on appeal to our Students' Union for hospitality for "hunted" Germans and Austrians taking refuge in Czechoslovakia from the men who were in authority over their own countries, had collected more than £77, and had found hospitality for more than twenty-two persons ; at the beginning of May the Principal of the college made a confidential statement to the College's Academic Board about proposals for action regarding University teaching in the event of war ; Professor J. D. Bernal, head of the College's Department of Physics, reported to the college that he had been appointed by the Lord Privy Seal to serve on a special commission which was to be entitled the Civil Defence Research Committee ; and it became known in July that Professor Dame Helen Gwynne-Vaughan, Head of the College's Department of Botany, had been appointed by the War Office to be Director, Auxiliary Territorial Service, holding in this the rank of Chief Controller, and had been granted by the Senate of the University leave of absence therefor. Already Lady E. Deller, one of our Governors, and Miss Marjorie Daunt, Reader in our Department of English, were ambulance-drivers. Late in May, the Governors' Library Committee resolved to advise such Heads of Departments as possessed books not kept in the college's general Library that it was a desirable precaution at the present time for volumes of periodicals published before the year 1910 to be kept in the general Library, where not long afterwards the windows were given some protection by a covering of wire netting. It was noted in June that, with the operation of the Militia Act, 1939, the concession of postponement of National Service, granted to full-time students at Universities, did not apply to part-time, that is to say, our evening students. The whole session had been in fact overshadowed by the sombre questions which all people felt or asked—whether war would come ; and if so, when ; but during the summer term it became even clearer that the question "whether" was being blotted out by the question "when."

Closing of Birkbeck College decided on

In July the Governors of the college acted on advice received from the University that the college should be closed if war were to break out ; and therefore resolved, if war came, to close the college, but, as in the war of 1914-1918, and in accordance with the policy which, it was understood, the University proposed to follow, if war again occurred, to pay all due salaries, allowances and emoluments of all the staffs (less what the members might be earning in employment elsewhere[1]) so long as the college received sufficient grant[2] from the Court of the University. There were indeed strong arguments for closing—probable cessation of normal life in London owing to hostilities by air, and therefore the end of studious work also, especially during the hours of evening when Birkbeck College held most of its regular courses ; and expected conscription of most young men over the age of eighteen into the armed forces. Neither of these arguments was proved by later events to be justified ; but in fact the part to be played by the college during war was finally decided by a quite different consideration, and the method of playing it was made inescapable by yet another. Whereas the duty of the college had been made plain by that decision of the Committee of Vice-Chancellors and Principals which advised that education in Universities should continue, the college's special function, among other colleges of the University whose functions were different, made it inevitable that its method of continuing, if it were to continue, should be by staying in London. Now came the one short time when the University and the College, faced with a difficult decision, hesitated in reasonable doubt whether the college could in fact do its duty even by this method ; it appeared that, if war broke out—and war was imminent—organised education and other activities of peace-time would indeed be impossible. As soon as that hesitation had passed, the way was clear, and the duty and the method were both translated into action. For the moment the Governors of Birkbeck College gave instructions to the officers of the college to close the college when hostilities began, and these instructions were

[1] This employment, taken on the assumption that the college would close, did not have to be "National Service" ; in more than one instance of appointments taken at this time by members of the staff, it was not such service.

[2] Sufficient grant from the Court was received throughout the war to come.

to be obeyed after dangerous chemicals had been removed and other precautions had been taken. The college's office alone was to remain open for any necessary business. This was, in a sense, our "zero-hour." While some institutions and departments of the University of London closed altogether, those which had resolved to leave London carried out carefully prepared plans, and were gone : Oxford, Cambridge, Birmingham, Bristol, Sheffield, Nottingham, Manchester, Leeds, St. Andrews, Glasgow, Aberdeen, Cardiff, Swansea, Aberystwyth, Bangor (North Wales), and other places—some of those named here proved to be none too safe—received them as arranged. The headquarters of the University, except the Library and the maintenance department, were transferred to Royal Holloway College, Englefield Green, Egham[1], Surrey. Each unit was destined to have exceptional experiences through going elsewhere ; ours were exceptional because Birkbeck College stayed wholly in central London.

Retirement of George Senter. Appointment of John Maud to be Master

From this time onwards an immense responsibility rested on the wisdom of our Governors and of the two persons who occupied in succession the Headship of the College after the retirement, on the 31st of August, of George Senter, Principal of the College since 1918, whose steady guidance during this uneasy year preceding the outbreak of war was his last active service to the college which he had led so well. On the 1st of September, John P. R. Maud[2] succeeded him as Master[3] of the College, while remaining also a full-time official, first in the Ministry of Home Security, then, from the 1st of November, 1939, in the Ministry of Food.

[1] Whence in 1941 a move was made to Richmond College, Surrey. By the Universities and Colleges (Temporary Provisions) Order, 1939, the University was enabled to make emergency statutes giving special authority to Chairmen of Councils and Committees and to the Vice-Chancellor.

[2] Later Sir John. Made C.B.E. in 1942, K.C.B. in 1946.

[3] Earlier in the year the Governors had expressed a desire to change the title of the college's chief officer from "Principal" to "Master." The Privy Council granted the Governors' request.

Outbreak of War. Birkbeck College closes

Events in Europe now reached and passed their horrid climax. Early in August, attempts by Mussolini to be a mediator failed, and on the 23rd, Germany made a pact of non-aggression with Russia, whereat all the world knew that war was at hand. The British Government at once took all possible measures of precaution, ignoring a chance to back out of their agreement with Poland, offered by Hitler's postponement of assault on that country by one week to the 1st of September. On that day, Hitler attacked Poland, and the British Government put all its fighting forces in readiness. On the 3rd, with Italy's declared neutrality as one of our only comforts, in lovely weather of summer Britain and France found themselves at war with Germany at 11 o'clock in the morning, and in a shocked world a great struggle for life and honour began, a war in which victory was forged in factory and workshop, a war of machines and movement as much as a war of men ; a war with long periods of waiting and watching, and violent bursts of action ; a struggle in which even an academic institution could say that it shared as a sufferer at home if not a fighter in the field. But Birkbeck College was now closed.

CHAPTER TWO

TENSION AND STRAIN

SESSION 1939-1940

The first events of War

CHAMBERLAIN had hardly come to the end of his speech on the wireless to a world-wide audience on the 3rd of September when there was heard in London the horrid long-drawn wail, rising and falling, of an air-raid "alert" as if to confirm one of our greatest anxieties. The alarm was false, and it was followed by the welcome "all clear" sounded musically on its level notes sounded together. Two more alerts, one in darkness on the 4th, the other in daylight on the 5th, likewise led to nothing. Neither in the next days nor months did air raids follow ; neither in France was there any noise of hostile aircraft nor in Britain, except the hum of a few on reconnaissance, and in some raids against the Firth of Forth on the 16th of October, and, during the winter, on our shipping along our east coast ; neither of defensive gunfire, bomb-explosions, falling buildings, nor of suffering humanity. Hitler's method was to concentrate on one thing at once ; the Germans like ourselves feared air-raids ; and our own on Germany consisted, for some time, owing partly to French opinion, in the dropping not of bombs but pamphlets. Moreover Hitler hoped to get Britain out of the war by means other than air-raids. Yet the outlook during the rest of the year 1939 was gloomy enough. Poland fell swiftly to Germany and to Russia which then obtained control of the Baltic States—Estonia, Latvia and Lithuania—and was soon at war with Finland. We rejected a peace-plan of Hitler. Our ships suffered losses, though we thwarted the magnetic mine. The Western Front in Europe waited ; Italy, though neutral, was hostile, Russia hardly neutral and certainly not friendly ; America and Japan were both outside the struggle.[1] At the beginning however of September, owing to the absence of raids, we almost felt that the worst was over, as indeed in one sense it was ; we were no longer awaiting but waging war.

Birkbeck College opens again

In our small academic sphere, while most members of Birkbeck College were away on vacation, welcome decisions were soon made. Though the college was closed, some people were present, and it was confirmed that in any raids they could use the shelter of the Field Press ; and certain new precautions were taken at the college's premises to safeguard books and other property of special value. Among the members of the college in general, it was widely felt that the duty of the college was to play its own part, fight its own battle, and, if need be, take a battering with the rest of London ; among the teaching staff especially there was a very strong opinion that it should re-open at once ; and within a fortnight after the declaration of war, John Maud decided to challenge the ruling which had closed the college. On the 14th of September, at a meeting called to consider the policy of continuing[2] work on our new building at Bloomsbury, he suggested that the college might open forthwith. He further discussed with the London School of Economics the prospects of holding evening classes. The policy of the college was indeed now manifestly indicated by its main function. It is a not residential school of London University ; and the college's chief task is to provide instruction in the evenings to students who have full-time paid occupations during the day-time, and must therefore be able to come swiftly from their business to their college. London itself with Middlesex sent more than half of the students, though many came from other counties nearby. Home County Councils thus had close interests with the college ; Surrey County Council, Middlesex County Council, and above all, London

[1] But in November 1939, America began to help us by introducing the system of war-sales on the basis of "cash and carry."

[2] On the 15th of September the builders were instructed to continue the work of building.

County Council had contributed nobly to its support with special reference to its new building ; so also had the Corporation of the City of London ; only in London could the college perform its proper task ; there were no air-raids ; therefore the college could remain and ought to re-open.

But the College could also, if it re-opened, extend its main function to include another. Whereas it had been expected that conscription into the armed forces would be applied to all men between the ages of eighteen and twenty-five or thirty years, the British Government decided, two days after its declaration of war, not to call up men under the age of twenty. This might increase the number of young persons seeking admission to our college as it certainly did in the case of the day-time institutions which had left London.[1] Many students through lack of means and others who were in reserved categories and had homes in London could not go to their chosen colleges, now in other parts of Britain ; those who were in the reserved categories would be lost to public services if no provision for them were made in London. The Polytechnics did not cater for subjects in Arts. Could Birkbeck College be a day as well as an evening college ? On the 18th of September the teaching staff were informed of the possibility of providing day-time courses. The Master of the college had informal discussions with certain members of the Academic staff of the college, and with members of the Council of our Students' Union. On the 29th of September (four days after the date formerly fixed for beginning a new session) at Connaught Hall (University of London), in Torrington Square, a Students' Residential Hostel of which the Clerk[2] to the Governors of Birkbeck College was the Warden, members of the college's Academic Board met and heard from the Master an explanation why the college had not left London, but had closed ; and why neither of the two reasons for closing (air-raids ; conscription) was justified by events. He confirmed the opinions

[1] The Government also allowed postponement of military service by men over twenty for not more than a year if their intentions were to sit for some examination which would mark a critical stage in the University career.

[2] G. F. Troup Horne, Secretary of Birkbeck College. He died on the 28th January 1953, a few months after retiring from his post at the college.

already held by members of the staff. He stated his belief that the existing situation was a challenge to Birkbeck College, and that there was a pressing need to make preparation at once, by way of experiment, for Intermediate courses by day, and for such evening courses as were likely to receive support. With a view to ascertaining the demand, a series of questions was being circulated to students of the college, asking whether they could attend courses, during the day or the evening, at Birkbeck College or some other college not situated in such a central position. The Academic Board of Birkbeck College was unanimous in its desire that the college should be re-opened as soon as might be until the enemy should make it impossible to continue work ; and appointed a sub-committee consisting of the Master, the two Deans of Faculties, and Professor H. G. Jackson and Professor E. H. Warmington, with power to consult such persons or bodies as might be desirable and to report direct to the Governors on the question of day-courses and, if feasible, evening courses, worthy of education in a University in London in war-time. The sub-committee met, and unanimously recommended that some form of full University education be begun in London forthwith ; it pointed out that although the interests of the existing students of the college should be safeguarded, any holding of evening courses for them in the way which was normal in the college, was doubtful ; for at this time the regulations for London prohibited evening-work of an educational kind within one-and-a-half miles of Leicester Square. There was however some demand for day-classes, especially in Intermediate courses, and this demand at least should be met at once, the numbers admitted to depend on the provision which could be made for protection in air-raids ; probably two hundred and fifty or three hundred students could be taken, and about twenty-five teachers would be required for them. The sub-committee made suggestions about fees ; and recommended to the Governors that full-time day-courses in preparation for a degree of the University in the Faculties of Arts and Science be arranged to begin on Monday, the 23rd of October. On the 4th, letters were sent to other colleges of the University of London suggesting that they might let Birkbeck College have, for day-courses, the names and addresses of such students of these colleges as could not be admitted to them through lack of space, and through other reasons, in the places, away from London, to which the colleges had gone. The University Grants Committee fully supported the proposal to re-open Birkbeck College, and had guaranteed continuance of grants at the present level for a period of six months at least.[1]

On the 5th of October, the Finance and General Purposes Committee of the Governors of Birkbeck College and then the Governors themselves, summoned by telegram, held special meetings at the offices of the Governors' Chairman, and gladly and unanimously confirmed the recommendations of the Academic Board and of its sub-committee, and agreed on the re-opening of the college. The classes would be held during the mornings and afternoons of all days except Saturdays and Sundays. It was decided to adapt space in the main building, in Greystoke Place, and in Field House, for sheltering about three hundred persons in case of raids. With a view to making our policy widely known, the British Broadcasting Corporation, the Ministry of Information, and daily newspapers and weekly publications were asked to help us. Further consultation took place with the University and other bodies concerned. But it was felt to be wrong to leave our normal kind of students, engaged in paid occupations during the mornings and afternoons, unprovided for; and indeed there were appeals coming in from existing students of the college. All the possibilities of opening in the evenings also were again carefully considered, and the Academic Board's sub-committee was able at last to recommend the opening of the college for evening classes also on the 30th of October. These classes would be held, according to the custom of the college, on all days except Saturdays and Sundays.[2] On the 20th of October an announcement was made by the Broadcasting Corporation. The Master met, on the 22nd, members of the Council of the college's Students' Union

[1] The Treasury's guarantee extended thus far only, but there was no difficulty in this matter throughout the war.

[2] The possibility of using the daylight and evening hours of Saturdays and Sundays was considered by some people, but was not pursued.

at Connaught Hall, and found heartfelt support. The numbers of students which the college could admit was limited by such sheltering from air-raids as could be provided in the main building and in Greystoke Place (through the able services of the contractors, Messrs. G. and L. Bray, who worked day and night in the week preceding the opening), and in Field House. The air-raid precautions, when they were completed, consisted, in the main building, of the adaptation of the Senior Common Room (the teaching-Staff Common Room) to the further function of an air-raid shelter, by the provision of quadrangular wooden columns stretching from floor to ceiling[1] ; massing of sandbags at the pavement-lights, the lower windows, and the entrance of the building ; and provision of an emergency exit ; in Greystoke Place, provision of another shelter ; and in Field House, by arrangement with the landlords, of a third ; moreover, fixing of efficient "black-out" material through all the premises, so that, after dark, no speck of light inside the buildings could be seen from outside ; the formation, from the staffs, of four fire-fighting squads[2] of six persons each equipped with the required apparatus (including Civilian Duty Respirators since these allowed much greater freedom of movement than ordinary gas masks), and organised by Dr. H. Henderson, with the help of Dr. D. Dakin, K. Wilson and others ; and the establishment of a First Aid Post in the office of our Students' Union.

With the goodwill of the scattered day-colleges, Birkbeck College opened its 117th session, for day-students on Monday, the 23rd of October (at fees based on those charged at Queen Mary College, it being understood that any existing students of Birkbeck College would be allowed to enter for the day-courses if they were able to do so and chose to do so, at the usual fees), additional time-tables having been prepared accordingly ; and for evening students on the 30th of October. The hours for

[1] Requisite timber for this and other purposes connected with air-raid precautions was obtained after some difficulty. After the war, the baulks which had formed the columns were used to make new benches in the laboratory of the Department of Physics.

[2] There was as yet no such system of night-time fire-watching as was created later when it was required.

day-courses were 9.30 to 4, for evening-courses 5.30 to 8.30. In the Faculty of Science the evening-courses would be for post-intermediate students, but, in the Faculty of Arts, for both intermediate and post-intermediate work. Before our opening, the Imperial College of Science and Technology was was also open at South Kensington for courses for students in their second, third or fourth year, and for post-graduate students ; but had asked Birkbeck College to receive some of its first year students, who had not been able to make suitable arrangements elsewhere. Birkbeck College willingly accepted them. The opening of our college had a wider effect also. In the earlier days of this autumn, when it seemed likely that there would not be any University-teaching in London, a number of students who would otherwise have gone to some college had decided to register as external students of the University instead of internal ; whereupon the University had resumed its Advisory Service for external students. But when Birkbeck College opened for day students as well as evening students, and when moreover Polytechnics also opened, many difficulties of students who had been unable to leave London were solved, and this Advisory Service was then largely employed in helping European refugees seeking advice about continuing the studies which they had abandoned in their own country. Early in October the University declared that internal students could receive a Degree after two years' study instead of the usual three years of attendance, if they produced evidence of National Service or were recommended by their school or college.

Thus the college was in full action during the hours of daylight as well as at evening-time, and had thus added to its tasks the duties of a day-college. It could take pride amongst the institutions of London University because it was doing more work in war-time than it had done in peace ; but it must be remembered that the college was not faced with some entirely different problems successfully solved by those institutions which had left London. Nor must it be forgotten that there was still academic teaching in Arts, or Science, or both, and in other Faculties, in other institutions of London University which were not away from London. Prominent among these were some Schools of the University :—Imperial College of Science as indicated above ; Royal Holloway College, which remained at Englefield Green not far outside the London area ; the London School of Economics and Political Science (evening classes only) ; New College ; and, on the outskirts, Richmond College. However, it was Birkbeck College alone which was now open in the area of London in two whole Faculties of Arts and Science ; it was this college which was able to provide during the war full courses for Degrees in arts subjects, as well as science subjects whose direct usefulness in the war kept them freer from the severe restrictions put upon the study of arts subjects. This was possible only because our students were engaged, when they were not at the college, on other work necessary for the nation.

Patrons and Officers of the College, October, 1939. Students' Societies and Clubs

The following lists of the governing, administrative, and teaching staffs of the college, and list of the students' societies, present the basis on which, with the indispensable services of an establishment staff also, the college now carried on its work.

Patrons and Officers, October, 1939

Patrons

His Most Gracious Majesty King George VI
Her Most Gracious Majesty the Queen
Her Majesty Queen Mary

Presidency

(Vacant)

Vice-Presidents

Sir W. Collins, K.C.V.O., M.D., M.S., B.SC., F.R.C.S., D.L., J.P.
The Right Honourable The Lord Mayor of London
Ada Crosby, M.B.E.
The Viscountess Rhondda

Governors

(* indicates Member of the Finance and General Purposes Committee)

The President, *ex officio*
*The Master, J. P. R. Maud, *ex officio*

Representative Governors

(*a*) *Of the University of London*

The Vice-Chancellor of the University—Prof. F. Horton, SC.D., D.SC., M.SC., F.R.S.
W. H. Coates, LL.B., B.SC., PH.D.
Prof. G. F. J. Temple, D.SC., PH.D.
The Right Honourable Lord Stamp of Shortlands, G.C.B., G.B.E., D.SC., SC.D., LL.D., F.C.I.S., F.B.A.

(*b*) *Of the London County Council*

*Lady E. Deller
*E. G. M. Fletcher, B.A., LL.D.
Mrs. S. B. Samuels, B.SC.
*H. S. Mount Somerby

(*c*) *Of the City Parochial Foundation*

*The Dowager Viscountess Harcourt, G.B.E., J.P.

(*d*) *Of the Academic Board of the College*[1]

*Prof. Dame Helen Gwynne-Vaughan, G.B.E., LL.D., D.SC., F.L.S.
Prof. E. H. Warmington, M.A., F.R.HIST.SOC.

(*e*) *Of the Corporation of the City of London*

*A. King-Hamilton

(*f*) *Of the Court of Electors of the College*[2]

*A. L. Bostock, LL.B.
O. W. Moss, M.SC.
Prof. S. Sugden, D.SC., A.R.C.SC., A.I.C., F.R.S.
*W. R. Wooldridge, M.SC., PH.D.

(*g*) *Of the Students' Union of the College*

Lena M. Chivers (President of the Union)
L. P. Huggett, B.SC., A.I.C.

Co-optative[3] *Governors*

*W. L. Hichens (Chairman of the Governors)
The Right Honourable Lord Justice Sir H. Slesser, P.C., J.P.
(*One vacancy*)

[1] See page 36. [2] See page 36.
[3] This word is looked upon by some people as one of our special treasures.

*E. J. Syer (Deputy Chairman of the Governors and Chairman of its Finance and General Purposes Committee).
*N. Rees, B.SC.

Staff

A. Administrative

Master : J. P. R. Maud, M.A.

Clerk to the Governors and Secretary to the College : G. F. Troup Horne, B.A.

Clerical Staff : Principal Clerks : S. H. W. Eames, M.C.
W. O. M. Gibson

Assistant Clerks : T. S. Jackson, Kathleen L. Lake.

Secretary to the Master : Hilda A. R. Keet, B.A.

Clerk to the Secretary of the College : Renée K. Suffield.

Library Staff

Librarian : Margaret Clive Hildyard, B.A., PH.D.

Assistant Librarian : Norah H. Evans, B.A., F.L.A.

Junior Assistant Librarian : Kathleen I. Garrett, M.A.

B. Academic

The Master

Faculty of Arts

(Dean : Professor J. R. Sutherland)

Classics and Ancient History
E. H. Warmington, M.A., F.R.HIST.SOC. Professor. Head.
R. P. Winnington-Ingram, M.A. Reader.
A. G. Way, M.A. Part-time Lecturer.

English Language and Literature
J. R. Sutherland, M.A., B.LITT. Professor. Head.
B. Marjorie Daunt, Final Eng. Hons. Oxford. Reader.
Charlotte R. D. Macdonald, M.A. Part-time Lecturer.

French Language and Literature
F. J. Tanquerey, D. ès L., O.A. Professor. Head.
Claudine I. Wilson, M.A., PH.D., Reader. Acting Head.
Marjorie Gould, B.A. Part-time Lecturer.
Alice Aubry, L. ès L., PH.D. Lecturer.

German Language and Literature
R. J. McClean, M.A., PH.D. Reader. Head.
W. D. Robson-Scott, M.A., PH.D. Lecturer.

Italian Language and Literature
A. Crespi, DOTT.LETT. Part-time Lecturer. Head.

History

A. Jones, M.A., F.R.HIST.SOC. Reader. Head.
W. P. Morrell, M.A., D.PHIL. Reader.
D. Dakin, M.A., PH.D. Lecturer.

Logic, Philosophy and Ethics

C. E. M. Joad, M.A., D.LIT. Part-time Lecturer. Head.
T. Greenwood, M.A., L. ès L., O.I. Part-time Lecturer.
Ruth Saw, B.A., PH.D. Part-time Lecturer.

Economics

J. K. Horsefield, B.A. Part-time Lecturer. Head.
Ellen S. Haines, B.A., B.COM. Part-time Lecturer.

Geography (*Also in the Faculty of Science*)

Eva G. R. Taylor, D.SC. Professor. Head.
H. C. K. Henderson, M.A., B.SC., PH.D. Lecturer.
A. C. O'Dell, M.SC. Lecturer.
E. C. Willatts, B.SC., PH.D. Part-time Lecturer.

Faculty of Science
(Dean : Professor W. Wardlaw)

Mathematics (*Also in the Faculty of Arts*)

E. H. Smart, M.A. Lecturer, Head.
P. Dienes, D.PH., D. ès SC. Reader.
C. Fox, M.A., D.SC. Lecturer.
R. G. Cooke, D.SC. Lecturer.
A. E. Ball, B.A. Part-time Lecturer.
F. W. Land, M.SC., PH.D. Part-time Lecturer.

Physics

J. D. Bernal, M.A., F.R.S. Professor. Head.
L. Simons, D.SC., F.INST.P. Reader. Acting Head.
H. R. Nettleton, D.SC. Lecturer.
H. J. J. Braddick, PH.D. Lecturer.
R. E. Siday, B.SC. Lecturer.

Chemistry

F. Barrow, M.SC., PH.D. } Joint Heads.
W. Wardlaw, D.SC., F.I.C. Professor. }
F. J. Thorneycroft, B.SC., M.SC., PH.D. Lecturer.
A. J. E. Welch, B.SC., PH.D., A.R.C.SC. Lecturer.
D. J. G. Ives, B.SC., PH.D., A.R.C.SC. Lecturer.

Botany

Dame Helen Gwynne-Vaughan, G.B.E., LL.D., D.SC., F.L.S. Professor. Head.
F. C. Steward, M.SC., PH.D., D.SC. Reader. Acting Head.
K. Wilson, M.SC. Lecturer.
Mrs. Q. E. Broadhead, M.SC. Lecturer.

G. Taylor, D.SC. Lecturer.
F. W. Jane, B.SC., PH.D. Assistant Lecturer.

Zoology
H. G. Jackson, D.SC., F.Z.S. Professor. Head.
A. Graham, M.A., B.SC. Reader.
Lilian Russell, B.SC., M.SC., F.Z.S. Lecturer.
Vera Fretter, B.SC., PH.D. Part-time Lecturer.

Geology
G. M. Davies, M.SC., F.G.S. Reader. Head.
L. F. Spath, D.SC., F.G.S. Part-time Lecturer.
F. Smithson, B.SC., PH.D., F.G.S. Part-time Lecturer.

Academic Board

The Academic Board was composed of the Master, the Professors, full-time Heads of Departments, and such other members of the teaching staff[1] as might from time to time be prescribed in by-laws.

Students

Court of Electors. The primary object now is to provide a means whereby former students who have graduated may retain their association with the College ; its original function was to elect representative governors. *Members :* the Governors, some former Governors ; such members of the college as are also life-members of it ; and some benefactors of the college admitted by the Governors.

Friends of Birkbeck. Founded in 1924, under the presidency of the Right Honourable J. Ramsay Macdonald ; in 1931 reconstituted, the main object being to collect funds for new buildings. There were in 1938-1939 about 3,536 Friends, mostly past and present members of the college.

Students' Union. All matriculated students taking a course for any degree or diploma, or doing any postgraduate work. There is no fee for membership of the Union. Other students can belong to it if approved and on payment of a fee.

[1] During 1943 a by-law defined "other members of the teaching staff" as all part-time Heads of Departments, all Readers, and four representatives of the Junior teaching staff—two from each Faculty.

Societies and Clubs
(Any and all are open to all members of the Students' Union without subscription).
Societies: Natural History, Physics, Chemical, Classical, Literary, French (Société Française), German (Deutscher Verein), Geographical, Historical, Catholic, Birkbeck Peace, Birkbeck International, Birkbeck Players, Birkbeck Student Christian Movement, University of London Animal Welfare Society (Birkbeck Branch.)
Clubs: Athletics, Cricket, Association Football, Rugby Football, Men's Hockey, Women's Hockey, Netball, Lawn Tennis, Rifle.

University of London Officers' Training Corps

The College's Company—G. Infantry Battalion—ceased its activities after the outbreak of war because the University's contingent was suspended.

Athletic Ground

The College has about eighteen acres at Greenford, Middlesex. The freeholders are the City Parochial Council which helped us in meeting the costs of the pavilion completed in the year 1928 for our use ; and contributed to its rescue, when a subsidence took place early in 1943.

Numbers of the students and of the staff were doing service locally at their homes or elsewhere as air-raid wardens or in other voluntary duties. The following members of all grades of staff were doing more extensive national service but were not all wholly seconded from the college. [1](i) On Government Service or in the fighting forces : Professor Dame Helen Gwynne-Vaughan,* Prof. J. D. Bernal,* L. Simons, Miss R. Suffield, Miss R. Bateman, A. G. Atkinson, F. J. Neale, A. Hamilton, A. Jenkins, R. W. Marsh, A. T. Jackson, J. Baylie, S. Baker ; (ii) On civilian service directly connected with war-work : John Maud, C. Fox, W. Morrell, W. Robson-Scott,* Miss M. Daunt. (iii) On civilian duties not connected with war-work : Prof. F. Tanquerey,* Dr. V. Fretter,* A. Ball. (iv) Abroad : T. Greenwood* (in the United States for teaching and research).

[1] * after the name of a teacher indicates total secondment.

Beginning of the new Session

The classes at Birkbeck College were attended by keen and spirited students, numbering by mid-November, at day-courses, 21 in the Faculty of Arts, 64 in the Faculty of Science, at evening-courses, 73 in Arts, 101 in Science ; included in their number were people employed by firms whose main business was carried on near the college. A Freshers' Social, held on the 4th of November, was more successful than a similar one held in 1938. Although the number of students enrolled was only a portion of the normal[1] at the beginning of a session, the number of lectures being given was much increased by duplication for day-students.[2] This placed added burdens on the teaching staff on the working days, Mondays to Fridays inclusive, but other feelings gave way to pleasure at being able to do one's work in spite of past fears ; moreover the many difficulties of the students were overcome by the efforts of all the staffs acting as one.

Public lectures

Under the conditions which prevailed in Great Britain during the first year (and especially the first autumn and the first winter) of the war, it was felt that Birkbeck College should if possible play a wider part than usual in the general life of the people. An obvious lack in London was public lectures of an academic kind, since the other colleges and schools and the headquarters of the University had withdrawn from the city ; lectures having some broader appeal also were not to be despised ; the public in the neighbourhood of the college was certain to be interested, especially in subjects having some bearing on the times in which the nation was then living. Thus

[1] Apart from anything else, a large proportion of our students were teachers in schools, and teachers had been dispersed from London by the scheme of evacuation, as had also the staffs of various offices and firms. In the University taken as a whole, the numbers of students in some Faculties such as the Faculties of Science, Engineering and Medicine, tended to remain high because more and more persons trained in these Faculties were wanted for the varied war-efforts of the nation.

[2] After discussions began with King's College (University of London), early in November, it was decided to bring thence to Birkbeck College the subjects Psychology and Spanish ; and courses in Spanish began at Birkbeck College before the first term of this session ended. See below, pp. 40-41.

it came about that, during the first term, began the delivery at the college of public lectures which became throughout the period of the war a welcome means of keeping active, not only within the membership of the college, but also among people outside it, interest and knowledge in various subjects of life and learning. The Hon. Harold Nicolson, C.M.G., M.P., Professor J. B. S. Haldane, F.R.S., and Dr. C. Joad, Head of the College's Department of Logic, Philosophy and Ethics, were invited to give at Birkbeck College, during the luncheon-hour, lectures on themes of their choice. Harold Nicolson gave four lectures on "The Background of the War" with special reference to Hitler's opportunities, successes and policy ; Professor Haldane three on "Science in Modern War" (Explosives, Gases and War-Hygiene) ; and Dr. Joad four on "Progress, its Fate and Prospects." The success of these lectures was greater than we had expected. For the first an ordinary room was held ready, but some time before the time of beginning it was clear that only the college's Theatre could take in the many people. To the Theatre therefore were the lectures transferred. Not only did the audiences vary between four hundred and nine hundred and more, but on more than one occasion people who came late failed to obtain entry—more than one hundred were turned away from Harold Nicolson's third lecture (Hitler's Policy and Theory of Appeasement).

Finance

During this term the Finance Committee of the Governors of the College followed a wise and careful policy in view of an uncertain future. It felt that the college must practise all possible economy, and took suitable action to this end, with special reference to the Library and to expenditure by Departments on maintenance. When the University asked the college to revise its estimates, the Governors found means to reduce these by about £5,000 for the session 1939-40. The reduction would hold good during the whole period of the war. To this act the Court of the University replied on the 9th of December 1939, expressing its grateful acceptance of what had been done, and its warm appreciation of the work being performed by the college. The term ended on the 16th of December.

The second term

The calendar year 1939[1] ended without disturbance from what was to be called the "waiting war." But early in 1940 Hitler's plans for invading Holland, Belgium and France had been formed; Britain prepared vigorously, France less so. In March, Russia and Finland made peace, but in April Hitler mastered Denmark and Norway, and our own Norwegian campaign fared ill. Thus early in the new year 1940 our second term (8th January—16th March) of the session opened in quietness indeed but with some foreboding of what spring and summer might bring. The number of students attending was now more than 440, of whom more than 120 were taking day-courses. A number of students working to become Bachelors of Science with the Special Degree in Science were obtaining permission to complete their subsidiary subject ; if successful in this part of the examination they might be allowed postponement of military service till June 1941, when they could take the main Final examination ; a number of students had their call-up to National Service postponed now in order to take an examination in the summer of 1940.

Psychology and Spanish from King's College

Very important additions were now being made to our teaching activities according to decisions taken in November 1939. (i) In the Department of Psychology of King's College, then at Bristol, there were, when war broke out, students resident in London whose studies in Psychology were still unfinished and for whom no classes could be provided at Bristol. Courses, on an intercollegiate basis with King's College, in General Psychology and Experimental Psychology were begun in the evenings of the second term by Professor F. Aveling, M.C., D.Lit., D.D., and R. J. Bartlett (both on the staff of King's College) in both Faculties at Birkbeck College, though

[1] For students' activities see below.

the students remained registered as students of King's College. This, of course, did not hinder the new subject from being a help to our own Department of Philosophy. (ii) The evening classes in Spanish at King's College could not continue in Bristol; and courses begun late in the first term at Birkbeck College were now further established, on an intercollegiate basis with King's College, by J. R. Carey (as supervisor), Janet Perry, and Señor D. R. M. Nadal, all on the staff of King's College, by arrangement with Professor A. Pastor, Head of the Department of Spanish there. Thus were added to Birkbeck College two new subjects of which both[1] later became departments of the college, that of Psychology reaching a height of importance and numbers (and of position and space in the college's new building) not contemplated at this time.

Hebrew; Proficiency in English; Map-reading; other projects. Departmental changes

Besides these, following a suggestion made in November 1939, facilities for the study of Hebrew were provided, on an intercollegiate basis with University College, at Birkbeck, on behalf, in the first instance, of one student of University College (which had removed to Wales) by Dr. S. Stein of the staff of that college. Furthermore a course for the Certificate of Proficiency in English was begun (it was repeated until the end of session 1943-1944) in our Department of English, by Miss Marjorie Daunt, for foreign students. The course included both written and spoken English; and in connection with it were courses for English-speaking students requiring training for teaching English to foreigners by the most modern methods. Information about these courses was sent to Embassies and Legations as follows: French, Italian, Spanish, Portuguese, Swedish, Danish, Norwegian, Swiss, Yugo-Slavian, Greek, Polish, Latvian, Netherlands, Roumanian, Hungarian, Egyptian, Saudi-Arabian, Turkish, Chinese and Japanese. The classes began informally before they were recognised. The first applicant was a Japanese girl who had intended to approach University College; soon came three Spanish priests, then several Chinese

[1] See pages 133-134, 167, 169.

people, and before long, exiles belonging to various other nations. A number of other students of other colleges in various other subjects also were enabled to continue and finish their courses at Birkbeck instead. In January 1940, the college submitted to the War Department of the British Government suggestions from our Department of Geography for instruction in map-reading for officers ; the War Department took advantage of this, and six day-time courses were arranged in the first instance through Brigadier-General L. A. Hawes, Eastern Command. Each course lasted for two weeks and was given to officers of the Eastern Command daily (except Saturdays and Sundays) from 9.30 to 4.30 by Professor Eva Taylor, Dr. Henderson and Mr. O'Dell. A further series broke down with the fall of France because the Eastern Command could not spare any officers. In the courses delivered, the object was to give officers the best possible knowledge of European maps, and each lecture was followed by a "practical," in which officers were taught to "read" large-scale maps as well as to "spell" them, and each officer was given a type-script manual. Among the testimonials which were received later, was one from an officer who after landing in Norway said that because of the teaching he had received at Birkbeck College he was able to grasp the nature of the terrain before going into the field. The college also said that, if the War Office should desire courses in Military Studies at Universities to replace courses, at other institutions, which had been suspended because of war, the college would do all in its power to help. On advice from the Government lectures to a small class were begun in the Department of Physics by a student demonstrator, E. P. George, on Radio-Communications[1], a subject which belongs properly to Electrical Engineering. Some special and secret work of national service for the Chemical Defence Research Department, Ministry of Supply, was being done by Professor Wardlaw and Dr. Ives in the College's Department of Chemistry. In the Department of German, Dr. Johanna Hamilton was appointed to fill the gap created by

[1] See below, pp. 76, 82, 83.

the seconding of Dr. W. Robson-Scott to the Censor's Department of the War Office ; in History, Dr. D. Dakin gave up his work because he was appointed by the British Council to be Director of Studies, British Institute in Rome, becoming later an officer in the Royal Air Force. A. V. Judges, of the London School of Economics, took over part of Dakin's work.

The study of Art. Public lectures

Another permanent feature of the college was destined to arise out of a series of six lectures (intended primarily for students, to broaden their outlook, but open to the public also) given, in concert with the Courtauld Institute of Art, by Dr. N. Pevsner[1] in the early evenings—a convenient time for our students—on "The Relation of Art to the History and Literature of Europe" and ranging from the eras of ancient Greece to the nineteenth century of modern times. In further co-operation with the Courtauld Institute, lunch-hour lectures on "The Enjoyment of Works of Art" were given by its Director, Professor T. S. R. Boase ("Pictorial Art"), Dr. Pevsner in place of G. F. Webb, then Slade Professor of Fine Art in the University of Cambridge ("Architecture"), Sir Eric Maclagan, C.B.E., Director of the Victoria and Albert Museum ("Sculpture"), and Desmond McCarthy, F.R.S., LL.D. ("Drama"). Four public lectures were given by Kingsley Martin (Editor of the *New Statesman and Nation*) on "The Technique of Propaganda" ; two by the Rt. Honourable L. S. Amery, M.P., on "The Strategy of War" ; and two by Admiral Sir Herbert Richmond, K.C.B., Master of Downing College, Cambridge, on "The War at Sea."

Musical Concerts

Of special interest was a series of musical concerts organised by Jean Hamilton (Mrs., later Lady Maud, wife of the

[1] Already a leading authority, he was not yet a member of our staff, but became one later and ultimately also Slade Professor of Fine Art in the University of Cambridge. Dr. Pevsner's interest was in a subject not yet taught at Birkbeck College—the history and criticism of Art. Art itself had ceased to be taught at the college in 1914.

Master of the College) with the help of Myra Hess, C.B.E.[1] and given in the second term during lunch-hours in the College's Theatre; which, in spite of the great success of Myra Hess' own inaugural recital, were not followed by further series because the size of the audience did not justify the project[2]. The concerts were intended for people working in the neighbourhood of Holborn, Fleet Street, and the Law Courts, and for others also whose duties made it impossible for them to attend the concerts in the National Gallery. The college's were: a pianoforte recital by Myra Hess; chamber music by the Menges String Quartet (Isolde Menges, J. Y. Dyer, Beatrice Carrelle, I. James); vocal music by the Fleet Street Choir, conducted by T. B. Lawrence; a concert of two violins (Jelly d'Aranyi and Adila Fachiri) and pianoforte (J. Sherrin); a vocal recital by Keith Faulkner (accompanied by Christabel Fullard); a trio recital (Kathleen Long, pianoforte; Eda Kersey, violin; J. Whitehead, violoncello); a programme of Bach (Elsie Suddaby, soprano; Eric Greene, tenor; J. Francis, flute; Jean Hamilton, pianoforte); a piano recital by Louis Kentner; and a vocal recital by the New English Singers (director, C. Kelly). The hospitality offered to the players and singers, as also to all public lecturers and many other people invited from outside the college, was, so far as possible, maintained at a high level,[3] as it was even in some later leaner years, through the culinary knowledge and skill and gastronomic dexterity, in vittles not forming staple diet, of that acknowledged master of taste in food and drink—G. F. Troup Horne.

Activities of the Students

During these two terms of 1939-1940 the students in their Union had, after some early difficulties, adjusted themselves

[1] Dame Myra Hess since 1941.

[2] The College was not so well placed for drawing large musical audiences as is the National Gallery where lunch-hour concerts were likewise begun and organised in 1939 by Myra Hess.

[3] The college had long been well spoken of because of its cookery for entertainment. When Winifred Bruce, a former member of our refectory staff, left the college to go to the University's headquarters and became permanently Catering Manageress there, the college felt gratified at her promotion; when she was awarded a B.E.M. in 1945, the college took some pride in the matter.

successfully to the changed conditions, under the able presidency of Lena Chivers, who, with L. P. Huggett, represented the Students on the Governing Body of the College. The usual gatherings took place, including Council Meetings and General Meetings as during the whole war, the Freshers' Social, other socials, a Christmas party, film-shows, dances and debates. Close touch was maintained with the National Union of Students, especially in this session with regard to students in straitened conditions arising from the war. Men's athletic clubs were able to continue, but women's lapsed because those who wished to partake in them were too few. The new Music Society was inaugurated by a pianoforte recital by the Master's wife, Jean Hamilton, in the first term, and was given another in the second term by Gabrielle Bernard, wife of Dr. R. G. Cooke, lecturer in the Department of Mathematics, and a third by singers of madrigals. Members of the Society diligently practised on recorders. Two large societies were made out of smaller : Societies in the Faculty of Arts, including the Birkbeck Players, were readily united into a new Arts Society, and the Societies in the Faculty of Science, after some hesitation, into a new Science Society ; both united societies being open to all students of both Faculties. It was agreed that the former separate societies might break away again at any time if they were supported well enough. The Music Society was treated as separate forthwith, and in the second term the Geographical and the Historical Society each held a separate meeting. Some activities, such as expeditions, were given up altogether. The new Science Society held inaugural meetings on the 12th of February 1940 (day-students' section) and the 16th February (evening-students' section). The new Arts Society showed a film on Finland in the first term, and one on the history of the cartoon in the second ; it was also in the second term addressed by Dorothy Sayers, Miss Scott Thompson, and Muriel St. Clare Byrne. On 15-16th March, the Société Française produced, between a scene from Kyd's "Spanish Tragedy" and Thornton Wilder's "The Happy Journey," J. Romains' "Le Déjeuner Marocain." The Student Christian Movement flourished as it did throughout the war, holding meetings in the church of St. Dunstan-in-the-West, through the kindness of the Rector, Dr. A. J. Macdonald. In the second term it commemorated the World Student Christian Federation and in the Easter vacation held its annual conference at Hockerill Training College, Bishop Stortford, instead of Ashford as hitherto. The Peace Society did its best by thought and debate to maintain its hard but honourable position. In November 1939, the Union resolved to support a Christmas Refugee Fund in aid of student exiles in China, Spanish exiles in France, and Central European and Polish exiles scattered in several countries of Europe. Three issues of the College's magazine, *The Lodestone*, which is produced by the Students' Union, were edited during the session by J. Hickman. The students, in council and in general meetings, kept a watchful and hopeful eye, as is a habit of theirs in no way relaxed at any time during the war, on the college's refectory, which, with the help now and then of other eating-places near by, sought to fill the intaking needs of the flesh. It was never a question of no food for the stomach, but sometimes the students had no stomach for war-food, or had some other grievance, and they then let our catering staff know this. They were, however, quick to give thanks and praise when they felt that they were deserved, and to make suggestions from their own experience outside the college. Nor were their vigorous expressions of opinion confined to the refectory. For example, when early in January 1940, a most subtle smell, which lingered long in nostrils and in memories, and was known as The Stink, spread throughout the college's main building and beyond, breathing even upon people in other premises, it was the students who, after many efforts to check the odour's wanderings and its makers—justly suspected of belonging to our Department of Chemistry—finally cleared the air. Histories of smells in colleges and schools would all surely take on one certain look, so to speak. These normal and healthy activities have been chosen by me from among many hints and signs of a healthy and normal college in war-time.

The fall of Holland, Belgium, and France

The summer term (15th April—22nd June), in which the weather in much of Europe was mostly beautiful and the events there so appalling, now seems to many people like a dream and a nightmare. Just after the Government in Britain had changed, and on the very day, the 10th May, when Winston Churchill became Britain's national leader, the Germans let loose their terrific onslaught on Holland, Belgium, Luxembourg and France. The fall of Holland came four days later, and Belgium surrendered on the 27th. The advance of the Germans to the Channel ; the ruin of our share in the defence of France ; the tension and relief caused by the famous rescue of British and Allied forces at Dunkirk (where Arthur Wensley, formerly sole lecturer in Economics at Birkbeck College until his resignation in autumn 1938, lost his life), complete by the 3rd June ; the declaration of war against France and Britain by Italy on the 10th ; the fall of Paris on the 14th ; the collapse of France as an ally, 17th—21st June—all these things became known to Birkbeck College as it pursued its appointed work. News of the fall of France, which meant that Britain alone was facing Germany and Italy, came to many of us when we were engaged in our classes. Not much was said ; feelings were perhaps too deep for many words. Some of us tried to utter a message of comfort to such French people as were at the college, where one could see some of the French spirit still alive and hot. There was some despair among us—but also a steely look in the eyes and an out-thrusting of the chin. Indeed we knew that Great Britain and the Empire would fight on ; and that this land would be attacked at last by air if not by invasion across the Channel. It may be that, at college, as elsewhere, the danger from air-raids was taken less seriously, before they came, than it ought to have been. Yet even in late May it was felt that academic examinations of early summer might be disturbed by air-attacks, and forethought was taken accordingly. Again, on the 3rd of June, the fire-fighting parties ready at the college were, on advice received, told where, in air-raids, should be sent seriously wounded people ; where the walking wounded should go if they were in need of care[1]; and where further fittings for gas-masks could be got. However, the uppermost thought in our nation's mind at the moment, next to grief for the woes of France and other lands, was the likelihood of invasion of England by sea. Even from mid-May onwards, men in civil life had been coming together, in the towns and villages of our land, as Local Defence Volunteers holding anything that could be called a weapon ; and early summer saw the beginning of their proper arming and training, and the change of their name to the Home Guard.

The third term. Plans for next Session. The New Building

Thus this summer term was much more trying than that of 1939 ; such students as had the normal anxiety about the coming examinations in their minds, suffered the further dread which all people in Britain felt at the fall of France, the surge forward of Hitler's invaders to the Channel, and the hardships of our own forces in the midst of fearful turmoil. However, the term was not otherwise an abnormal one. The number of enrolled students at the end of session was 493, of which 147 had attended day-courses. A certain number out of the total were exiles from other countries. In view of the success of the six courses in map-reading for officers, our Department of Geography was prepared to give, for Local Defence Volunteers, similar but more elementary lectures on map-reading, on which the War Office looked with favour, but these were not delivered. Early and careful consideration had been given to the policy of the college with reference to the coming session 1940-1941. It was hard to look ahead, partly because it was not certain[2] whether absent colleges and schools

[1] In a memorandum from Mr. Troup Horne to Dr. H. Henderson we read: "serious casualties are to be sent to the Central Criminal Court and walking wounded in need of attention to Wyman's, New Street Square." See the map. On the 25th of June an air-raid warning was heard in London, but no trouble followed then.

[2] The events in Europe went far towards damping the hopes of absent schools and colleges of London University that they might return as most of the Medical Schools had done ; the raids of September finally overthrew such hopes.

Steel framework of new building

of the University would return to London or not ; but in July it was decided after some consultation with other colleges and schools to provide full evening courses—a policy which, as will be seen, the college was unable to follow because of air-raids; and, if these portions of the University did not return, to arrange day courses in the coming session as in the present session if numbers justified it. Arrangements were made so that Colonel G. A. Bayley, C.B.E., D.S.O., lecturer in charge of Military Studies in the University in succession to Brigadier-General E. B. Mathew-Lannowe who died in January 1940, and had been Reader in this subject, could give in session 1940-1941 at Birkbeck College another[1] course of special lectures which in peace-time would have taken place at King's College. From the Department of Economics, J. Horsefield departed for work in aircraft production. The following were appointed Acting Heads of their departments for the coming session 1940-1941 : Dr. P. Dienes[2], in Mathematics in place of the Head, E. H. Smart, retiring after thirty-nine years of faithful service in the college ; Dr. L. Simons, in Physics, Mrs. L. Simons[3], in French, Dr. F. Steward, in Botany. In view of the active work of the Master of the College for the British Government, the Governors of the College gave him sanction to appoint a Vice-Master if he should deem it necessary to do so. Because of scarcity of labour and material, and first rights of the Government in the use of these, work on the college's new building in Bloomsbury was stopped in June, and the arrangements with Prestige and Company were ended by mutual consent.[4] The great steel framework, weighing eleven hundred tons, of the building stood complete, and was later protected by painting. With great wisdom a quarter of a million bricks and sixteen hundred yards of Burma teak flooring had been

[1] The lectures in Military Studies during the present session were given in part of the vacated building of King's College in the Strand, London.

[2] He remained Acting Head until he became Professor and Head in 1945. He died in 1952.

[3] Claudine Wilson, who married Dr. L. Simons on the 1st January 1940. She remained Acting Head throughout the war, and until 1948.

[4] Arrangements for completion on a larger scale were renewed with them on the 13th of June 1947.

bought at prices very much smaller than these would have been after the war. These materials were placed in stack and store next to the building site.

Public lectures. Social Activities

To the various public lectures given in the autumn of 1939 and the winter-spring term of 1940, were added during the summer term lectures by Graham Pollard on the History of the Newspaper (the Chairman at the first lecture being Major The Honourable J. J. Astor, M.P.), and by Señor D. R. M. Nadal on Contemporary Spanish Poetry. It was a privilege of the College to become henceforth a meeting-place of certain University bodies, such as Boards of Studies and Boards of Examiners. In this session we also welcomed the University Musical Society ; the Old Students' Association of Queen Mary College ; the Physical Society of London ; the Metropolitan Branch of the Training Colleges' Association ; and moreover members of the "B" Division of the City Police and associated workers in Air Raid Precautions, with their guests. At their meeting on the 8th of April, the Chief Commissioner and the Deputy Commissioner of Police were present, and the whole audience was very large indeed. The programme included contributions by the City Police Band and the Ilford Dramatic Society. At Greenford the college's sports-ground was made available for persons not connected with the college. It was decided to close the college during the vacation of summer, except the Library, to all save staff, students doing research by special permission, and students attending such special courses or classes as would be held.

Retrospect

Thus did the college pass its first session of war-time without mishap. It had been in effect working during twelve hours of the day, but patience and good-temper had been shown throughout. Three-quarters of the attendant staff had been called away to the Navy, from which they come to the college ; yet the rest made no complaint. The refectory was very crowded, but the Librarian aided here by arranging for willing helpers. No use was made either of any air-raid shelter or of any First-Aid Post ; gas-masks, which all students carried by order, in examination rooms of the college during Intermediate examinations conducted by the college, and B.A. and B.Sc. examinations conducted by the University, were quite unnecessary ; nor mercifully were they ever destined to be used by anyone, except as a protection against smoke and heat in hard fire-fighting later on. For some teachers this session was the hardest in their experience because they had held classes during week-ends as well as during the evenings of mid-week. Of those teachers who were engaged on full-time work for the British Government, some managed to put in, at the college, hours about equal to the normal of peace-time. The students had acted splendidly. Not only did they face the conditions of "black-out" so successfully that the social life at the college was perhaps livelier than ever before[1] ; but they also pursued their academic studies with such zest that in the examinations held at the end of the session the college gained a larger number of successes in the Intermediate examinations in the Faculty of Science than any other college of the University, except one ; nor did the achievement in the Faculty of Arts come far behind. In the Final examinations of the University a higher proportion of candidates from Birkbeck College entered, and a higher proportion gained eminent success, than in any recent year.[2] Some students owed much to a Joint Recruiting Board or to Hardship Committees through which had been granted postponement of call-up to enable students to take examinations. Lastly, the college may rightly claim that it had become, for the people of the general public whose work lay in the neighbourhood, a centre of that form of good living, as applied to the mind and the brain, which is commonly called culture. People

[1] In some of the academic work done in the Faculty of Science black-out was a help, not a hindrance.

[2] The University decided to award no "War Degree" as such. Some concessions and adaptations were made in existing requirements, so as to meet the conditions of war-time. But there was no lowering of the University's standards. Important at this time was the decision to allow, in cases of a University career interrupted by National Service, credit in certain papers and subjects taken at the Intermediate or Final Examinations before the interruption or when interruption was expected.

had come crowding to us for profit and pleasure in subjects belonging to politics, science, literature, art, philosophy and music. All this may seem an impossible feat, but performed it certainly was, just as the concentration of most classes on to week-ends alone was successfully achieved during the sessions to come. It might with some truth be said that man's brain was borne up by the stress of the times.

Prospect

At the end of the session, with France fallen and the Germans lining the southern coast of the Channel, while the British Government was making ready to resist invasion which might come from one or more directions, the students and staff of Birkbeck College were mostly absent for the vacation of summer. It was an interval full of keen but calm excitement ; in which news of the process by which Russia received control of the mouths of the Danube, and completed her absorption of the Baltic States—Estonia, Lithuania and Latvia—by the 6th of August, did nothing to calm our anxieties for the future, while the Germans, during July and the first part of August were, in the hope of invading, after mid-September, the eastern half of the north coast of the Channel, massing men and shipping in northern France from Calais to Brest ; and were directing air-attacks on ships and other targets along the promontory of Kent and the south coast of England, in what may be taken as the first phase in the "Battle of Britain".

CHAPTER THREE

STRUGGLE AND DISASTER

SESSION 1940-41

"Bombers, the enemy's loaded arm,
Flog to bright blood the bones of streets."
G. Tillotson, *Criticism and the Nineteenth Century*, p. 229.

The "Battle of Britain." The raids by night. The neighbourhood of Birkbeck College

In order to invade Britain along our south coast, Hitler tried first to control the skies above the Channel and southern England, because the British Navy kept the seas. Hence came about, in July, August, September, and October of 1940, the famous "Battle of Britain" wherein the Germans, after the first week of August, in fine weather, tried to smash the British forces out of the air and to overawe the people below. Through the skill and valour of those who manned our fighter-planes, the "Hurricanes" and "Spitfires," and the cleverness of those who planned and controlled their actions, these efforts of the Germans failed utterly. Thwarted in this way, the Germans, on the 7th of September, at a time when our airfields, our machines, and our men were all taking grievous harm and loss, foolishly changed from attacks by daylight to attacks chiefly by night, London being now the main target, on which began a long series of raids lasting from dusk of evening to twilight of morning. The wide-sprawling city faced attacks on eighty-two out of eighty-five nights ; and of those eighty-two, fifty-seven were consecutive. As in many other parts of London and of other British towns which suffered grievous harm through blast and fire, stout indeed was the structure of our buildings in mere mass of hard bricks, stone and steel ; yet far stronger was the steadfastness in the hearts of the men and women who worked in them and defended them. In this wearisome and trying time, and throughout the session, Birkbeck College, as a small portion of London, played its part in an area which is now in places not recognisable for what it was. It is widely believed that falling bombs were by technical means turned aside with success from the great terminal railway stations at Euston, St. Pancras, King's Cross and Liverpool Street; and that the districts of London containing the City of London and Holborn and their neighbourhood, with the area in which Birkbeck College lay, suffered in consequence more than they would have otherwise. But the opinions which I here indicate are both wrong; nor is it known whether the Germans aimed at these railway targets. It is, however, most likely that they did so ; and the districts mentioned did in truth receive more high explosive bombs than other parts of similar size in London. The fearful damage and loss of life caused within and near our area of it occurred for the most part immediately east, south-east, and north-east of the college ; much less destruction within the area[1] occurred to the north, though this involved the worst blow which the college suffered ; not much took place to the north-west and little or none to the west, south-west, and south.

At the College in July and August, 1940

When the raids began on England, the members of the staff and students of the college away on vacation wondered what was the fate of the college from day to day. In fact, a nerve-racking, exciting and dramatic sequence of events led to such decisions and action by the college not only at the moment, but also during a whole session, as may well prove to be the most striking in the varied history of the college. The critical moments were slow in coming, and during July and all August there was for the college a pause, tense indeed and watchful, but also over-hopeful. On the 10th of August, after a meeting which included members of the teaching staff, it was decided by Birkbeck College, in view particularly of the intended return to

[1] Not far outside the college's area (as defined on page 14 in Chapter I), south, south-east, east, north-east, north and north-west of it, very severe damage was done. About one-third of the area of the City of London suffered destruction.

London of the Faculty of Arts of University College, and the extension of the courses at Imperial College of Science to include students in their first year, that day-courses at Birkbeck College in mid-week should not be repeated in session 1940-1941 ; there would be evening-courses only. In the departments of Science some precautions were taken to safeguard such precious material as could be moved to securer parts of our premises. This was wise, because German aeroplanes broke through to the outskirts of London on the 15th and 16th of August, and from the 23rd onwards single aeroplanes were appearing over central London also.[1] During the day and night of the 30th and the 31st, our area heard four alerts which lasted in all nearly nine hours ; and on the 31st and the night following there were seven alerts covering more than eight hours. There was one day on which there were fifteen alerts in daylight. But, although the sirens thus gave their warnings frequently, whereupon people on the college's premises took shelter, the raids were widely scattered, and during the month of August our neighbourhood was not touched.

September. The first attacks over the College's area

The area received its first shock when, during the second phase of the "Battle of Britain," in which between the 24th of August and the 6th September the Germans aimed at forcing an easy way to London by shattering the Royal Air Force in the air and on its grounds in southern and south-eastern England, two high explosive bombs, falling by night in Took's Court, off Cursitor Street, north-west of the college, on the 2nd of September, destroyed some property and caused the death of a woman, wife of a sub-editor on the staff of our neighbour the newspaper *The Daily Mirror*.[2] Two more bombs

[1] The "City" received its first bombs on the 24th.

[2] It is of interest to note that between these two dates, on the 5th, a meeting of the Council of our Students' Union took place at which was read a letter from the occupant of a house adjoining our sports-ground at Greenford, complaining that during a recent air-raid cricketers had continued playing their match, thus endangering themselves and the whole neighbourhood ; as the screens had not been put back afterwards, the field was thus rendered a suitable landing place for aeroplanes. Though there were trees and houses on two sides of the field, which would impede landing, the college proceeded to enforce the replacement of obstructions after every game. It was noted that there was apparently going to be a new system connected with the sirens, in which case a game would probably cease on receipt of a warning.

fell shortly afterwards. On the 7th, the Germans, after delivering hard blows along the Thames during the afternoon, began constant night-attacks on London with about two hundred bombing aeroplanes every time ; on that day and on following days struggles in the air over the huge city were very hard and long. The nine days and nights from the 7th to the 15th of September presented London, in daylight and in darkness, with nearly all the features of German air-raids at their worst ; three successive nights, those of the 7-8th, 8-9th, 9-10th, being very horrible. The attack which began on the 7th, causing some harm even to the centre of London where Birkbeck College lay, brought death to 306 people and grievous hurt to 1,337 ; in the next raid, which began on the 8th, hardly any district of London escaped, 286 people being killed and at least 1,400 badly injured. On this day a heavy bomb burst in Chancery Lane, not far from the College ; on the next day, the 9th, another burst on the roof of the office of *The Evening Standard* newspaper, at the northern end of Shoe Lane north-east of the college, breaking many windows far and wide. The onslaught made on the 9th and 10th left 400 dead and at least 1,400 badly hurt ; nor did the nights following give any respite. Details of the numbers of the killed and injured were not made public ; but people rightly judged at the time that the raids were severe. On the 15th the Germans made a most determined attack on the city by day with many bombers and attendant fighter aeroplanes[1]. Further, from mid-September onwards were added much nuisance from delayed-action bombs,[2] and the deadly effects of very large mines, each dropped with a parachute.

Professor H. G. Jackson becomes Vice-Master of the College. Postponement of the opening of the new Session

Such menacing onset of danger brought anxiety to John Maud, the Master of the college, because the first term of the

[1] Perhaps it was the failure of this culminating effort that made Hitler decide to give up the plan of invading Britain.

[2] They were used in August also.

session 1940-1941 had been fixed to begin on the 30th of September, and the Council of the Students' Union had held a meeting at the college on the 5th. Moreover, he found it a very hard task to bestow his full care on the college in a time of urgent need, in view of his important work in the post of Deputy-Secretary to the Ministry of Food. This difficulty he was able to solve without delay ; he now acted on the sanction of the Governors to appoint Professor Harold Gordon Jackson (Head of the Department of Zoology) to the post of Vice-Master of the College, and obtained Professor Jackson's acceptance on the 16th of September. This action by John Maud was indeed a stroke of mastership, because Gordon Jackson, a man of wisdom and courage, was destined to guide Birkbeck College through later troubles to ultimate peace, after the end of Maud's leadership. At the same time, Jackson consented to be also Dean of the Faculty of Science (instead of Professor W. Wardlaw, the Dean designate, who had accepted an appointment at the Ministry of Labour)—an action which was confirmed later by that Faculty. On the same day, the 16th, by which date two bombs had fallen within 75 yards and two within 125 yards of the college, the Master decided to postpone the opening of the first term of the coming session from the 30th of September to the 14th of October. This would fit well with such day-institutions as might be opening. Birkbeck College had given up any idea of resuming day-courses of its own. In reporting these acts in a letter dated the 16th of September, and addressed to the members of the College's teaching staff, Maud wrote as follows:—"At the beginning of August, University College informed me that their Arts, Law, and Medical Faculties would be returning to London this session, and Bedford College that it would also return. More recently the London School of Economics gave me similar information . . . . It remains to be seen how far those plans materialise.[1] But meanwhile it seems unnecessary for us to organise day courses at Birkbeck, and we can concentrate on

[1] In fact none of those here mentioned did so. On the 18th-19th September the buildings of University College in Gower Street were damaged badly in a raid ; the Senate House also of the University was damaged, again too in November.

our normal functions as a college for evening students. In this present phase of intense aerial bombardment, it is difficult to guess how far our normal evening work will prove to be possible . . . . (*decision to postpone opening*) . . . . But, apart from that change I think we should plan to carry on full evening courses as usual, and announce our intentions at once. When we see how many students are forthcoming, and what conditions of life here in October are like, we may, of course, have to modify our plans accordingly".[1] Needless to say, we knew nothing then about the hopes and hesitations of the Germans, which caused Hitler on the 30th of August to postpone the beginning of his invasion from the 15th of September to the 21st; on the 11th of September to postpone it to the 24th; on the 14th and the 17th to delay it further; and on the 12th of October to put it off until the spring of 1941. But we did know, after Churchill's broadcast on the 11th of September, about the ominous movement and gathering of ships by the Germans.

The College is damaged, 25*th of September*, 1940

The policy of the college during the coming session was finally decided not by raids during daytime—these in any case became unimportant after the last great daylight-raid, that of the 15th, in which the attackers were routed—but by the adoption of the Germans, after the 6th of September, of bombing

[1] For the policy which the college did in fact follow see below, pages 68ff. A little more than an hour had passed since I was putting some touches of revision to this book when I heard with deep regret of the death of Mr. Troup Horne, on the 28th of January 1953. I give here a letter which, written to me from college on the 20th of September, during the "Battle of Britain," is typical of the man. "Many thanks for your card. You will by now have had the Master's letter. The situation will probably be a little easier in a fortnight's time. All merry and bright here—with that grim gaiety of Winston's happy phrase. We've had six inners—bombs within 125 yards, three of which were less than 75 yards away, but no direct hit so far. At the Hall (*that is, Connaught Hall*), they knocked over a couple of houses just behind me and smashed a pane of glass in my bedroom—damned impudence. Winnington-Ingram was not so lucky. His wife was in yesterday reporting that they had been evacuated with nine unexploded time-bombs (*delayed-action bombs*) surrounding all their 'lares et penates.' Happy remembrances to your wife." Speaking of another occasion during this session when, as I know, death came near him, he said to me: "owing to a physical disability from which I have suffered for over thirty years, I didn't turn a hair on top."

London every night. By the 24th[1] of September the bombs fallen near the college included one which damaged a pinnacle on the Public Record Office very close to us ; and one which fell on Field House, fifty yards from the college's main entrance, flinging part of a girder seventy yards' distance to Greystoke Place. Then followed real trouble for the college. Not long after dark on the 24th of September a raid on London began in which our area received its first incendiary bombs.[2] These came showering down not only on West Harding Street, Gough Square, and Nevill's Court, and other places in the area, but also, between two and three in the morning, British summer-time, of the 25th, on Breams Buildings and Greystoke Place, bringing damage to the college. Of the six incendiary bombs which now fell on our premises, without injuring anybody either at the moment or in the process of fire-fighting, the one which came down in the courtyard of Greystoke Place was harmless ; but that which fell on the roof there caused a fire ; and this, though it was possible to confine it to the part of the roof above the staircase, took more than an hour to quell, and the front part of the roof was burnt off. The water let loose by the fire brigade ran down even to a cellar and wetted some zoological material already stored there. A makeshift roof was soon made, but a part of the building was for a time unusable. The four bombs which fell on the main building brought us far greater loss in material things. Swift action was taken by the Clerk, G. F. Troup Horne, who was on the premises as on most nights since the bombardment of London by the Germans began. He now put out three of the bombs before the coming of members of the London Fire Brigade. Two members of the fire-fighting squad of the newspaper *The Daily Mirror* gave valuable help. Unluckily the blazing bomb which still remained could not be effectively reached until the arrival of help from outside our vicinity, since it had rolled into a large wooden structure situated on the roof and

[1] On the 23rd the steel framework of our new building at Bloomsbury, having received a slight peppering from shrapnel earlier in the month, was hit by a bomb which then fell in soft earth just outside a basement retaining wall, and there exploded.

[2] Incendiary bombs were little used by the Germans until mid-October.

used as a store in the adjacent Department of Chemistry ; and as the fire which it caused could not be put out until many hours afterwards, the bomb did much damage, leaving what had been the two highest floors, which held laboratories, in a very bad state, and our College Theatre a partly roofless and useless shell. Water applied by the fire-fighters, and also rain, when it came down through the gaps in the roofing, increased the effect of ruin. People who came early after daylight were met by the sight of a fire-engine outside the premises, two hoses disappearing into the gloom of the college's entrance hall, and water flowing out into the street ; and by a long-lasting smell of charred stuff of various kinds. At lunch-time the firemen were still at work.

Details of the damage and of salvage

Most of the structure affected by this disaster was occupied by the Departments in the Faculty of Science. The whole of the Department of Zoology, including two laboratories, the largest of the laboratories of the Department of Physics, with a workshop, a dark-room, and a private room of that Department, and the store of the Department of Chemistry, were all completely gutted ; and the south Chemistry laboratory and two research laboratories of the Department of Botany were made, like the Theatre, unfit for use. In the workshop of the Department of Physics, shell-bases were being made by C. Dobb (steward in the Department of Botany), who was teaching other members of the college's staff, and some boys belonging to Mercers' School near by, to help him ; this work was now ended. The Department of Geology lost a good epidiascope and a projection microscope and nearly all its geological maps which had been stored in a loft to hinder their falling into enemy hands in case of an invasion ; sets of specimens not in general use had likewise been stored in that loft. By raking away the ashes, G. M. Davies, Head of the Department of Geology, was able to recover, undamaged, some black garnets and other things. Most specimens, however, had cracked in the heat, and a series of rich gold-quartzes from the early Australian discoveries was hopelessly blackened. Professor

Jackson, the Vice-Master of the College, and Head of the Department of Zoology, lost the whole of his personal notes (including the results of valuable research), his specimens, his annotated text-books, and other documents.

Throughout the day, in addition to the valiant energy of the fire-brigade, the splendid work of salvage by the administrative, establishment, and teaching staffs continued, and the departments of Chemistry, Physics, Botany and Geology were able later to resume work under much difficulty in such space as remained to them or could be found for them. The Department of Zoology moved remnants across to Greystoke Place where much museum-material and some books had been transferred before this damaging raid. There the department occupied and adapted as a store the cloak-room belonging to the women, who cheerfully and with good grace retired to the main building. The downward flood of water in 20 Breams Buildings, made greater by a fire-fighter obediently keeping it flowing until he should be stopped by an order (which through an oversight never came), reached the building's basement, where were stored not only the costly microscopes belonging to the Departments of Botany, Zoology and Geology, but also invaluable apparatus belonging to the Department of Physics ; all the precious instruments were wetted by water which was several inches deep. The chemical liquids especially which came down with the water did great harm to the fine equipment made for research on X-rays and Crystallography in that department. It was hard to extract safely from the rubble of the same department, and then across a floor whose joists were nearly burnt through, the lathes and other heavy machinery. This task was supervised by Dr. H. Henderson, of the Department of Geography, and by Mr. H. Bell, helped by several others of the Physics laboratory-staff. All Superannuation Policies belonging to the staffs, the National Savings Certificates of the college, and inventories of property belonging to the Departments of Science had been placed for precaution's sake in the vaults of the Chancery Lane Safe Deposit which was also devastated by fire ; yet all these documents came back to the college, soaked indeed by water, but otherwise unharmed.

Here I quote an account given me by A. Graham, who became later Professor and Head of the Department of Zoology. "The whole of the Department of Zoology in the main building had been rendered completely uninhabitable, standing open to the sky, and there was a great hole in the floor going straight through to the Theatre ; the benches and chairs in the laboratories were burnt and useless ; the whole of the books and journals kept in room 16 were destroyed. Professor Jackson's room, and the little bay off the passage outside it, which formed the place where Miss L. Russell worked, were utterly ruined, and seemed to have formed the kernel of the fire : not only were the books, research material and papers destroyed, but a considerable quantity of china and similar bric-à-brac, with which these two loved to surround themselves, was completely smashed. The intensity of the fire in this region may be judged from the fact that the books, closely packed on the library[1] shelves, which did not burn readily, were so black that even central pages were useless ; and, of course, what fire had spared, water had ruined.

"The text-books in room 15, under their dogfish boards, had escaped burning (though the dogfish boards were and still are charred on their bases), but were wet. So, ultimately, they were gathered up by the Librarian, Miss Hildyard, and sent off to be trimmed and rebound. What must happen then but that the bindery be bombed too and all our books lost, except a few which happened to be out on loan at the time ! "[2] To this record may here be added that G. M. Davies saw Graham and Dr. Vera Fretter[3] salvaging animals' skeletons over the gaping hole in the floor, with a drop to the Theatre below if they stumbled. The moulded plaster of the ceiling of the Theatre had to be pushed off the joists by walking on these and prodding,

[1] The departmental library of the Department of Zoology, separate from the college's main Library.

[2] Books in the Department of Botany were saved from wet by glass-fronted cases and were below the range of the fire. Some of the botanical periodicals were sent to Royal Holloway College.

[3] Before the war began she was lecturer part-time at Birkbeck College and part-time at Royal Holloway College ; after war broke out, she became a full-time teacher at Royal Holloway College ; but helped us during this time and afterwards with classes, keeping her connection with Birkbeck College permanent.

because of the persistent smouldering of the hair included in the plaster. Graham continues, "For the next few weeks John Baylie and I, with occasional help from Dr. Vera Fretter, Miss L. Russell, and Botany-assistants and others, sifted and riddled the ashes of the department and collected out of the mess whatever seemed to be worth salvage, often with a good view, through the hole in the roof, of a raid in progress. A great deal of what we found was barely worth the trouble of searching for it, but we did collect an enormous amount of material—" of which a good number of microscope-lenses, in their metal containers, were very valuable—"from the rubbish, and slowly got it dried and cleaned and taken across to Greystoke. The more valuable apparatus, such as microscopes, which had got wet, were despatched in charge of Mr. and Mrs. Dobb" (steward and assistant steward in the Department of Botany) "to Royal Holloway College ; the two of them spent an energetic month there dismantling, cleaning, and reassembling microscopes and microtomes and similar apparatus, and, I have no doubt, saved much of it from destruction, or at least from much more expensive repairs, by their devoted care.[1] Since the classes were now very small, it was decided not to bring much of this material back to College, and instead it was stored in the loft of the Botany Department at Royal Holloway College.[2] We owe a real debt to Miss E. Blackwell, head of the Botany Department there, and to Miss J. R. Bacon, the Principal, for the generous way in which they put space at our disposal during the war." Equipment of great value was taken for safety's sake to Berkhamsted in Hertfordshire, where it was kept in store at Berkhamsted School by the kindness of the authorities there ; some of it was brought thence into London by Mr. Dobb at times when it was required at the college.

Dr. L. Simons, Acting Head of the Department of Physics, wrote to me[3] in May 1954, the following :—"I have before me a

[1] Mr. and Mrs. Dobb applied their patience and skill in putting into good condition equipment and apparatus of the departments of Botany and Geology as well as Zoology, and for all this the college was duly grateful.

[2] A quantity of museum-specimens and teaching-specimens was also stored in and outside Vera Fretter's bedroom at Royal Holloway College.

[3] I would gladly have given personal records of other people also, but here, as elsewhere, a limit had to be set.

pathetic letter from John P. R. Maud dated Wednesday, 25th September 1940, which starts 'Dear Dr. Simons. This morning, between 2 and 3 a.m., the main College buildings, and also Greystoke, were hit by a number of incendiary bombs . . . The fire, however, could not be put out before considerable damage had been done to the main buildings, especially to the Theatre, the Zoology and Geology Departments and parts of the Chemistry, Physics and Botany Departments.'

"I was working in an Admiralty Department at this time at Slough, and was coming up to Birkbeck as often as I could in the evenings and at each week-end, in order to help in keeping the teaching going. On the receipt of this letter, I hurried to the College and my first impression was one of astonishment at the completeness of the destruction by fire of nearly half of the Physics Department. I stood on the charred rafters with Dr. Braddick and I think that we were both a little awestruck. The southern side of the Physics landing on the third floor led to a large general Physics laboratory, at one end of which was a partitioned-off optical dark room and at the other end there was a partitioned-off workshop. In one corner of the laboratory was my private room and up on a main wall there was a gallery cupboard full of expensive apparatus. The next room was used by the Geology Department with a partitioned-off end that Miss Russell used for her own work in Zoology. The last room on this side of the landing was a fine Zoology Laboratory and Museum with partitioning for a private room for Professor Jackson and another for Mr. Graham. The whole was above the main ceiling of the College Theatre. Now this ceiling was of special interest because it was hung from enormously deep and strong lattice steel girders which, in turn, supported our floor. The girders themselves occupied an air space, between ceiling below and floor above, of three or four feet. This space insulated the fire from the Theatre below and probably saved the whole College. I noticed particularly that the fire had not distorted the girders, but here and there one could see that the lattice steel work was a little buckled and twisted. The girders are still in use.

"The destruction of these rooms was complete; not a bench nor a partition remained, nor did I see any recognizable piece of apparatus. My own private apparatus, mostly made at home, had totally disappeared and that was a very sad personal loss. Many of the tougher Zoology specimens were salved. The evil did not end there. The many chemicals in the affected departments had been liberally diluted with water from the hoses and had seeped down the walls, through the various floors, to the Physics Research Laboratory in the basement. This room had just been equipped with new and expensive X-ray goniometers, X-ray tubes and automatic devices for their operation for the combined personal researches of Professors Bernal and Wardlaw, Dr. Llewellyn and an American citizen, Dr. I. Fankuchen. The sulphates and the nitrates bit, like dragons' teeth, into the fine mechanism."

Problems of policy

Meanwhile it was unlikely that the college would be ready for students even by the 14th of October. It was hard to get labour and materials for swift repair of the damage (caused to the building itself and to supplies of electricity, gas and water), which was judged to involve a cost of about £16,000 in money value of that time. Mechanism for electric light and power had been put out of action in both the main building and in Greystoke Place. Said the Master in a letter to staff dated the 24th of September : "It now remains for us to take heart and secure that if possible (and for my part I have no doubt of the possibility) what has happened to-day proves only to be the starting-point of a new phase in the progress and prosperity of the College." The Master sent an inquiry to all such students of the college as had begun in previous sessions studies not yet completed, and all new applicants, about choosing between evening classes during mid-week, and week-end classes during hours of daylight. The difficulties of the moment proved to be less than they might have been because less than one-fifth of the usual number of students could attend. On the other hand, the number of courses to be given could not be reduced, whereas the number of hours available at week-ends would be less than those available in mid-week. It would have been an easy thing to close the college for three months and to employ some large firm to repair all our damage ; but in such a case all our undergraduates would have lost in effect a year's work, because it would have been impossible to drive part-time students, such as ours are, through a whole session's work crowded into twenty weeks. Therefore only such repairs, both makeshift and other, were decided on as were wholly necessary and could be done in a short time ; and these were put into our jobbing contractors' hands. Besides the rescue of apparatus and specimens, furniture and rooms had to be cleaned ; new space adjusted to needs, time-tables re-cast, and the question of air-raid shelters reviewed. We had also to bear in mind depletion of the teaching staff through transference of some members of it to government posts and to other work. With great reluctance the Master now ordered not the closing of the college but a further postponement of opening. But when a little time had passed, after consulting Mr. W. L. Hichens (Chairman of the Governors), Professor H. Jackson (Vice-Master and Dean of the Faculty of Science), and Professor J. Sutherland (Dean of the Faculty of Arts), he decided on the 3rd[1] of October that the opening should in any case take place. The teachers of the staffs of both faculties were called to a meeting to be held at the college on the 16th of October, and therefore those teachers of the college who had not returned to London did so now with feelings of nervousness, excitement and gladness mingled.

Death of W. L. Hichens in an air-raid

Meanwhile air-raids on London and other places continued by night and at times by day, London being attacked nightly by about 200 bombers during most of September and all October. Just before 9 o'clock in the morning of the 8th of October a sneaking raider[2] dropped a bomb which killed, near Chancery Lane Station, about a dozen people who were on their way to

[1] The afternoon was rainy with low clouds, and there was an alert then lasting three hours, during which much gunfire was heard. But the decision held good.

[2] It was one of several German aeroplanes which dropped bombs in our neighbourhood during the very long alert of the 7th and 8th. It destroyed a motor-bus.

work. This happened just outside our area ; but much worse things occurred soon after. On the 9th, about 9 o'clock in the evening, a high explosive bomb fell into a trench-shelter near the college to the east-north-east, killing fourteen and badly injuring eight more of the twenty-five people who were in refuge there. None of these persons was connected with the college ; but members of the college had a share in the sad tasks which followed the blow. On the 14th the college suffered a loss which, as it became known, brought a personal shock graver than could be given by merely material damage. Mr. W. L. Hichens, who was co-opted on to the College's Governing Body in 1922, and had been its Chairman since 1927, was killed instantly by a bomb which fell in the early hours of darkness on Church House, Westminster. For nearly twenty years the college had had the benefit of his wisdom, advice, integrity and inborn charm, all bestowed in the midst of a business life full of wonderful energy. Not long before his death he was at the college discussing policy and the repair of the damage recently done. "The highest tribute we can pay to his memory, as Governors, Staff, Graduates and Students, is for each of us to do all in our power to ensure that Birkbeck does its duty despite the mischances of war. He fell where his duty called him, and where he wished to be, in the heart of the battle".[1] He was one of about five hundred people who were killed in this raid. During its course on the 14th and 15th, explosives and incendiaries and delayed-action bombs were dropped not far from the college, and there were some fires in the area of Fetter Lane. On the night of the 15th of October, when the Germans dropped on London about 386 tons of high explosive bombs and mines, and about 70,000 incendiary bombs, our area escaped, but a heavy bomb fell near it to the west and another near to the south.

Meeting of the Teaching Staff. The College to re-open

On the 16th of October the meeting of the teaching staff, with the Master presiding, took place in the main building as

[1] Quoted from the College's magazine *The Lodestone*, Autumn 1940 (Vol. 33, No. 7, p. 3).

arranged. We were all glad to see each other, and though some of us felt worried and somewhat in need of sleep after yet another disturbed night, we were very much awake and ready for anything. We had all steeled ourselves against any discouragement in the face of nightly air-raids and interruption or total lack of sleep through the noise of German bombs and British gunfire.[1] At the meeting the Master reported fully on the state of affairs. In reply to the inquiry which had been made, 112 of our existing students had said that they would prefer to attend during the daylight hours of week-ends. A small number were bold enough to state that they would be ready to come in the evenings of the other days of the week. There was also a small demand for daylight courses during those days. After discussing the possibility of re-opening the college in central London ; the safety of the available air-raid shelters ; and the types of courses which might be offered, the teachers present resolved :—"(i) Unanimously—that the college re-open in some building this session ; (ii) by fifteen votes to six[2]—that the college reopen in Birkbeck" (*that is, in the main premises, No.* 20 *Breams Buildings*) "and Greystoke on the understanding that air-raid shelter accommodation be improved so as to give maximum safety ; (iii) unanimously—that courses be arranged for Saturdays and Sundays" (*in hours of daylight*) "to cater in particular for present students of the college ; (iv) unanimously—that courses be arranged for other

[1] This gunfire was very violent on the 10th of September, and became, though less intensely, a regular method of defence except when our night-fighters ("Blenheims" and "Defiants") were in the air.

[2] The dissentients from this proposal had a deep and reasonable anxiety lest by opening at the college we would be courting disaster and risking fearful tragedy, without need for it, to crowds of students. They felt that we should make a new start elsewhere and laid emphasis on the uses of correspondence courses. Their loyalty to the College was quite unshaken as their subsequent actions showed throughout the war. That the college did take great risks is manifest ; it was acting against an idea which had governed the advice given to the University by the Lord Privy Seal before the war broke out—the idea of avoiding concentration of groups of persons in London if the city was attacked from the air. Yet the college can claim that it was not unreasonable in its belief that it might very probably be spared the more deadly forms of disaster not through mere good fortune so much as the Germans' continued policy of choosing, for their fiercer attacks on London, the night-time, when the college was not working. The course of this history will show how far the college proved to be wrong.

days of the week" (*in hours of daylight*) "if students present themselves in sufficient numbers ; (v) unanimously—that week-end courses begin not later than Saturday, 26th October." The meeting also gave approval to courses to be provided by postal correspondence (for students who could not attend college at all) in such subjects as could be taught by these means ; and the continuance of public mid-day lectures if this should be possible. The members then split into separate meetings of the two Faculties to discuss details. On the 17th of October the Governors met and gave their approval to these resolutions, and decided that the college be opened during daylight hours on Saturdays and Sundays from the 26th of October onwards, for a limited number of students (who would normally have attended in the evenings of mid-week) ; and that, should a sufficient number of applications be received, these week-end courses be extended over other days in daylight hours, to meet the needs of day-students, the working principle being that students who in time of peace would be attending as part-time students in the evenings, must attend in daylight on Saturdays and Sundays, and full-time students also must attend on those days in daylight and on other days also as might be necessary. The hours on Saturdays and Sundays were fixed between ten in the morning to four in the afternoon for the present, but it was recognised that the times would later be changed to fit the seasons, and, if need be, according to ways and means of travel. The vacations would be shortened in order to increase the time available for teaching-work. The Governors further decided that the college's air-raid shelters be improved, if possible, in the light of recent experience.

By thus transferring the proper times of our classes from the evening hours of five mid-week days to the daylight hours of Saturdays and Sundays, we did our best to provide for our proper students what was their due, and enabled both them and such members of our teaching staff as were employing their special abilities during mid-week in helping the national war effort, and then taught at the college during Saturdays and Sundays, to spend their hours of evening as they thought fit so far as air-raids allowed this. This change meant work on all seven days of each week for most of our students, nearly all of them being engaged on reserved national tasks in various ways apart from the college. Every day during this time, as the darkness of evening came on, the sirens sounded the "alert," so that, quite apart from danger and noise, transport in the hours of darkness was uncertain. The decision made to teach in hours of daylight only, when raids were not severe and were carried out by small groups of three or even by single aeroplanes, was inescapable. With raids taking place after every sunset, the likelihood of interruption of classes and the possibility of sudden disaster, quite apart from difficulties of travel, made any holding of evening classes foolhardy even if it were allowed. It was inevitable that numbers of students would be much smaller than was usual. Because of National Service there would be very few men over twenty years old (most of these would be in the Faculty of Science, finishing studies for a degree in some reserved subject) ; and many persons had left London with their schools, firms, departments, or offices, at the time when war began or since then. Moreover, this session, like the last, was beginning late. After the still harder strain of the previous session the concentration of work on to two days was not expected to be so fatiguing as it might have been ; and so it proved for most teachers, though sometimes the week-end was very tiring when air-raids brought sleeplessness, and also, for some students and teachers, hard and painful labour in rescue-work at any time.

Precautions against air-raids

Preparations were now duly made for greater safety, by day as well as by night, of persons at the college (whose presence in the buildings was, so far as air-raids were concerned, entirely at their own risk), and of the buildings of the college, by re-formation, in September, from members of our staffs, of fire-fighting units for duty in Breams Buildings and Greystoke Place, by night as well as by day, and of other services ; and by the promulgation of rules for taking shelter, with special reference to roof-watchers[1] on the adjoining premises of *The*

[1] Commonly called "roof-spotters," they received also another popular name, " Jim Crows."

Daily Mirror Newspapers Limited. Because of the system there long established, it was not necessary for Birkbeck College to have its own roof-watchers ; and grateful thanks of the college goes out to all those provided by *The Daily Mirror*, who carried out their lonely task day and night throughout the war to our advantage. The sounding of an "alert" on nearby sirens no longer meant interruption of work ; it was simply a warning to be ready for more serious alarm-signals which would be given if hostile aeroplanes seemed to be coming very near or overhead. After any alert, we were to be guided by signals given by *The Daily Mirror*. On the approach of peril, a first intermittent ringing of their bell indicated "imminent danger," whereupon people went on with their work but were tautened into readiness for what might come next.[1] On a second intermittent ringing, "action-stations," which meant that there was danger coming right overhead,[2] work ceased and every post was manned. These signals from the alarm-bell of *The Daily Mirror* could be transmitted to Birkbeck College. The second ringing of the bell became known popularly as "Divo" because it meant "*D*anger *I*mminent *V*ertically *O*verhead," and the coined word suggested, with no feeling of panic, the need for seeking sudden shelter at once and quickly. It was soon clear that risk run from raids during daylight[3] was very small compared with the dangers of raids by night ; none the less, further precautions was taken. At the beginning of the session instructions were placed on every lecturer's desk that, on the sounding of the signal for "danger overhead" everyone who was not on duty in defence of the buildings must take shelter. When by the end of November no such final signal had been given within working-hours, reminders were issued to the staff and displayed on the notice-boards for general affairs. In our main building the existing shelter of the Senior Common Room was extended to

[1] Such was the general behaviour. But any people who wished to go into shelter, on hearing an alert, could do so.

[2] Roof-watchers in and near our area were much helped by a red flag which was hoisted by the Air Ministry on the top of Bush House when danger was coming near.

[3] The coming of cloudy weather at the end of September encouraged "sneak-raiders," singly or in pairs, to try their luck. These did some harm, but were only a slight menace in contrast with the night-raiders.

include other parts of the basement, the central landings of the ground floors, and the adjoining staircases ; the shelter at Greystoke Place was likewise extended so as to take in part of the staircases. Moreover, roomy shelter in Field House was available as hitherto. All possible efforts were made to strengthen also the main building. Bricking up of doors and windows and the making of baffle-walls were all that could be done to hinder blast ; in addition a gas-proof chamber was prepared and arrangements were made for "decontamination." The college, though it was closed during the times of "black-out" except to persons on special duty or with special permission, was never left unoccupied by day or night.

The change in methods of protection caused by the use of fire-bombs by the Germans spread in mid-October throughout London, so that during raids a part of the people went, not down to basements and cellars and the like, but up on to roofs with no protection except a hat of metal. Before November a huge organisation of fire-watchers and fire-services, covering all London, began to work. In our part of the street Breams Buildings this new method was already centred in *The Daily Mirror*, to whose system were linked the simpler schemes not only of other firms nearby, but also of our college, in the manner described already. Before long the local fire-brigades were united into a National Fire Service to which was added the great Fire Guard of trained civilians. Air Raid Precautions received a new title—Civil Defence Service.

The fire-guard of Birkbeck College

For most of those people who served at various times, during the next five years[1], on the guard by night at Birkbeck College, the memories of how the time was passed when things were quiet, or not too noisy, are more pleasant than not. The Senior Common Room became the guard-room also, and in it were placed beds for members of the guard, who could, as they wished, talk, read, pursue academic or other work, play chess or some other game, listen to a wireless, play a piano and,

[1] Not until the end of March 1945 did the vigilance of our fire-guard become unnecessary. See p. 171.

in turn, sleep. At dead of night, even when all was quiet, there were at times innocent disturbers of rest in the form of loud snorers or of sleepers pestered by bad dreams. When no raid was in progress, any teacher on the guard was able to give additional guidance to students who, with special permission, came or stayed for this purpose ; and scientific experiments were carried out all night at the college. In calm and restful moonlight hours, at times after the raids in darkness had slackened off or ceased, one could, on climbing out on to the roof, appreciate the quiet of central London ; and sometimes one could hear little else than the talk of other watchers nearby. Memories of evenings and nights spent on the task of fire-watching were still very vivid at the time of this writing, and arose as much from the good fellowship of peaceful periods as from the excitement of air-raids. Members of staffs and students of all kinds have borne witness, which I can well confirm, to prolonged contact and friendship with each other such as they would never have had otherwise. There are some people whose total of nights spent on duty is very large. I do not here add in full either their names, or the stories which could be told about them and about many others ; but, by narrator's privilege, give just one name and one anecdote. There was an occasion when I was roused from sleep, at the beginning of my turn at watching, by a watcher with the words, "I've wakened ye to say ye need not wake, but can stay asleep while I take the last watch also, before going to Mass." He was a member of the attendant-staff of the college, old J. Wilson, an Irishman (as you may have guessed) who had served in several wars.

Re-opening of the College. The first term. Departmental changes

On Saturday, the 26th of October, the college at last began a new session after the usual raid[1] by night, abandoning, by substituting week-end day-courses for mid-week evening-courses, a policy which had been pursued for well over a hundred years. The re-opening proved to be a most inspiring success,

[1] For some nights past the raids had been much less severe than before.

under the reciprocal leadership of the Master and the Vice-Master, in spite of the long and dreary series of interrupted nights.[1] The whole college was open for all seven days of the week. Both staff and students were determined that the work of the college should go on however great the hardships might be. The council of the Students' Union made very clear their pleasure at the decisions taken by the Governors, and at the efforts made by the administrative and teaching staffs to put this policy into action, and the Union gave up their Common Room to be used as required by the Department of Chemistry, and for other purposes. Our ravaged departments of Science were able to do their work ; the Department of Zoology was enabled to use the badly damaged laboratories of Botany for the small class of Intermediate students ; Alastair Graham and Vera Fretter took turns in travelling to and fro every week between Birkbeck College and Royal Holloway College, carrying the needed practical material in a heavy rucksack from which the animals' bones peeping out roused wondering comment amongst fellow travellers.

By mid-November there were 93 students attending in the Faculty of Arts, and 77 in the Faculty of Science. They were spread in about the usual proportions over all the subjects in both Faculties. Most of them were taking some Honours course, but a number were studying for the General and Intermediate examinations. It was hardly possible to provide, in the Faculty of Science, full one-year Intermediate courses, but some changes in these courses in Science were approved by the University ; at the college, limitation of choice to two practical subjects was deemed to be workable. Certain lectures on days of the week other than Saturdays and Sundays were given or planned according to the ability and desire of students to attend. The mere fact of the war and the fall of France in

[1] We knew that London was suffering much, but we did not then know that by early November the number of persons killed in and near London was about 9,000, and the number of the badly hurt about 16,000. The night of the 3rd of November was a most memorable one, because then for the first time during nearly two months London heard no sound of alarm. But conditions varied much. On the 15th there was a heavy raid which brought more damage east of Fetter Lane ; on the 19th and 20th there were no alerts at all in daylight ; and on the 25th there was no night-alert.

particular and her occupation by Germany had cut off our students in modern languages and other subjects from many benefits of linguistic experience, from the use of foreign libraries and laboratories, and so on, of the European mainland. A number of students unable to attend the college were now being dealt with by postal correspondence ; needs were varied, and efforts were made to satisfy all. Some defects in teaching by post were made good by interviews held now and again at college or at a teacher's house. Since so many persons had been called up for National Service or had been sent elsewhere in their employment, the Governors decided to suspend[1] the awards of such college scholarships, studentships, and prizes as were competitive within the college, and were not earned as the result of gaining a First Class in a Final Examination. Secondment (besides those mentioned above in the second chapter) of R. P. Winnington-Ingram*[2] to the Ministry of Supply ; of K. Wilson to the Ministry of Supply ; of Mrs. E. Haines to the Ministry of Information ; of J. Horsefield* to the Ministry of Aircraft Production ; of Professor W. Wardlaw* to the Ministry of Labour ; of A. Welch* to the Imperial College of Science and Technology ; and of Dr. H. Braddick* to the Ministry of Aircraft Production for work on bombsights, was a handicap for the working of the departments, for it was difficult to fill the gaps caused by their absence. A. G. Way, in the Department of Classics, became full-time lecturer ; H. Kestelman, from the staff of University College, became part-time lecturer in Mathematics ; Dr. F. J. Llewellyn was made a full-time lecturer in Chemistry ; and Dr. Rosemary Freeman part-time lecturer in English in place of Mrs. Charlotte R. D. Macdonald who had resigned her post at Birkbeck College. In the Department of Philosophy, Ruth Saw continued the work of T. Greenwood who had likewise resigned.

[1] When the Council of the Students' Union had protested against this decision, the Governors in the second term referred the matter to the Academic Board ; which in March recommended that for 1941-42 not less than four Final Studentships be awarded ; and the Governors approved. When these were in fact awarded (in autumn, 1941) they were made available for students who were in even their second year of a Final course provided that they had taken their Intermediate Examination at the college and not elsewhere.

[2] * indicates total secondment.

Radio Communications (Radio-Physics)[1]

Early in December, as the result of a letter from the Right Honourable Lord Hankey, received near the end of November, and subsequent information, the Department of Physics began preparations for the provision, in a new and more regular form, of important instruction in Radio Communications, on which E. P. George had been lecturing since early in the war. The object of the scheme, in which Birkbeck College decided to take a share, was the training of men and women in skilled radio work and radio-location for the fighting forces ; additional apparatus could be supplied ; persons to attend courses would be for the present chosen by the Government in January 1941 ; students in Science other than Physics would be eligible ; the matter should be regarded as secret to the extent that neither the total number of persons required by the Government nor the number in any category must be disclosed.

Public lectures. Students' social activities

Public lectures could not be given so easily as before because the college could not use its Theatre for very large audiences. The heating in the Theatre, always difficult, was worse in coming winters under a makeshift roof ; the bricking up of the main doorway of the college, and the curtailment of easy passage through the entrance-hall, forced us to limit the persons gathered in the Theatre at three hundred. However two lunch-time lectures given in the Students' Common Room by Dr. C. Joad on "Some Problems of Philosophy" were, with more by him and by others in the second term and three more in the third term, very welcome to the public as well as to the college. The social activities of the students, though some efforts were made, could not be carried on as they were during the previous session owing to the concentration of work over week-ends in daylight, and to the air-raids after dark ; luncheons took the place of dinners ; dances could be held only on a few afternoons. However, the students became more and more used to the conditions of strain which air-raids were causing ; by the end of the year they numbered 104, including

[1] See pages 82, 83.

55 women, in the Faculty of Arts; 111, including 34 women, in the Faculty of Science. Normal meetings of the Council and Union of the students were held. At a cheery Christmas luncheon and party, the Union entertained some Norwegian sailors brought by Dr. McClean. The term went on to its end on the 18th of December without further damage to our buildings and without loss of life among staff and students. The college was, however, grieved to learn that Alfred Drake, President of the Students' Union in 1932-3, and representative of the Students on the Governing Body in 1932-4, was killed accidentally in October while he was on duty, not of course at the college, in Air-Raid Precautions.

Air-raids. The College is again damaged Sunday, 29th December, 1940

At the college the rules for taking shelter (see page 71), were maintained, the procedure holding good of course not only for the classes and other meetings held in the day-time, but also for evening gatherings where no routine-work or duty was being done. At one of the first public lectures of the session, as soon as an alert was sounded, everybody took shelter without need. But alerts at following public lectures caused no such interruption, because the signal for "danger imminent vertically overhead" was not needed and was not given, and people were more familiar with the general ruling. During the term,[1] within the college's area a bomb had destroyed a building in Dean Lane; and another, on a night when some incendiary bombs had already fallen along the length of Fetter Lane, had left a crater thirty feet wide at Thavie's Inn, causing the sudden disappearance of a four-storied building and the death of the one person—a woman—who was inside it. The "land-mine" or parachute-bomb—one of thirteen which fell in the City of London alone during the war—let loose on an earlier night over Holborn (and weighing a ton and a half) which

[1] From mid-November 1940 onwards, the Germans had been attacking industrial towns other than London, besides London itself. Towards the end of 1940 and onward into 1941 our enemies seemed to follow up any severe raid on London by another, one night or two nights later.

hung itself harmlessly over a lamp-standard in Ludgate Circus, passed, with weird sounds of flapping, low over the college's area, dropping its base on to the roof of *The Daily Mirror*. In December the first week was the quietest that London had had since early September. There was a severe raid on the 8th which came near to us. In mid-December there was another quiet week, and Christmas was free from raids.

Then at the end of the year, during the vacation, the college itself[1] suffered again. On the night of the 29th of December, when a severe onslaught with thousands, perhaps even one hundred thousand, of fire-bombs and tons of high explosives—most of them fell not far east and north-east of our area—destroyed so much of east-central London,[2] two of the incendiary bombs fell on our main building and a third on the roof of the premises belonging to *The Daily Mirror*, close to the greenhouse of our Department of Botany. The college's fire-guards, A. J. Massey and C. Smith, both being laboratory assistants attached to the Department of Physics, true to their duties, helped to put out this third bomb, and found one of the others in a most awkward position just beneath the roof in the Department of Chemistry. After about forty-five minutes the fire caused by the bomb was quelled. The main credit belongs to Massey, who faced steadfastly a task hot and hard while he was sprawled on a beam for a long time. Here are Massey's own words : "We spent a considerable time on the roof earlier that evening watching the 'fun' and eventually decided to go below for a period. Whilst coming down the ladder leading past the Chemistry stores, I was rather disconcerted, to say the least, to observe that the glass top panels of the door were transmitting the light from some conflagration within—and that is how we discovered it. There was so much going on 'up top' that both of us failed to observe the neat little hole in the roof that the bomb made upon impact. The remainder of the story is a routine one—use of stirrup pump until extinction of bomb (and exhaustion of operator) supervenes ! " Mean-

[1] Late in the term some further damage was done to the steel framework of our new building in Bloomsbury.

[2] The main target on this occasion was the City of London.

while the other bomb, which had fallen in front of the stage of our Theatre, was seen by a member of the fire-guard of *The Daily Mirror*. He forced his way into the Theatre, whereupon he and three others of the same guard extinguished the bomb. They promptly received a token of gratitude from the college, which likewise took the opportunity to express to the Directors also of *The Daily Mirror* thanks for this example of neighbourly behaviour and for the manner in which the staff of *The Mirror* was guarding readily and willingly the area next to our main building. The college lost one hundred and ten books in this raid.

People who took a walk round our area after daylight on the 30th saw how near had come destruction by fire. The ruin stretched from Shoe Lane almost as far as Fetter Lane ; New Street Square looked fearfully burnt and Gough Square was badly mauled on its northern side ; Dr. Johnson's house had suffered. Fire still flickered against clouds of smoke and puffs of steam. One scarcely wished to think about what might follow, so that the lull during the next two nights seemed too good to be true—or too true to be good.

End of the year 1940

We had now passed through about one-half of the first period of German attacks by air on Britain. A few of us had already suffered death or mutilation ; a few had seen the killing or mangling of kin or friends ; some had seen these grievous things come to thousands of other people ; more of us had gazed upon destroyed or shattered streets and homes—many of these were our own—and damaged roads and railways ; and bore discomfort through lack of water, gas and electric light and power ; many of us were sharing in the troubles of refuge in outdoor "Anderson shelters," forerunners of the table-shelters which were used later, or in some other more or less secure place ; most of us slept, when we could, in homes or lodgings which had little protection of any sort ; all of us were part of nearly one million people who travelled every day to and from work in London ; all of us felt the strain of foreboding and of sleeplessness.

As a fitting end to a record of this short but exciting and trying term there follows here a quotation from an application made by the Court of the University of London to the University Grants Committee and the London County Council after receipt of two letters from the College :—"The two letters . . . . . tell the tale of a very gallant and successful fight against odds. The Court are convinced that the Grants Committee will wholly endorse the view expressed : 'That staff and students, almost all of whom spend a large part of their days in earning their daily bread, should insist on continuing academic work of a University standard in the middle of London, not only throughout the first winter of the war, but also in October and November 1940, is perhaps a not unhopeful sign for the future of higher education in Great Britain.' "[1]

Air raids in January 1941. *The second term. Increase of the college's fireguard. The strain slackens*

On new year's day water was still being shot from hoses on to scorched and battered buildings, and another raid came after dark. On the 2nd of January, during the afternoon, people were startled and puzzled by a sudden sound which turned out to be the explosion of dynamite used to bring down such buildings as were no longer safe as they stood. Then followed a much quieter time, including three nights free from raids. But an attack[2] on the night of the 12th—13th brought more fire-bombs and explosive bombs rather near us ; still nearer were bombs dropped along Fetter Lane on the night of the 15th—16th. The rest of the month was again much most restful, night following night without raids, until, after an increase of alerts by daylight, a raid on the 31st brought fire-bombs—the first to come near us by day—not far away. These things added further point to the requirement that new plans for fire-fighting in the area of the City of London should be sent in by the 5th of February.

[1] Quoted from Governors' Minutes, 16th Jan. 1941, Minute 96.

[2] On 10-11th and 16-17th trifling harm was done at our new building.

The second term of the session, which began on the 4th of January 1941, instead of later as had been formerly arranged, proved to be less of a strain that the first term had been ; for raids on London were less persistent, and most people had become more hardened to the unusual demands made on mind and body ; they were now cheered by American aid in material, and were confident that Britain would remain uninvaded,[1] and that Germany and Italy would in the end be laid low. Hitler had already decided to attack Russia and was looking south-east and south as well, in hopes of cutting our communications in the Mediterranean and the Atlantic. An expansion of the college's fire-guard was now made in view of the danger of further attacks by fire-bombs. Hitherto it had been kept by the various staffs of the college. The number was on the 1st of January 1941 increased from two to four members,[2] and students were added from such as volunteered and were not already engaged on duties by night elsewhere. They had long desired to have a share in the protection of the college. The Students' Union made itself responsible for providing the guard of every Saturday night—Sunday morning, which meant that its members would not have an additional journey to and from home during week-ends, when classes were held. Further, those students who stated that they would prefer to take duty on nights other than the Saturday—Sunday, were worked into the rota of staff-members. Meanwhile during January and February bad weather continued to hinder German air-raids against this country.

Prospects

During January careful consideration was given to the possible provision of other working-premises should the college be further damaged. On the 29th came a Proclamation

[1] The Germans revived plans for invasion in 1941, putting them off again in July until the spring of 1942, in which year, on the 13th of February, the whole idea was allowed to lapse.

[2] They received some payment for expenses. At first the students protested at the idea of receiving anything at all. Through the introduction now of a compulsory system of fire-watching duties and training, many members of the college divided their duties between their home-districts and their places of work.

which made young men aged 18 or 19 liable to military service. This announcement, and the plans to conscript young women into industry, were bound to affect Universities seriously. But there was universal agreement when our Academic Board stressed its belief that the policy of the College should still be to afford University education as long as possible for students in London, and to provide also for continuing and extending research, maintaining further all work connected with the war. This last was conducted mainly in our departments of Science. Members of our Allied Governments and Forces, and their children of student age, were admitted to any of our established classes. The Academic Board also considered carefully the possibility of offering special lectures and courses of instruction of University standard for people in all Forces.[1] Some members of the teaching staff were ready to give instruction at centres of the Army and Air Force. But in March, after Major-General H. Willans, representing Army education in London, had visited the college by invitation, it appeared, from the useful information which he gave, that the college could not take action yet, but might do so in the next session. It was known however that the Army authorities would welcome correspondence-courses of a University standard, and the delivery of lectures of educational value but more popular in appeal; and it was hoped that members of the teaching staff of the college would be added, as opportunity arose, to an already existing register of persons able and willing to help in the matter.

Radio-Physics

In Radio Communications E. P. George continued with a class while new equipment was being got in readiness for a succession of elementary and advanced courses, on syllabuses laid down by the British Government, each lecture in both courses to be followed by practical work. Our department of

[1] The University of London had representatives on a Central Advisory Council for Education among His Majesty's Forces established under the auspices of the Young Men's Christian Association early in the war ; and had set up a Regional Committee which had arranged courses of instruction for troops.

Mathematics also helped in the task. The whole subject was later, under the title of Radio-Physics, made an integral part of studies for the Bachelor of Science Degree, by means of an examination which could be taken instead of normal papers in Physics, and was of a general type ; so that classes were not confined to students chosen by the Government.[1] The courses continued throughout the war ; nor did the subject lapse during two years after the war was ended.

Relations with Norway. Map-reading for Commando troops. Departmental changes. Public lectures

Our Departments of Geography and German in the college gave help to the War Office in a matter which at the time had to be kept secret. This consisted of training in map-reading by A. O'Dell—with the help of Dr. McClean, who provided a Norwegian translation of topographical terms—given to Norwegian-born Commando-troops in preparation for the first raid on the Lofoten Islands off north-western Norway, on the 4th March 1941[2] ; in which two hundred Germans were taken prisoner and three hundred and fourteen Norwegian volunteers were brought away. At the request of the Norwegian Government, Dr. McClean also arranged, in the College's Department of German, a special Norwegian-English language course for a dozen young Norwegian women who afterwards became nurses. Further valuable work for the war was done through our Department of Geography by A. O'Dell,[3] who was seconded in February 1941, to the Naval Intelligence Division, and helped in the writing of the Admiralty Handbooks published under the editorship of Dr., later Professor, H. C. Darby, at Cambridge, where the Cambridge Centre of the Geographical Section of the Naval Intelligence Division was working. In place of Mrs. Haines, who gave up academic teaching for work in the Ministry of Information,

[1] See below, p. 101.

[2] A second raid on the Lofoten Islands took place on the 26th of December 1941.

[3] He later joined the Scott Polar Research Institute at Cambridge ; in 1943 he was transferred to the Department of Health for Scotland as a Research Officer, South-Eastern Scottish Area.

E. Grebenik and Douglas Smith, both of the staff of the London School of Economics, were, on the advice of the Director of that School, appointed to take their places in our Department of Economics. In Botany, K. Wilson, doing work at the Ministry of Supply, was unable to continue with us after the spring of 1941. In Mathematics, since Dr. F. W. Land had been called to the Navy, his work was entrusted to H. Kestelman. In Classics, J. H. Mozley, of Queen Mary College, was appointed part-time lecturer to take over the work of A. Way when he was called for military service. The Department of Psychology suffered a blow through the sudden death of Professor F. Aveling on the 6th of March ; whereupon R. J. Bartlett became responsible for the department. Dr. Ives, of the Department of Chemistry, was allowed to help at the Imperial College of Science during the rest of the session. Dr. Dienes, Acting Head of the Department of Mathematics, began lectures on Statistics with the help of Mr. M. Kendall, whose task was to give a demonstration on "Statistical Method in Practice" after each lecture. This instruction in Statistics was likely to be of very great value to persons in Government Departments in particular. Dr. N. Pevsner now began public lectures on the Cathedrals of England.[1] Dr. Joad gave two more public lectures on " Some Problems of Philosophy" ; and Professor Eva Taylor three public lectures on "Geographical Aspects of National Planning." The upper floors of Breams Buildings and of Greystoke Place were treated with a fire-resisting substance. The makeshift roofs, made of corrugated iron, which had been put on the top of the tower of Greystoke Place and later on top of the Theatre, and were "camouflaged" in paint, served their purpose well enough. But the galvanised iron and the sheets of tarpaulin began to be blown about and ripped by wind and rain. At one of Dr. Joad's lectures in the Theatre, falling snow came through the roof and dropped flakes on lecturer and audience. In the week following, because of great cold, a small electric fire had been fitted into the portable reading desk placed on the lecturer's

[1] Slides prepared for these lectures, and others also used at them, were afterwards presented to the Courtauld Institute of Art.

table. The heat produced in this way was too much for the desk, which went up in flames, to the immense anxiety of the audience for the lecturer, who, however, was unharmed by the mishap. As the days lengthened, it was possible to do more and more evening work in mid-week to supplement the week-end courses ; but Honours students were finding the two uninterrupted days of each week-end both preferable and sufficient.

Students' social activities

On the social side, the students were able to do more than had been possible during the first term. The Arts Society revived and was addressed by Dorothy Sayers on "The Un-Free Press," and gave a private exhibition of the film "The Lady Vanishes " to a crowded gathering in the Students' Common Room, since the Theatre was not in full use yet. The Science Society underwent some reconstruction ; the Music Society revived in a modest way and at the end of the term heard a lecture on Beethoven and a piano recital by Jean Hamilton. The Student Christian Movement flourished as last session and again held its annual conference at Bishop Stortford in April. Active touch was kept with the National Union of Students in regard to the new call-up and the provision of books for use in air-raid shelters and for prisoners of war. Not only did students from Birkbeck College attend the great congress of the National Union of Students held in April at Cambridge, but B. Chibnall (see p. 124) became this Union's Secretary. The College's Union was fortunate in having Miss Lena Chivers as its President for a second year running. She was the first student in the history of the college to have this honour of a second year's Presidency, and much gratitude is due to her for her tireless energy, keenness, tact, and common sense, which made the students' activities much more effective than they would have been otherwise. On the Governing Body she was ably supported by the other representative Governor, L. R. Perry.

Death of Lord Stamp in an air-raid

Severe air-raids[1] on Great Britain during March and April included one of the severest single German attacks of the whole war—that which, directed against London on April 16-17, killed more than two thousand three hundred people and badly hurt more than three thousand others ; and destroyed in our area the large premises of T. Wallis and Company and in their place left ruin extending from the parts near Holborn Circus to Fetter Lane. This and other raids which touched our area did not harm the college, though some explosive bombs, let loose by aeroplanes guided by the glare of Wallis' burning building, fell unpleasantly near. But elsewhere on 17th April the college in time of vacation suffered the loss, through enemy action in this air-raid, of the Right Honourable Lord Stamp of Shortlands, Governor (representing the University of London) of the college since 1925, and deservedly to be remembered by us for his services in connection with the college. With him died his wife and his eldest son.

Light and shade of the War

The larger events of the war were like mingled light and shadow. From the beginning of 1941 Britain had the benefits of "Lend-Lease" through the generosity of the United States of America. The Italians fared ill against Greece and against General Wavell[2] in North Africa and in Abyssinia. But when Hitler went to Mussolini's aid in April, Yugo-Slavia, and then, in spite of our efforts, Greece, and in May, Crete, fell to the Germans ; and Bulgaria, Roumania, and Hungary had all become "satellites" of Germany. Rommel and his German forces were sent to restore the Italian cause in Cyrenaica, and there met with some success.

[1] They formed part of a second phase in the air-attacks on Britain. The raids of March were mostly not on London, which however did not escape, especially on the 8th-9th, the 14th-15th, and the 19th-20th of March.

[2] From 1947 to 1950 Field-Marshal The Right Honourable Earl Wavell, G.C.B., G.C.S.I., G.C.I.E., C.M.G., M.C., LL.D., was President of Birkbeck College.

The third term

The session's third term, which began on the 18th of April with 140 students in Arts, and 122 in Science, is memorable because of the shocking disaster to the building and equipment of the College during the last great air-raid[1] carried out by the Germans—among the most destructive of all the night-attacks on Britain—before they turned their might against Russia. On Saturday the 10th of May, our Librarian Dr. Margaret Clive Hildyard wrote about the Library for *The Lodestone*, as follows: "Last session we kept practically to our normal hours of opening. This session we began modestly by being open from 10 a.m. to 3.30 p.m., extending later to 5 p.m., and during this term until 8 o'clock. Our busiest days are Saturdays and Sundays, and even with so limited a number of students the issues for last session amounted to 3,341 which compares very favourably with the figure for the previous peace-time session, which was 4,464. Though our expenditure has been very much curtailed, there has been no shortage of essential books other than the inevitable difficulty and delay in obtaining both books and periodicals from America. It has been our privilege during the last two sessions to lend books to other libraries on a much larger scale than before, and we have also been able to welcome readers from other colleges whose libraries are no longer accessible in London . . . . . . On an old library at Berne is the inscription 'Let no profane person enter.' May our own remain intact ! "[2] Towards the close of the same day began the great air-assault by the Germans, which early on the next morning added bitter pungency to these words.

The air-raid of 10-11*th of May*, 1941

It is worth while giving here in some detail the nature of the disaster which came upon our area, and the manner in which it was faced by the people who shared in it at the college. On the night of Saturday, 10th of May—Sunday, 11th of May, the fire-guard on duty at the college consisted of five students in

[1] London had had no trouble since the 19th of April when a heavy raid had taken place.

[2] *Lodestone*, Summer Term, 1941 (vol. 33, No. 9), p. 29.

the Department of Physics, and a laboratory attendant—Wright (leader), Wilson, Eiduss[1], Loveless, Shaw and Singer, about whose coolness of spirit (if not of the flesh), steadfastness and bravery in confronting a terrible danger, this record can bear but feeble witness. The full moon was shining brightly. At 23.00 hours (11 o'clock in the evening) British summer-time, on the 10th, the alert was sounded, and before long the guard received the signal of "Danger Imminent Vertically Overhead" (see p. 71), put on their kit, and took up their positions, one man on the roof and two in the entrance of the main building, two in the entrance of Greystoke Place and one in readiness near. During the following five hours and a half, the German aeroplanes came over at intervals of about two minutes, dropping thousands of incendiary bombs, interspersed with high explosives up to six at least in one "stick," central London being the main object of attack. In our parts the assault began with high explosives, then fire-bombs likewise came down in groups, and the blaze of fires glowed grimly east and south-east, as later also north-east and north of the college. Soon after midnight, when the conflict seemed to be at its height, a high explosive bomb burst open a water main[2], to the disgust and dismay of the many gallant fire-watchers and firemen, to whom water was then so precious, both inside and outside the area under so violent attack.

Progress of the raid. Fire threatens the college

About 01.00 hours (1 o'clock in the morning) on the 11th, a shower of fire-bombs fell in Fetter Lane, where on the east side great fires were started, and in the street Breams Buildings; a few came down immediately east of the college's main premises, on the adjacent building not belonging to the college, and began a blaze of fire which in the end destroyed that building, and brought great danger to the college's main premises also. Then two fire-bombs fell through the makeshift roof of corrugated iron on our Theatre, and caused fires which were, after

[1] Who was later specially thanked by the College for his conduct.

[2] One of nearly one-hundred-and-fifty water mains broken in this raid. The low tide of the river Thames was another hindrance to fighting the fires.

some trouble, quenched by the guards with stirrup-pumps. Two more which soon came down in the courtyard of Greystoke Place offered no difficulty. But a new menace to the College was now growing ; besides the building[1] east of our main premises, others north of Greystoke Place, and separated from this by a few feet only, were burning fiercely. At 02.35 hours, reports by telephone made by the leader of the guard to the Clerk G. F. Troup Horne at Connaught Hall, of which he was Warden, caused that big sturdy figure, a personification of London, to move quickly through smoke and heat, to the help of the college, adding one more to the fire-guard. When he came, the building lying east of our main premises and adjoining them, and those which were directly north of Greystoke Place were burning so violently that it looked as if the whole of the college would be destroyed by the fires. Three things, however, united to save the college's main premises in Breams Buildings :—(1) the fire-guard, fearful lest the top of the fabric should set alight from heat and passing sparks, removed all curtains and black-out materials from the windows, and caused water to be sprinkled over the hottest places through a hose-pipe fixed to a tap. This alone probably saved the main building. (2) Members of London's fire-fighting forces agreed to pump the water from a dam holding 3,000 gallons in Rolls Buildings on to the east wall of our main building. From our side, the interior part of this wall, although there was a small space between it and the west wall of the next building, had to be watched carefully and constantly even later during the hours of daylight, when this at last became visible through the smoke which covered much of central London. (3) There was a shift of wind at 03.45 hours, which lessened the danger.

Destruction of the College's Library, 11*th of May,* 1941

But unfortunately this change of wind was much worse for Greystoke Place. Windows there on the higher floors were cracking ; paint bubbled and smoked with heat, and, in the Library, books standing against the windows opposite the rest of Greystoke Place began to be scorched. The members of the

[1] Property of Wyman and Sons Ltd.

guard wore respirators because heat and smoke made seeing and breathing very hard. Of necessity lacking much-needed help from others, they struggled manfully to keep window-frames and floors wet, and moved furniture which was in front of windows. Blazing windows were desperately pushed out. All was in vain. They might have saved the Library if they had not been forced to rush to and fro in order to deal with outbreaks of fire elsewhere in Greystoke Place. When, about 04.40 hours, the roof caught fire, the guard, with the help of Troup Horne, began to save as much of the Library's contents as they could, beginning with valuable books in the Librarian's room, the New English Dictionary, and the catalogue ; next, loyal to their duty as physicists, a number of books on Physics. Soon, however, they were forced to give up. The main reason for the rescue in the end of more books in Science than in Arts was the nature of the fire and the arrangement of the Library itself. A fire-engine and a second fire-squad from Essex had arrived soon after the roof of Greystoke was set ablaze. The members of this party did their best to help. They came from Rayleigh near Southend, about fifty miles outside the area of London, and were unfamiliar with the conditions which they found. Had their hose-junctions fitted the hydrants in London, our Library might well have escaped with nothing more than damage by water. But the delay which took place before this difficulty was overcome, and the great shortage of water after the bursting of the water-main mentioned before, made impossible the task of saving the Library and part of Greystoke Place. All that the tired and blear-eyed members of our fire-guard could do now was to help the firemen in their successful protection of Field House west of Greystoke Place. When anyone stood on the top of our main building, only reddish masses of smoke and bursts of flame could be seen ; it was after 05.00 hours before the already present daylight could appear. Of the two thousand and more fires caused in all London in this raid, hundreds were still out of control when the signal for "all-clear" so long awaited was at last heard, shortly before 06.00 hours. Before then, while part of Greystoke was

Looking down on the Library after the fire

Ground-floor view of the Library after the fire

still burning, our Library of 40,000 books was blazing fiercely, to become shortly a flaring smouldering sodden mass of ruin and ashes in a shell of hot bricks.

Fire, smoke, wreckage. Approaches to the College

People who were coming into London in bright sunny weather after dawn on the Sunday morning could see over the city the immense pall of false cloud which was real smoke. There were but few who found such evidence as might make them even so much as guess at the number of persons who lost their lives in this raid—one thousand four hundred and thirty-six ; or the number of the injured who were much more than this. But the sight which met all who approached the college's area and other parts was nevertheless weird and then shocking. Of all the damage suffered in it during the six years of the whole war, about four-fifths had been done in the preceding night. Among the members of the college, some, like the Vice-Master—Professor Jackson—who was called in by telephone, came very early ; most arrived according to their duties of the day ; all could tell a striking story of what they found. Approach to the college from the north, along Fetter Lane, could be made only by scrambling through broken glass over the collapsed fronts of buildings. The blazing wrecks of these had been given up as hopeless ; any policeman or fire-fighter whom people saw was so weary that he merely stood a passive figure in a landscape livelier than he. Persons who came from London Bridge had to walk to the college by way of St. Bartholomew's Hospital because all roads between this and the river Thames were closed. On all that were open, broken glass lay deep ; here and there in the streets one could see sand-bags which had been used to stifle blazing bombs ; and long hose-pipes were lying about like dead snakes. The present writer came through Lincoln's Inn where small pieces of burnt paper and other material were falling like a thick storm of black snow ; the eastern end of the street Breams Buildings was shrouded in smoke ; there were also dying fires and vast clouds of smoke all over the parts north and north-east of the college and of the intact Public Record Office south of the college in Fetter Lane. Furnival Street and Fetter Lane were closed, but Chancery Lane and the street Breams Buildings remained open. At the college itself people as they came saw both the disaster which had fallen on it and also the tasks of quenching and salvage still going on. Of many records and memories of this day which might be given, I can include one only, which must suffice. Dr. L. Simons wrote as follows:—" By May 1941, it had become a routine matter for my wife[1] and me to start out in our car on a Sunday morning, from our temporary house in Datchet which was near the Admiralty Department where I worked, to do our day's work at the college. We always turned the Fleet Street—Chancery Lane corner at 9.30 a.m., and we carried with us our customary packed lunch. But on this Sunday morning of 11th May we already knew that something a little more serious had happened in London overnight. From Datchet we saw the angry red glow over London and the scintillations of the exploding shells had been denser than usual. That morning we never got as far as our Chancery Lane corner. From Hyde Park corner, looking east, the town seemed to be covered with an extra black London fog. By devious routes, to avoid glass and hose pipes, we eventually parked our car in Bell Yard, next to the Law Courts. My class was waiting for me as usual, but I took the precaution of posting someone to warn us, whilst lecturing, if our roof had caught. A number of senior Arts teachers, including my wife, had gathered in the Junior Common Room, left of the main entrance, where they sat around in isolated groups to give their customary classes."

Classes and salvage combined

About the usual hour, which was 10 o'clock, as Simons indicates above, students and staff were at college to attend the morning's classes, some of which began as usual, though not in Greystoke, but in any place which could be found. For example, French and German classes were held at the same time in separate groups in the Students' Common Room in Breams

[1] See page 49.

Buildings. A number of the classes there took place, on different floors, in rooms bounded on one side by the eastern wall; now and again a student or the lecturer would feel the inner surface of this wall to see whether it was becoming too hot for safety. But the work of teaching in different parts of the college was mingled with active help given, especially between classes, to a busy throng of salvagers who, following the example of Professor Jackson and Miss Hilda Keet[1] (Secretary to the Master), spent the whole morning in conquering flames and saving documents, books, specimens, furniture and other equipment. These were carried through smoke and murk from Greystoke Place, by students, teachers and others, across planks laid down over the water-flooded forecourt, while all was filled with smoke and deep in hot water, and flames and smoke were still to be seen round window-panes and rafters. Some specimens belonging to the Department of Zoology were brought out and set up against a wall. Most of the apparatus belonging to the Department of Geology, and housed in sheds near the Library, was retrieved. When Dr. R. J. Bartlett reached his room, he found on guard at the entrance a fireman, who was not sure whether the floor would stand under any weight. Stand however, it did, and soon some students in Psychology, with the help of Bartlett and a visitor, Dr. Philpott, of University College, were moving their apparatus across to the main buildings ; where on the suggestion of the Vice-Master, these salvagers were soon attending a class in the Council Chamber. I was helped in bringing out books from rooms in Greystoke by several students on whose skin the pale patches amidst the black were not enough for recognition of persons. This seemed natural enough. But in the afternoon (and even before), more startling sights were seen when students came unwashed, with dirty hands and black faces and filthy clothes, to classes, and listened to teachers who looked no better than they. Never perhaps had such grimy faces, hands and clothing been

[1] We could not easily think of a nature farther removed than Hilda Keet's from any sort of warlike violence ; yet now we saw her, topped with a borrowed metal helmet—a "tin hat" most unlike the softer samples of her own varied millinery—spurring on students and others to become busier.

seen at academic lectures ; nor such quantities of them together in such a state.

"After my lecture I hurried out to look at the scene," says Dr. Simons. " The building on the east side of the College was well alight, but there was little danger from there because its west flank wall was independent of our east flank wall, against which it abutted, with a few inches of air-space between them. We had a few windows in the well in our wall, but there were none in the other wall, and so I felt that the fire would not get through to us. This proved correct. The Law Stationers' building, off-right from our front, was alight, as was Greystoke and most of the east side of Fetter Lane.

"Only a few hose pipes carried water. I found one discarded nozzle and tried my hand at scientifically spraying the Law Stationers', for water loses its efficiency if the temperature of the surface on which it falls produces what is known as the 'spheroidal state.' The surplus water, falling on the Greystoke forecourt, was being scooped up in a pannikin by a woman student and passed to someone trying to cool off the books in the Library, whilst E. P. George, sitting astride a wall, was handing out smouldering books as fast as he could. The staircase of the building next to the College to the east looked exactly like the interior of a blast furnace."

After the first floors of Greystoke Place were cleared, the salvagers did their best at higher levels. Dr. Henderson and Dr. Llewellyn, by forcing a way into Miss Marjorie Daunt's room, removed some books and other valuable property of hers. Of the Library the upper floor had been wholly destroyed, and the lower library had caught fire through the heat of the concrete which lay over it, and was still burning strongly. When the stairs to and from the main library were burned away, the firemen were busy trying to tackle the fire in the lower library through a hole in the floor. But a new attack on this part of the burning building was begun when Dr. Henderson seized an axe from the belt of a fireman ; with this he and Professor Jackson broke in the upper panels of a door, hidden by shelves and books on the inside, but approachable from a passage.

This enabled them to use a hose ; and here the fire was quelled. More could not yet be done, because people were thwarted by heat and smoke. However, some persons, wearing gas-masks, sprayed with stirrup-pumps, on to the remnants of the Library, liquid supplied by a human buckets-chain leading from puddled water in the forecourt to a jutting piece of the ground-floor. Growing difficulties were eased when expert firemen came with two large hoses, whereupon the stirrup-pumps were used to sprinkle the smouldering roof, afterwards removed, of Greystoke Place. More water was obtained from a cistern and then from drains. There was no control ; but nothing was lost as a result of this, and at length all the fire-fighters and salvagers retired to have their hurts tended and to receive hot drinks. Our Mrs. E. Francis, despite her well-lived seventy-five years of age, of which most had been spent in devoted service to the college, despite also the hindrances of smoke, rubble, glass, and kindly but useless efforts of a policeman to guide her to an easier approach, had long before reached the college to direct the service of catering ; and at 12.30 after noon, the refectory having opened, one hundred and fifty lunches were served without aid of gas or water. The fire-fighting party from Essex continued to give their services until, after twelve hours of work, they ate beef and drank beer, late in the afternoon, and received our grateful thanks.

We looked with foreboding towards the night to come ; but to our relief nothing was heard except one or two alerts. On the night of the 12th—13th fires were still glowing along Fetter Lane, Shoe Lane, and elsewhere ; and water was still being applied from hoses on the 13th. Fetter Lane remained closed for a long time.

Salvage from the Library

The bitterest shock of all this fierce turmoil fell on Dr. M. Clive Hildyard. She saw the destruction of the library of which she had charge. She and her assistant staff, Miss N. H. Evans and Miss K. I. Garrett, with ready and welcome help from others in both Faculties, began, even while Greystoke Place was still burning, to gather and arrange the remains of the

Library in new quarters in the main building—a task at which they worked steadily and untiringly for days. On Monday, the 12th of May, a discovery was made which brought some comfort and encouragement. The lower Library, which contained the lending section, could now be entered, and it was found that a good part of the books there had survived. Many were badly scorched, and nearly all were soaking wet, those which were below table-level having been under water for many hours ; but large numbers, tightly packed even before the raid and now swollen by their soaking, looked worthy of salvage because the pages of print between the covers seemed to be unspoilt if not dry, and might still be read easily. After some use of a crowbar, each book was carefully brought out by the staff of the Library—helped by B. Chibnall and some other students, such as he could collect from day to day to aid him—and cleaned ; all that were still damp were laid down separately and open or partly open out of doors in the forecourt of Greystoke Place, so as to be dried by air and by the welcome sun which by good fortune shone brightly during much of the next fortnight. Passers by on the highway Breams Buildings could see, beyond the gravestones which remain from the long disused burial-place, rows of books, and, behind them, lines of animals' bones belonging to our Department of Zoology. By the night of Wednesday, the 14th, all of the usable books, about 4,000 in number, had been removed before the rain of that night began to fall. The general sections devoted to Classics, English, History and Biography, French, German, Italian and Spanish were totally destroyed, as were all the periodicals and all the Zoological books[1] recently housed in the main Library ; most of the Geographical books also were lost. The books ultimately saved included those which were in the lending section as described above ; nearly all the books in the subjects Mathematics and Economics ; and also a large and most valuable book borrowed from another library in London. It was stained and sodden, yet every letter and stop was legible on its return to the lenders.

[1] They included such as were out on loan when the departmental library of the Department of Zoology was burnt in September 1940 (see pages 60-62), together with some others acquired since then.

The Lending Library after the fire

The Reference Library after the fire

Disposal of rescued books. Replacements

Generous offers of help were received from University College and King's College less than a week after the disaster. A new place was found, for the surviving books and for replacements and further books, in the committee-room in our main building—a room which, as many a single book itself did for some years, retained a faintly scorched smell for a long time. Newly acquired books not needed for present use were sent away outside London until safer times should come. The College owes special thanks to one of the Governors, The Dowager Viscountess Harcourt, who introduced our Librarian to Lady Caroline Grenville, living at Shackleford, near Godalming in Surrey. Lady Caroline kindly put a room at the disposal of the college and housed some hundreds of books during the war-years to come. Bound periodicals from the Department of Chemistry were taken in by Dr. Ward, Principal of Guildford Technical College ; botanical periodicals were received by Royal Holloway College, at Englefield Green, Surrey; and many books were also taken to Greenford. Bookcases for the makeshift skeleton-library in the college's committee-room were borrowed from various parts of the building ; and the London School of Economics kindly lent us some steel bookshelves until the war should be ended. Appeals for gifts of books or money, and gifts made without appeal, had brought more than one thousand books from kind well-wishers before the end of June, and very many more before the beginning of the next session. One of the earliest donors was Dr. G. P. Gooch, who earned special thanks for his generosity. Books of his own which he gave to our Library included the Dictionary of National Biography and a large number of French, German and Italian texts to replace those which had been destroyed. Other outstanding donors were Professor R. W. Chambers, Professor Oliver Elton, Dr. Albert Mansbridge and Mr. G. F. Troup Horne ; and, among others now, and later, the British Academy, the Early English Text Society, Friends of the National Libraries, the National Central Library, and the Royal Geographical Society. Our Zoologists were able to remain in Greystoke Place, but later their material was gathered into the College's Theatre, and soon all the skeletons of animals and other specimens were taken partly to the Department of Botany at Royal Holloway College, and partly to Dr. Vera Fretter's room there.

Rooms in Field House. Examinations

There was a meeting of the Governors on the 15th of May ; a general meeting of the Students' Union on the 17th ; and a meeting of its Council on the 19th. On Saturday and Sunday, the 17th-18th, the week-end classes took place as usual. Teaching went on steadily. Some classes were held in the open air of the forecourt of Greystoke Place. But within a week after the raid excellent space had been provided for classes in Field House, consisting of eight rooms of moderate size and one smaller one, to which was soon added another room for Psychology. These rooms were generously offered by the Directors of the Field Press at about half the normal rent because of their long connection and their sympathy with the college in its difficult situation[1]. The Directors' very thorough scheme for protection against air-raids, installed at much expense, was free of all cost to the college ; which decided later to provide a fire-guard for Field House on Saturdays and Sundays by day during term-time. Moreover in Greystoke Place a few small rooms off the staircase were again in use. Books scorched and newly dried were being read by students preparing themselves for examinations. Personal discussions with teachers, and loans of books and notes by them, helped further the students' task of revision. Once more were examinations held in our main building by the College and the University without interruption[2]; once more the proportion of our students who entered for the University examinations, and the successes gained,

[1] The College was looking also for a place elsewhere whither it could move without confusion if further attacks should make this necessary.

[2] There were alerts but no more, on the 1st of June (three hours) ; the 4th (three hours) : the 6th (short) ; the 19th (one hour) ; and the 26th-27th of June ; also on the 27th-28th of July.

were greater than they were during earlier years of peace.[1] The unexpected respite was caused by Hitler's earlier decision to turn his arms treacherously in a mighty attack against Russia, which he did without warning on the 22nd of June, and air-raids of any sort on Britain were rare until 1943-1944.[2]

Plant-life and animal-life on the bombed sites

The terrible havoc wrought by the raid described above created east of Fetter Lane a wild and gaunt waste of which only a small part had been built on again at the time, in 1953, when this history was finished. In the years which followed the raid, the ruined spaces became covered with many kinds of plants, especially pink rose-bay willow-herb, and yellow "Oxford" ragwort which was in due course discovered by crimson-and-dark cinnabar moths. A number of other insects of the countryside were often seen there, and found their way into the buildings which the college occupied until 1951. One or more pairs of London's new breeding bird, the black redstart, nested in the ruins of this area every year from 1943 onwards to 1951, and the song of the male birds could be heard at the college even during lectures throughout the months of

[1] The damage sustained in 1940 and 1941 by buildings belonging to institutions of the University of London indicates that in some cases, if the institutions had not gone elsewhere, the work of internal students in them might have ceased altogether. The buildings of University College were more than once attacked by explosive and incendiary bombs, and a large part of them was destroyed, including about 100,000 books which had not been taken away with the college ; King's College's building in the Strand was damaged as were also two of its hostels, and, elsewhere, its Library at Bristol which had been moved thither. About one-third of the buildings of Bedford College was destroyed by fire. The buildings of Imperial College, Westfield College, the School of Oriental Studies, King's College of Household and Social Science, and the London School of Hygiene also suffered. Nearly all hospitals attached to Medical Schools of the University met with severe damage, and the Medical College of St. Bartholomew's Hospital was almost wholly destroyed. The London School of Medicine for Women was damaged badly. The last great raid, besides ravaging the old buildings of Birkbeck College, as recorded here, did also some harm by the steel skeleton of its new building in Bloomsbury, and there caused the closing of Connaught Hall. As a result, the Warden of the Hall, G. F. Troup Horne, became a permanent member of our fire-guard at No. 20 Breams Buildings.

[2] Through air-raids on Britain during the year extending from June 1940 to June 1941, 43,381 civilian people had been killed and about 50,856 badly hurt.

spring, summer, and early autumn. The removal of an isolated ruined building in Fetter Lane opened up still more fully to the college a view which included St. Paul's Cathedral and the Old Bailey, and was utterly unknown before. Lovers of the charm which old houses bring will regret most of all the loss of Nevill's Court with cottages built, it seems, in the seventeenth century and provided with gardens of which bushes of privet still remained when the college moved from the area. Several of the foundations of destroyed buildings were turned, in precaution for the future, into tanks of "static" water, swarming later with "water-boatmen" insects, and favoured by visiting mallard ducks and, from late summer to spring, yellow-breasted grey wagtails ; but destined not to be put to the uses for which they had been intended. In the summer of 1941, however, no living wild thing of any sort, except house-sparrows and " London " pigeons, could be seen or heard among the ruins.

Foundation Oration. Future policy. Radio-Physics

The college was much heartened towards the future by the delivery on the 18th of June, after the Administrative and Establishment Staffs had done hard work in preparing the war-scarred theatre, of the Foundation Oration[1] in celebration of the college's 117th anniversary, by His Grace the Lord Archbishop of York, Dr. Temple, on the subject of "Education in Peace," the Vice-Chancellor of London University, Professor F. Horton, F.R.S., being in the chair. There was on this occasion much less ceremony than is usual on "Foundation Day," a fact which, in view of the hardness of the times, helped to make still vivider our memories of the speaker, soon to become, when Archbishop of Canterbury, President of the College for a short time before his death. On the 19th of June our Governors resolved that in the coming session the college should offer courses in hours of daylight on Saturdays and Sundays, from the 6th of September onwards, using other days of the week if need arose ; and that a statement be issued to the public, to

[1] The first since the war began. The Foundation Oration is traditionally celebrated every year, as near as possible to the 2nd of December. It became widely movable because of the war.

the present students, and to new applicants for admission as students, saying that all usual courses would be provided if this were possible, and if the number of students justified such a policy ; there would be in general no day courses for full-time students. Day-courses were however approved for holders of State Bursaries in Radio-Physics (Radio Communications), who would take Physics, Mathematics and Radio-Physics ; and in Chemistry, who would take Chemistry, and Physics or some other subsidiary subject, in order that the former class might be trained by 1942, and the other by 1943. Successful candidates in Radio-Physics would be given a University Certificate of Proficiency, and their results would count towards a B.Sc. Degree if they took the rest of a Final Examination later. However, none of these "Bursars," who were to be allocated to institutions of universities, were immediately sent to Birkbeck College. But the courses in Radio-Physics were, under the Government's earlier directions, now fully developed by E. P. George, in the college's Department of Physics. An elementary course with practicals began on the 1st of July, to be continued, except for a short interval in August, during session 1941-1942 ; and an advanced course with practicals was appointed to begin in January 1942. In the Bachelor of Science (Special) Degree, alternative papers and a practical in Radio-Physics were worked into the University's syllabus.

Professor H. Jackson becomes Acting Master

On the 15th of May 1941, the Master had been informed by the Minister of Food that he had been appointed Deputy-Secretary to that Ministry. The Governors refused to accept his proffered resignation from the Mastership of the College, granted him leave of absence, and resolved to appoint, for the time of such leave, an Acting Master, having functions and duties identical with those of the Master ; and appointed to be Acting Master, from the 1st of August 1941, Professor H. Gordon Jackson ; and the office of Vice-Master, hitherto held by Jackson, lapsed forthwith.

Students' activities

Special interests among the students during this third term of a remarkable session, and in the vacation following, included an inaugural meeting, held on the 4th of May, of the new Socialist Society, and a flourishing season for the Cricket Club and the Tennis Club at the college's sports ground at Greenford, which was now used also by troops stationed near and by others in the various services supporting the war. From the beginning of the year 1941 onwards, part of our pavilion there was let to A. Gallenkamp and Company Ltd., a firm of chemical manufacturers who had been forced to leave their office in Bishopsgate through action by the enemy ; and a fund created out of the rent was reserved for the restoration of the ground after the war. The three parts of the session's *Lodestone* were edited by J. Hickman and Effie Campbell. The session saw also the creation of the Birkbeck College National Savings Group. A "Friend of Birkbeck"[1] who by his wish remained unknown had, in the summer of 1940, provided £1,800 wherewith by agreement the Treasurer of the "Friends of Birkbeck" bought £1,800 worth of National War-Savings certificates in blank, and placed them at the college's disposal, open[2] to all connected directly with the college and to their dependants and friends, for re-purchase at fifteen shillings a unit, all of the first issue being dated the 1st of August 1940, and bearing interest from that date no matter when they were re-bought. Payment was on an instalment-plan, being spread over twelve months. As the purchase-money was repaid, it was re-invested in further certificates placed at subscribers' disposal for the duration of the war. All the original certificates were taken up in the first year ; and by the summer term of the session this Group had, after appeal, paid for seventy-four parachutes for airmen.

Books for prisoners of war and others

In July and later in the year the college was in communication with some members of the War Organisation of the British Red Cross Society and Order of St. John of Jerusalem,

[1] See p. 36.

[2] Five hundred certificates were reserved for undergraduates.

Books and Specimens drying outside Greystoke

Open-air lecture

with special reference at first to the obtaining of books for a former student at the college, Sergeant J. Hawes, a prisoner of war in Germany (for whom a Friend of Birkbeck provided books[1]) to be sent by the Society ; and then with regard to the general project of giving books for the Educational Department of the Red Cross so as to enable prisoners of war to continue their academic studies. Books were also given by members of the staff through Marjorie Daunt during this session for people, especially children, who every night took shelter from air-raids in the underground railway-stations of London.

End of the Session

At the end of June there were 143 students in Arts, 128 in Science, so that in this session the college was at a very low ebb of students' numbers (not as a result of the fiery ordeal during May), but at a high tide of zest for recovery. The drop in numbers caused by the coming of the war seemed to more than one department to be accompanied by a drop in quality also among students taking undergraduate courses, but the results of examinations brought no general assent to this view; moreover in at least one department the numbers and quality of post-graduate students were better than they were before the war. There may be no significance in these impressions. It is noteworthy that whereas in session 1937-8, out of 972 students 122 (12½%) graduated, in session 1938-9 out of 938 students 98 (10½%) graduated), and in 1939-40, out of 488 students 75 (15%) graduated, and in this session 1940-41, out of 272 students, 56 (21%) graduated. The second year of the college's experience in time of war left us all full of hope and confidence in the future. There were some of us who had been stricken by sudden death ; some had been injured ; the homes of some had been destroyed or shattered ; the buildings of our college were in sad shape and shabby condition ; we had faced problem after problem in some of which differences of opinion were very sharp ; but in all our difficulties we were helped by something mental which seems to inspire all who join the college for any length of time—something which stifles quarrels and which we have come to call "The Birkbeck Spirit."

[1] The Germans apparently confiscated one of them because its author was a Cohen ; whereupon another book was sent for Sergeant Hawes.

CHAPTER FOUR

RESPITE AND RECOVERY

SESSIONS 1941-1942 AND 1942-1943

(1) Session 1941-1942

Progress of the War

WITH the end of the session 1940-1941 the dramatic tension of the college's history slackens, because during more than two years, while Britain, Russia, and then the United States, in spite of dismal disasters and setbacks, were working everywhere the slow ruin of Germany, on Britain air-raids were rarely made ; and though they were harmful where they occurred, our area escaped with but very slight damage. Despite the cessation of air-raids, Britain like all the free world was filled with desperate anxiety as Russia reeled before Germany's appalling onslaught. All who remember those days can hardly have names such as Brest-Litovsk, Minsk, Smolensk, Vyazma, Kalinin, Tula, Kiev, Kharkov, brought to mind without recalling also their capture one by one by the Germans. Early in December, Moscow was almost surrounded and besieged. Yet Russia fought and toiled and stood ; that mighty and monstrous machine of Germany was halted. In Africa we had done well enough by the end of the year. In the Far East a new menace had appeared as early as July. Japan seized vantage ports, absorbed French Indo-China, and became an ally of the "Axis" ; but on the 7th of December, by her violent attack on Pearl Harbour, she brought the United States of America into the war with us.

Working-space for the College. Fire-guard. Classes and teachers

The loss of space by Birkbeck College during May, 1941, had been made up by the renting of rooms in Field House, which proved to be a great boon to us. The best possible use was made too of the standing ruins of Greystoke Place, and the Theatre became available once more. Even so, some anxiety was inevitable lest still further damage should leave the college without enough space and equipment necessary for the teaching of all its students ; and arrangements were discussed whereby the college might use the vacant buildings of Bedford College (in Regents Park) ; the newly closed Connaught Hall (in Bloomsbury) ; the buildings still available for the University of London in South Kensington ; and possibly, at week-ends, The Imperial College of Science. Cessation of air-raids made such forethought needless, but at the same time brought steady increase in our students' numbers, as will be seen. For the better protection of our buildings against fire-bombs in particular, the daily inspection of the whole premises before nightfall included henceforth a tour of the roofs of the main building. After mounting through the ceiling of a laboratory in the Department of Chemistry, the party moved along the gullies and climbed the roof-slopes at a steepish angle by the aid of duck-boards. One had to keep one's head as well as one's feet, because a slip or a fall might have led to a drop of eighty feet to the ground. In the western gully, explanation was given to new and other members of the guard about the method of lowering injured persons from the roof by means of a rope-cradle. The tour ended with an exercise, inside the building, in which the whole party moved swiftly down the stairs in darkness from top to bottom without using any lights, in case such a descent should be necessary during an air-raid. In these tours over the roofs the guard made the discovery that Troup Horne, a man of goodly size, added to his many gifts a nimble agility and an unexpected look of lightness, whenever he led the guard on this, for newcomers, hair-raising adventure. Members past and present of the fighting forces who, on visits to the college, were taken over the roof, had the impression that it was better to be in the army. The winter of 1941-2 added to the normal tasks of the guard, since its members had to clear thick snow from the duck-boards. The absence of air-raids freed the minds of the guard from almost all foreboding ; yet in no way were care and watchfulness relaxed ; and in 1942 transmission to the college of any alarm-signal from *The Daily Mirror* was made surer by means of a microphone on a window-sill, an amplifier in the office of our Students' Union, and a loud-speaker in our fire-guard's room.

After the opening of the first term of the new session 1941-2 on the 5th of September, the college followed the policy which had been so severely tested and so luckily justified in the previous session. The holding of classes was kept within the hours of daylight on Saturdays and Sundays, beginning at 9.30 in the morning and ending in the evening or afternoon half-an-hour before the national time for "black-out," or not later than 8 in the evenings so long as "black-out" time came later than 8.30 ; and the evenings of other days were used only when the students could go home daily before the time of "black-out" began. As in session 1940-1941, members of the teaching staffs of Bedford College, King's College, University College and Queen Mary College, and of the London School of Economics (none of which returned to London) and further the Chelsea Polytechnic, were of great help to us during week-ends, while during mid-week our teaching staff was helping the Imperial College of Science, and King's College, Queen Mary College and Bedford College, and also the Universities of Reading and St. Andrews.

The first term. Increase of students' numbers. Difficulties of students

Under the guidance of Professor Jackson the Acting Master, both the Faculty of Arts (Dean : Dr. McClean), and the Faculty of Science (Dean : Dr. Barrow), found an active session before them. By the end of September the numbers of students were 178 in Arts, 199 in Science, a good increase on the numbers at the beginning of the last two sessions ; and by the beginning of December, 226 in Arts, and 218 in Science ; and the Faculty of Science then felt that it could hardly admit more under the present conditions. Indeed, the Departments of Chemistry and Physics, in spite of the provision of an additional Physics Laboratory for the use of holders of State Bursaries[1] but not yet required for such use, were full before mid-October, and the Departments of Botany and Zoology nearly full by that time. The Department of Zoology was able to spread itself during this and two following sessions in Greystoke Place to help its needs. When the Intermediate classes in Zoology grew in numbers of attending students, the Department used also two rooms in the Department of Botany. When those who were attending a Final course became very many, the theatre of the Department of Chemistry was borrowed. Material required for classes was fetched from Royal Holloway College every week and returned thither. In addition to this, Vera Fretter now came regularly from Royal Holloway College to teach our students zoology at Birkbeck College, while A. Graham in mid-weeks lectured in return to her students at Royal Holloway College. The hindrance to good study, for Honours courses especially, caused by the loss of our Library, was the more serious in the case of students in Modern Languages, in that, for a long time already, they had had no access to Europe. But exiles in this country were of welcome use to them. In London, The Linguists' Club and L'Institut Français du Royaume-Uni were available ; to some, the British Institute in Paris, as it was still called, proved helpful by holding holiday-courses for students who could not go abroad, and several people got into touch later with the Université d'Algiers by letter.

Departmental changes

Professor J. D. Bernal,[2] Head of our Department of Physics, was able to take charge of this Department while still continuing to serve with the Ministry of Home Security. Dr. L. Simons, who therefore ceased to be Acting Head of the Department of Physics, nevertheless found it best to give up his duties at the Admiralty in order to give his full time to the

[1] See above, p. 101.

[2] Professor Bernal wrote three pamphlets on the bombing of London. In 1941 he was associated with Bomber Command and in 1942 became Scientific Adviser to the Chief of Combined Operations.

work of Physics at the College. E. P. George continued the elementary course in Radio-Physics (Radio-Communications) which had been started in July. In the Department of Geography, Miss M. E. Odell was appointed to be a temporary part-time lecturer, since members of its teaching staff, except Professor Eva Taylor, had taken posts in Government Departments : Dr. H. C. Henderson was Flight-Lieutenant in the Royal Air Force ; and Dr. E. Willatts was seconded entirely to the Ministry of Works and Buildings (Lord Reith's Regional Planning Scheme), and later resigned his post at Birkbeck College. The Department of Philosophy, in view of the large increase in the number of students, was glad to obtain the re-appointment of Ruth Saw of the staff of Bedford College. In Botany, the return of Professor Dame Helen Gwynne-Vaughan, Head of the Department, was likewise most welcome ; the acceptance of a government post in the Ministry of Aircraft Production by Dr. F. Steward, who now ceased to be Acting Head of the Department, and the marked increase of its students' numbers, caused the appointment of Dr. H. Duerden, of the Chelsea Polytechnic, to be assistant lecturer. In Economics arrangements were made for an Intermediate Course at Birkbeck College, during the absence in war-time of the London School of Economics from London, for external students intending to take the Degree of Bachelor of Science (Economics) later.[1] The courses in Psychology conducted by R. J. Bartlett of the staff of King's College, and by Dr. C. A. Mace, of the staff of Bedford College, and the courses in Spanish by R. J. Carey and Miss J. Perry, both of King's College, were continued at Birkbeck College.[2] Our Department of Geology now lacked the services of Dr. F. Smithson ; and the Department of Chemistry the services of A. Welch ; both teachers having gone to take up appointments elsewhere. From the latter Department also Dr. F. Llewellyn was partially seconded to the Ministry of Supply.

[1] Birkbeck College was naturally not recognised by the University in the University's Faculty of Economics ; so these students could not be Internal. In our Faculty of Arts however, Economics subjects were available for Internal students in both Intermediate and Final (B.A. General) courses.

[2] See above, pp. 40, 41.

Public lectures

Further series of lunch-hour lectures were arranged to be delivered by The Hon. Harold Nicolson (two on Problems of a Peace Settlement) ; Dr. C. Joad (three on Our Civilisation and its Future) ; Dr. N. Pevsner (six on the English House from the Middle Ages to the Present Day) ; Sir Bernard Pares, K.B.E. (one on Russia) ; G. Faber (one on Books of To-morrow) ; and A. G. Street (one on the Countryman's Place in our National Life ; and one on Farming after the War). Through the kindness and public spirit of Professor Jackson, the Acting Master, the present writer, Professor E. H. Warmington, being Head of the Department of Classics, and Miss E. C. Gedge, were allowed to revive the London Branch of the Classical Association (inactive since war began) at Birkbeck College, which from now onwards, until the session following the end of the war, afforded space for lectures open to the public and given by experts in the old Greek and Roman civilisations, some coming from various parts of the country as guests of the college. There was thus a sort of nucleus of this Branch in existence at the college only, for four years, with Professor Warmington as sole officer, until the return of members to London. The lecturers who helped us in this connection, and the lectures which they gave, mostly in the Students' Common Room, during the present session were : Dr. N. Pevsner (in the first term one lecture on the Spirit of Greek Architecture, in the second term one on the Spirit of Roman Art) ; R. P. Winnington-Ingram (one on Ancient Greeks and Modern Europe ; one on Aeschylus the Feminist) ; Dr. C. Joad (four on Greek Philosophy, Plato and Aristotle, which during the winter-spring term drew many people to our cold and patched-up Theatre) ; and Professor E. H. Warmington (one each on the Discovery of Britain and the Baltic by the Ancient Greeks ; the Circumnavigation of Africa by the Ancient Greeks ; and the Discovery of India and China by the Greeks and Romans).

Students' activities

In the Students' Union, with E. P. George as President, and Lena Chivers as the other representative on the Governing

Body, increase in numbers enabled a welcome extension of social-academic gatherings to take place, including both the Arts Society and the Science Society[1]. From the Arts Society, the Literary Society in a vigorous revival, and the Société Française, the Historical Society, and a new Philosophical Society, all separated off as was allowed in the arrangements made in 1939. Assemblies large and small were addressed by members of the staff and by students on various subjects. A Squash Club was formed in the first term ; but no outdoor winter games took place during the session. The Union now began to take a more active part with the National Union of Students, with which it was always in close touch, in inter-collegiate activities. The Music Society heard on the 23rd of November a lecture by Professor Jackson on "The Orchestra of Handel and Bach," which was followed later in the session by two piano recitals by Jean Hamilton (Mrs. Maud), on the 21st of February and the 2nd of May. Since some of the students and the staff had joined the Association of Scientific Workers during the last session, a branch for the students and staff of Birkbeck College alone was begun in October. The Students' Common Room was often used for lectures. Socials also were held there and outside the college in other premises, because the Committee Room had become the Library since the fire of May.

Centenary of the death of the College's Founder

In December the college remembered with gratitude its Founder, Dr. George Birkbeck, who died on the 1st of December 1841. The Public Press of Britain gave wide notice to the great services rendered by him for education, and to the striking story of the growth of his London Mechanics' Institution into Birkbeck College of the University of London. The college also produced a special study of Dr. Birkbeck, by Professor J. Sutherland, as a supplement to its Report for the Session.[2]

[1] For these Societies see p. 45. The Arts Society owed much for its revival to Miss A. Moore, whose work in this respect deserves high praise.

[2] *The Lodestone*, Autumn Term, 1941 (Vol. 34, No. 1), likewise marked this centenary.

Loan of apparatus by the College

Late in the term (which ended on the 19th of December), after an appeal from the Ministry of Supply for the loan of apparatus, twenty-four microscopes from our Departments of Botany and Zoology, three petrological microscopes from the Department of Zoology, and eight balances from the Department of Chemistry were lent by the College to the Ministry and were gratefully received with a guarantee for return in good condition and repair.

age 111, fifth line of the
narrative: 'Department of Zoology'
should be 'Department of Geology'.

eful thanks,
f the College
the credit of
our New Building Fund. In a letter of thanks, Her Majesty was informed of the present condition of the College and the harm sustained by it in May, and illustrations of the damage done were sent to her.

The second term. News of the War. Courses for Jewish refugees

In spite of the entry of the United States into the war, and the close co-operation established between the Americans and the British in December 1941 and January 1942, the opening months of the year 1942 were miserable enough. Hong Kong, Malaya, Singapore, the Dutch East Indies, the Philippines, and Burma all fell before the Japanese who were not checked until May and June. Throughout 1942 the menace of German submarines was very great.

[1] In 1935 Her Majesty, when she was Duchess of York, joined with the Duke of York, then President of Birkbeck College, before he became King, in launching from the Mansion House an appeal for funds in aid of the College's new building ; to which she made a most generous contribution ; which also she opened, when Queen Mother, on the 28th April 1953, in the reign of her daughter Queen Elizabeth II. "We cannot forget the interest which you, Ma'am, and His Late Majesty King George VI showed in the life and activities of the College during a period of great moment in its history."—From the address of welcome to Her Majesty the Queen Mother, by the Master, Dr. J. Lockwood (successor to H. G. Jackson) on that date.

When our second term (9th January—30th March) of the session began, a few more students had been admitted. At the request of the organisation of Jewish Pioneers for Palestine, responsible for the welfare of exiled students who were of Central European Jewish parentage, arrangements were made to give at the college, to groups of such students, five-week courses on Elementary Agriculture and other subjects which might prove useful to them if they went to live in Palestine. The result was agricultural seminar-studies which consisted of an intensive course of lectures and practical work in the fundamental principles of agriculture, with the expert help of Sir John Russell and the staff of the Rothamsted Experimental Station and with the support of the British Council. The keenness and intelligence of the students helped much towards the success of this venture.

Education in the Forces

At the end of January 1942, the Master reported to the Academic Board of the College that the suggestion made by him a year ago to the London Regional Council and to the authorities of the Army about provision of education in the Forces had been adopted, but units in the London area seldom stayed for more than nine weeks and were liable to dispersal at any time; moreover there were few large concentrations of troops where personal instruction was worth while. Members of the staff, though registered, had not been called upon to act ; but Dr. R. J. McClean had delivered at Chigwell, Essex, a course in German attended by about twenty-four men and women of the Royal Air Force stationed there, and also gave instruction at the college in Dutch and Norwegian to persons singly. The latter experiment proved to be of importance for the college later,[1] as will be seen.

Public lectures continued. Economics

The public lectures which were begun during the first term, as described above, were continued. After requests made by some students working for the Intermediate Examination in the

[1] See pp. 114, 115, 142, 179.

Faculty of Economics with a view to the Degree of Bachelor of Science (Economics), R. C. FitzGerald, LL.B., of Lincoln's Inn, once a student at the college, became lecturer, in our Department of Economics, on the British Constitution.

Students' activities

Among the activities of the students, the Société Française produced "L'Anglais tel qu'on le parle," on the 28th and 29th of March ; and the Birkbeck Players on the same days gave most interesting performances of Shakespeare's *Comedy of Errors*. The Student Christian Movement held on the 7th of March a debate with the Philosophical Society, besides its weekly meetings at St. Dunstan's during the whole session, and in the Easter vacation Thatcham, near Newbury, was the place where its conference of this year was held. The sports-ground at Greenford was again available for people not connected with the college, particularly members of the Home Guard. The college learnt with regret that when on the 14th of February, 1942, an aeroplane fell to earth on the sports-ground, the Polish pilot was killed.

Deaths of men prominent in the college's history

Several persons to whom the college owed much died during the first part of the new year, and shall receive special mention here. On the 22nd of January 1942, died Cecil Delisle Burns, M.A., D.Lit., Lecturer, in the Department then called Philosophy, Psychology and Logic, 1921-1927, and author in 1924 of a "Short History of Birkbeck College" ; on the 1st of February, as the result of an accident, A. W. Baker Welford, M.A., Lecturer 1920-1925, then Head of our Faculty of Laws, which was dissolved in 1938 ; on the 14th of March, George Senter, Ph.D., F.I.C., Head of our Department of Chemistry, 1914-1932, Principal of the College, 1918-1939,[1] who had recently accepted, with gratitude, advice from the

[1] See above, p. 23.

college in his new interests in archaeology and ornithology[1] ; and on the 24th of March, Professor F. J. Tanquerey, D. ès L., O.A., Head of our Department of French, whom it had been resolved in March to recall from the University of St. Andrews in order to take up again, as he had long wished, his work at Birkbeck College[2]. Another death deeply felt at the College took place on the 11th of April, when Bernard Neville, B.Sc., passed away. He was President of the Students' Union of the College in 1910-1911, and a Governor 1912-1936. His whole life was a superb triumph of soul and mind over a crippled body. He was one of a group of students whose steady pressure obtained rightful representation of students on the Governing Body and helped to hasten the development of the "Institution" (which already had the name Birkbeck "College") into a College recognised in the University of London. Died also, on the 29th of June, Henry Birkbeck, grandson of our founder. Recently he had received from the College a print with a portrait of his grandfather, the centenary of whose death the college had celebrated in December 1941[3].

The third term. Dutch and Norwegian languages. History of Art. Departmental changes

In the summer term (24th April—22nd June), the college considered a suggestion that provision be made for the teaching of Dutch and Norwegian at the college, with financial help from the Dutch and Norwegian Governments, and possibly from the British Council. At this time recognised courses in Dutch and Norwegian were lacking in London through the absence of other colleges. First, Dr. McClean, at the request of the British

[1] Already a generous contributor to the Fund for our new building, he bequeathed without conditions £1,000 to the college. The Governors resolved to provide in the new building a laboratory to be known as " The Senter Physical Chemistry Laboratory." He bequeathed also five hundred books to the college.

[2] Since it was not possible to get into touch with relatives of his in France, about two thousand of his books were kept at Greenford ; they were later bestowed on the College by his sister. In 1943 the students established a Fund in his memory.

[3] See above, p. 110. Another of Dr. Birkbeck's grandsons, Arthur Birkbeck, died on the 24th of June 1945.

Council, provided, in our Department of German, special teaching in Middle Dutch texts and historical Dutch grammar for an external student whom the Council was helping. Next, on the advice of the Ministers of Education of the two Governments concerned, the College appointed, for the session 1942-1943 in the first instance, Dr. Theodoor Weevers (who held a joint Readership at University College and Bedford College), as Lecturer in the Dutch Language (which remained permanently as a subject taught by him at Birkbeck College), and Lieutenant (later Captain) Ingvald Marm, as Lecturer in the Norwegian language[1] ; both Lecturers to provide Intermediate courses, and to be independent of other Departments. Both courses would be mainly for persons whose mother-tongue was English ; but Norwegian, Dutch and Flemish people might use them for improving their knowledge of English. On a request made by the Academic Board the College established also, for session 1942-1943 in the first instance, a part-time Lectureship in Art, for the benefit particularly of students of Languages and History in the Faculty of Arts ; this subject, which consisted of the history and appreciation of Art, likewise became permanently established, by its teacher Dr. N. Pevsner, under the title History of Art, at the college, independent of other Departments, but helping them. In the Department of Geography it was resolved to appoint for session 1942-1943 A. Moodie, a graduate of the College, as a temporary part-time Lecturer (after that session, he was re-appointed) ; in French, R. P. Legros, Reader at Bedford College, as part-time Lecturer ; and in Mathematics, to continue employing F. V. Cantalamessa for special tutorial work.

Public lectures. Dr. W. Temple made President of the college. Honour for John Maud

Public lectures were given by Dr. N. Pevsner (four on the Art of the European Nations), and F. D. Klingender (two on the Napoleonic War as seen in contemporary caricature).

[1] Teaching of this subject at the college continued until the end of the war only.

The eleventh[1] Haldane Memorial Lecture was given in the Theatre on the 20th of May, by the Right Honourable Lord Hankey, G.C.B., G.C.M.G., G.C.V.O., LL.D., F.R.S., on "The Development of the Higher Control of the Machinery of Government." The Vice-Chancellor of the University, Professor F. Horton, F.R.S., was in the chair, and the Lord Chancellor, The Right Honourable Viscount Simon, also spoke. In celebration of the 118th anniversary of the college, the Foundation Oration was given on the 24th of June by the Right Honourable Viscount Samuel, G.C.B., G.B.E., on "The World after the War." On the 29th of June, His Grace the Lord Archbishop of Canterbury (formerly Archbishop of York), Dr. W. Temple, accepted the Governors' invitation to become President of the College. The College learned with pleasure that the Master, J. R. P. Maud, had been created a Commander of the Order of the British Empire.

Progress of the Library

In May, Miss Hildyard reported on the progress made with regard to the Library in one year after the destructive fire of May 1941. Since then, the Library had acquired 6,600 volumes, of which about 5,000 had been given by one hundred and seventy persons. Many of these were very generous and some were complete strangers; seventy-five had had no previous connection with the college. Some books had come from the University of London[2], University College (London), King's College (London), and the University College of Southampton. Our staff and students had given also £160, and the Thomas Wall Trust £20. More than 5,000 of our books and periodicals were housed free meanwhile at Royal Holloway College, Richmond College, Guildford Technical College, Greenford, Shackleford, and private houses at Newport, Essex. At least 300 books required by Honours students were kept by members

[1] The first since the war began. A Haldane Memorial Lecture is normally given at the College every year in memory of the first Viscount Haldane of Cloan, K.T., O.M., F.R.S., President of the College, 1919-1928.

[2] The University Library remained in the Senate House at Bloomsbury. It was closed to readers in person, but maintained a service to borrowers by post.

of our teaching staff and brought into the college when required ; other texts urgently needed but which could not be bought were borrowed through the National Central Library. Replacements included important works of reference and critical works. Cataloguing was not yet complete ; the card-index had been copied and the original sent elsewhere. Loans of books on Psychology and Spanish had been made by King's College, and on English, French and History, by the Northampton School for Girls. Five hundred books had been bequeathed under Dr. Senter's will. It will be seen that much credit is due to the Librarian and her staff because of the success of their efforts to restore the Library after the disaster of the previous year.

Visitation by the University Grants Committee and the London University Court. Needs of the College

On Friday, the 19th of June, representatives of the University Grants Committee and London University Court, including Sir Walter Moberly (the Chairman of the Committee), Professor A. V. Hill, W. Chesterman, Sir George Barstow, Sir Henry Dale, the Vice-Chancellor, the Acting Principal of the University, and the Acting Clerk of its Court, visited the college in order to inspect the damage caused by fire, and to discuss the question of temporary working-space for the college and other matters connected with this[1]. Sir Walter Moberly congratulated the college in its difficulties ; and the visitors expressed surprise that the college had been able to maintain its work when so much of its premises was out of use. The main problems were the need for completing the new building at Bloomsbury as quickly as possible after the war ended, and the provision of enough space for present and future needs with special reference to a large intake of students during the time before the new building would be ready for occupation. With regard to the Faculty of Arts, if the rooms at Field House should not be available, rooms suitable for immediate needs might be found at the Mercers' School near by. It would also be desirable that

[1] Minutes of the Governors of Birkbeck College, 18th June 1942, Minute 325 ; 16th July 1942, Minute 377.

the parts of the Library at present housed elsewhere be brought back to London when the war was over ; for this purpose further space would be wanted. The Faculty of Science which through past damage had no proper means for research in Zoology, Chemistry, Physics, or Botany, could adapt the gallery of the College's Theatre and the ruins of Greystoke Place. With the agreement of the visitors, the Governors resolved that the gallery of the Theatre be turned into a lecture-theatre in the Department of Physics, so that this department's existing lecture-theatre might be made into a laboratory ; that the south laboratory of the Department of Chemistry, at this time used as a store, be made fit for students' use, and that a store be found elsewhere ; that the back of the ground-floor of the college's Theatre be adapted for receipt into store of library books stacked in the Committee Room, so that the space gained in this room might be used for study, and the back of the Theatre might receive further, after the war, the books at this time housed in the country; and lastly that part of ruined Greystoke Place be roofed to form a laboratory in the basement for the Department of Zoology[1]. It was decided not to build huts in the forecourt of Greystoke Place'[2] In view particularly of the continued difficulties which the Department of Zoology was forced to face, it was with gratitude that the college learned that during this session the Royal Society had not only awarded a grant to R. E. Siday, in the Department of Physics, for the continuance of his research, and, through the Librarian, had offered various runs of periodicals and of the Society's Transactions, but had also awarded to Professor Jackson a grant for the salary of an assistant in order that his zoological research, interrupted and indeed wrecked by the fire of September 1940, might be continued.

[1] Except the adaptation of the gallery in the College's Theatre, it was not possible to proceed yet with these plans (in spite of Government's permits received) which were still under discussion in session 1943-1944.

[2] The question of huts here was revived later ; they were at last built after the war ended, not in Greystoke Place but in the ruined space just east of the college.

Students' activities

At the end of June the numbers of students were in Arts 299 (177 of them being women), and in Science 241 (180 of them being women). In the summer term a Fencing Society (Club) was formed, and became active if not positively violent at once and during the vacation. The Société Française was very active independently of the Arts Society, and the Philosophical Society held meetings. The Science Society continued its united activities. The desirability of having a fourth term added to the normal three in an academic session was now being vigorously discussed by students. *The Lodestone* was edited in the autumn of 1941 by E. F. Fitzpatrick, the other two issues being edited by A. Godfrey. Lena Chivers, ex-President of the Students' Union, played a prominent part during the session in managing the Caxton Hall meeting on International Students' Day. She, with E. George, the President, took part also in a broadcast to Empire-listeners on research by young scientists of the war. In May, Flight-Lieutenant J. Tilsley, prisoner-of-war in Germany, in reply to enquiries from him through the British Red Cross Society about studies in French and Spanish, was sent such information as could be provided. The Birkbeck National Savings Group continued to flourish. When the first certificates were absorbed, a further £1,800 worth was bought, and when these went a third issue was procured. The Group had provided by mid-session enough money to defray the cost of 140 parachutes at £40 each. For the "City of London Warship" Week the Group saved enough to buy 102 parachutes ; the organizers then determined to appeal for 500 life-belts, and got 1,800 of them. The Theatre was used for a Civil Defence Organisation ; for a variety concert once in April, and three times in July ; and by St. Albans Church School, Holborn, for several performances in a worthy cause. The college had been able to provide a meeting-place for the Committee of its Court of Electors,[1] and for the

[1] For the Court of Electors, see p. 36. During the war, no full meeting of the Court of Electors was held ; but its Committee of the years 1938-1939 remained in office and resolved to hold no large entertainments but only small social gatherings from time to time. Having met once only in 1939 (February), and once only in 1940 (June), the Committee resumed much more frequent meetings in 1942, beginning in July and continuing through the rest of the war-years.

University's Boards of Studies and for Boards of Examiners as before ; also for members of the governing body of Westfield College, and for conferences and committees of the National Union of Students.

Congratulations to the University of London from its Chancellor

Later in the year the college received from the Vice-Chancellor of the University a letter which told us that the Right Honourable the Earl of Athlone, K.G., Chancellor of the University, who was at this time residing in Ottawa as Governor-General of the Dominion of Canada, had stated, after learning of the work of the University in the academic year 1941-1942, his desire to congratulate all who had shared in that "work during a year in which so much has been accomplished in spite of the difficult times through which we are passing.[1]"

Hopes and fears about the War

The course of the war was not such as to bring much relief from anxiety. In the spring the Germans renewed their pressure on Russia into the regions of the Caucasus. By the late summer the Russians had made awesome sacrifices of men, material, land and other resources. Sebastopol fell in July, and in August began the fearful battle for Stalingrad on the Volga. In North Africa the Germans advanced until they were only sixty miles from Alexandria and the Nile. However, the foe was checked at Stalingrad and at El Alamein ; and some extremely heavy bombing raids were made on Germany by the British and the Americans. Perhaps the hopes and fears of our people were balanced evenly ; at worst or at best there might be a "patched up" peace.

(2) Session 1942-1943

The first term (4th September—21st December) of the session 1942-3 began without pressing anxiety for our future, the working days being Saturdays and Sundays as before,

[1] *The Lodestone*, Christmas Term, 1942 (Vol. 35, Number 1), page 2.

except that the new courses in Dutch and Norwegian, which were well filled, were held on evenings of other days.

Students and National Service

Had Birkbeck College been an ordinary day-college for students not yet engaged in any profession, the new Government Regulations with regard to students in Faculties of Arts would have reduced our numbers greatly. But at Birkbeck College most of the students had their call-up deferred not because they were students but because of their occupations during the day-time ; thus the college was affected probably least of all such colleges of Universities. Yet much sympathy was felt at this college with a suggestion, made by the National Union of Students, that some male students might be retained at all Universities, but it was well recognised that the needs of the war must certainly come first. As things were, our position was fortunate, and moreover, there was a larger number of students in Arts than in Science ; and by far the greater part of them in both Faculties were genuinely part-time students engaged in other occupations during the week.

Rooms and students. Great increase in numbers of students

More rooms at Field House were now available ; adaptation of the Theatre's gallery into a lecture-theatre for Physics had been achieved ; and more furniture was bought for students' use ; but some of the proposals made in the previous term for the adaptation of existing space in our main premises, and, for Zoology, in Greystoke Place, remained unfulfilled, although the Psychologists were able to use it. As a precaution, negotiations with the City's authorities with regard to the use of shelters in ruined Nevill's Court and in New Street Square took place, and even better arrangements than before were made for air-raid protection for people using Field House. By mid-October the numbers of students admitted, in Arts 408 (270 being women), in Science 307 (106 being women), were much larger than they had been at the beginning of the previous session. All such as were serving in the Forces while at college were henceforth charged one-third only of the fees. The numbers were up to 457 in Arts, 333 in Science, by the end of October, giving a total of 790 as compared with 444 admitted by the end of November, session 1941-42. Even by early September no more Intermediate students could be accepted in Chemistry or Physics ; and before long the Intermediate classes in Latin were full. In mid-October it was decided that in case of danger, students using the third floor of Field House should go to shelters at the east and west ends of Nevill's Court and in Colley House, New Street Square ; they would go as members of the public without favoured treatment. Practices in taking shelter were held ; and at Field House we provided a day-guard at week-ends during terms. In December, before the first term ended on the 21st, the Academic Board considered carefully rules for admitting students in the next session 1943-4 ; and its recommendations included one that no student could take the Intermediate Course either whole or in part during more than two sessions unless the Head of his or her Department and the Dean of the relevant Faculty allowed it ; and that "occasional students" might not take more than two subjects in any session except in special circumstances.

Courses

The Deans of the Faculties were, as for 1941-2, of Arts Dr. McClean ; of Science, Dr. Barrow. Mutual help between other colleges and ourselves continued. All courses (except special short ones) given during last session held good for the present one also. The elementary and advanced courses in Radio-Physics (Radio-Communications) were run concurrently, the laboratory being available in vacation as well as in term time. Two agricultural seminars, like the instruction given in the session 1941-2[1], were held with expert aid from the Rothamsted Experimental Station, East Malling Research Station, and the School of Agriculture at Cambridge, as well as help from our own staff. Dr. N. Pevsner was now part-time lecturer in the History of Art, which proved to be of great value to students

[1] See p. 112.

of various subjects. In our Department of Logic, Philosophy and Ethics, in which Honours Classes were now held, Professor H. Hallett, of King's College, gave help.

Public lectures

Public lectures were given during this and the second term by Dr. Theodoor Weevers (on "Dutch War-poetry from 1939 to 1942 ; Chairman : Herr Dr. G. Bolkestein, Minister of Education of the Royal Netherlands Government), and Lieutenant I. Marm (on " Norway under Nazi misrule") ; and, in connection with the London Branch of the Classical Association, by Professor E. H. Warmington (on the "Persecution and Triumph of the Christians under the Romans"—two lectures), and H. Mattingly, Assistant Keeper in the Department of Coins and Medals in the British Museum ("The Roman Imperial Government and Public Opinion"—three lectures). Other public lectures were :— by Kingsley Martin ("News from America" ; Chairman : E. Murrow, Director of the Columbia Broadcasting System of the United States of America) ; Sir John Russell ("Agriculture in the U.S.S.R. and Palestine" ; Chairman : Sir Herbert Emerson, G.C.I.E., K.C.S.I., High Commissioner for Refugees, League of Nations); Dr. A. Bulling (she gave six lectures on the "Spiritual Foundation of Chinese Civilisation") ; Dr. G. M. Davies (one lecture on "The Stones of London," and one on " London's Water Supply, Past, Present and Future") ; Professor J. Sutherland ("The Education of a Poet"), and Dr. N. Pevsner (three lectures on the "Appreciation of Sculpture").

Russians visit the college

At a time when we were cheered by the wonderful stand of the Russians at Stalingrad and by the victories of General B. L. Montgomery at El Alamein, Birkbeck College gained a brief but welcome glimpse of Britain's all too little known Russian allies. On November the 8th, under the charge of Miss Lena Chivers, who was now an official in the Ministry of Information, three representatives of students in Russian Universities, namely Junior Lieutenant Lyudmilla Pavlichenko (she was a member of the Order of Lenin), Senior Lieutenant Vladimir Pchelintsev (Hero of the Soviet Union and member of the Order of Lenin), and Nicolai Krasavchenko, Chairman of the Soviet Delegation, visited the college, inspecting the premises and the damage done to these by German air-raids, visiting lectures then in progress, and addressing in the Theatre about 600 of our students. They thus gained their first experience of life in English Universities. They spoke in the Russian language, expounded by interpreters. We were pleased to entertain these three sturdy people as friends and allies. The Acting Master gave a speech of welcome. In the College's Visitors' Book they wrote and signed a message in Russian which, translated into English, runs as follows:—"To dear English students from the Students of the Soviet Union. We send our heartfelt war-greetings. We are awaiting the moment when our efforts will bring about the downfall of Hitler-Fascism, and the ensign of freedom and happiness will be flown over the whole world. With warmest greetings." Not long after this interesting visit, the fighting fellow-countrymen of our guests turned the long and bloody battle of far away Stalingrad into a splendid victory by their attacks in the latter half of November. During the next months other vital places were retaken by the Russians ; the Germans began a long retreat ; and the hopes of us their enemies began to rise.

Other activities of the students

The large increase in the numbers of our students[1] enabled the Union, under the Presidency of B. Chibnall, with E. P. George as the other representative Governor, to enlarge its activities to an intensity which recalled the period preceding the war. Debates, dances and socials were held throughout the session. At the Freshers' Social on the 19th of September, the Birkbeck Players produced in the Theatre "French Without Tears." Various societies were independently active, the

[1] At a General Meeting on the 20th of September 1942, a student "deplored the increase in the serious study that was being done in the common-room" ; perhaps the Refectory or a room in Field House could be used for study. Such was the growing problem of space. After this the Refectory was in fact more frequently used as a sort of "reflectory" also, as students put it.

Deutscher Verein renewing its separate self in the first term; the Historical Society had revived its expeditions—it had visited St. Albans even during the past summer vacation; and the Science Society co-operated with the Association of Scientific Workers.

The second and third terms

The second term (8th January—5th April) and the third (30th April—21st June) proceeded as successfully as the first, there being at the end of the third term 514 students (325 of them women) in Arts, 360 (including 140 women) in Science. Another course held in connection with Jewish refugees and lasting a few weeks began on the 11th of March. Speakers at the college were Professor Susan Stebbing on Physics and Philosophy, and André Philip in connection with World Youth Week. On the 20th of March Dr. Temple, Archbishop of Canterbury, and President of the College, paid an informal visit to the College, addressed the students in the Theatre on "The English Tradition of Morality", and answered questions in a crowded common-room. The Birkbeck Players performed A. P. Herbert's "Two Gentlemen of Soho"; N. Coward's "Hands across the Sea"; and Nathaniel Lee's "The Rival Queens" (first produced in 1677 and now rarely performed). Meetings of Students' Societies included one in which the Socialist Society was addressed by D. N. Pritt, K.C., M.P. A Choral and Operatic Society was revived by Miss B. Knowles. In the Easter Vacation the annual conference of the National Union of Students was held at the college. In May the Geographical Society revived its separate activities. All the issues of *The Lodestone*, in small format, were edited by R. Glascock. In the "Wings for Victory" Week, when the Birkbeck National Savings Group aimed at getting £2,000, the amount subscribed was £2,437 10s. 0d. On Sunday, the 11th of July, a meeting of the Association of Scientific Workers was held in the Theatre while a like meeting was held in Moscow on the same day. One of the objects of the meeting at the college was to raise funds for equipping a laboratory in the Stalin Memorial Hospital.

Help for prisoners of war in the enemies' hands

The college maintained efforts to help such prisoners of war in enemies' hands as were formerly students at the college. One of these, Captain C. Selby Boothroyd, had written from Germany, through the Red Cross Society, that he was anxious to do some literary studies. Books were got and sent away, and reached him safely. Other such prisoners were Flight-Lieutenant J. Tilsley and Sergeant J. Hawes in Germany ; Captain K. A. Frazer in Italy[1] ; and Captain F. Boyer and Sergeant G. Porteous.[2] Friends were encouraged to write to them. Our students moreover shared in help given through the International Student Service to other students of all kinds, and of various races, who were prisoners of our enemies.

Public lectures

In May an interesting series of four public lectures was given, on "Developments in Modern Warfare," one each by Admiral of the Fleet the Earl of Cork and Orrery, G.C.B., G.C.V.O. (on The Royal Navy) : Chairman—Dr. D. Pye, Provost of University College, London ; Air Chief Marshal Sir Philip Joubert de la Ferté, K.C.B., C.M.G., D.S.O. (on Strategic Employment of Air Forces in Modern Warfare) : Chairman—Marshal of the Royal Air Force the Viscount Trenchard, G.C.B., G.C.V.O., D.S.O. ; Lieutenant-General Sir Douglas Brownrigg, K.C.B., D.S.O. (on The Mosaic of an Army) : Chairman—Admiral of the Fleet the Earl of Cork and Orrery, G.C.B., G.C.V.O. ; and Chief Controller Dame Helen Gwynne-Vaughan, G.B.E., Head of our Department of Botany (on The Future of the Women's Services) : Chairman—Captain the Earl of Munster. The 12th Haldane Memorial Lecture was given on the 3rd of June by Sir Gervais Rentoul, K.C., Metropolitan Magistrate for West London, on "The Art and Ethics of Advocacy" : Chairman—Alderman Sir Frank Alexander, Lord Mayor of London ; and the Foundation Oration for the 119th Anniversary of the College was given on

[1] Captain Frazer escaped from Italian custody on the 9th of September 1943 but after six months was recaptured and transferred to Germany.

[2] Not all books sent from the college reached captive men.

the 24th of June by the Right Honourable Sir William Jowitt, K.C., M.P., on "The British Commonwealth" : Chairman—The Vice-Chancellor of London University (Professor Frank Horton, F.R.S.). For the London Branch of the Classical Association public lectures were given during the second and third terms as follows : R. P. Winnington-Ingram gave one such and Professor E. H. Warmington two, on Ancient Greek Drama ; F. G. Simpson one on Hadrian's Wall ; Professor P. N. Ure one on "Gregory of Tours, Historia Francorum" ; and Professor A. H. Armstrong one on "Magic and Religion in the Later Roman Empire."

Compensation for war-damage to the College

Negotiations with the Government assessors, in regard to damage arising from action by the enemy, resulted in our estimate of the amounts of compensation being confirmed or but slightly reduced except in the cost of the Library. The damage in question was caused to the Departments of Chemistry, Physics, Geology, Botany and Zoology, and to the Theatre, on the 25th of September, 1940 ; and to the Library, the furniture of Greystoke Place, and to Departments on the 10th-11th May 1941.

Progress of the Library

The Library had done well during the session. Even early in it, by the end of October 1942, the staff, the students, the Court of Electors[1], and donors outside the College had contributed between 5,000 and 6,000 books, besides gifts of money, so that the total of books acquired since the fire was nearly 9,000. When the Librarian reported in June on another year's progress in restoring the Library, she announced that since the previous summer it had acquired about 3,750 more volumes, of which 1,734 had been given, in addition to £69 contributed to the Library Reserve Fund for buying books. We were indebted also to the Friends of the National Libraries, the Royal Empire Society, the Royal Historical Society, the Royal

[1] For this, see above, p. 36.

Society of Literature, the Seafarers' Educational Service, the Trustees of the British Museum, and the Libraries of London University, University College, and Welwyn Garden City Library. Since the great fire more than 12,000 volumes had been acquired by gift and purchase ; of these about one-half were books new to the library which now contained 18,000 books. All books hitherto kept in other private houses had been collected and sent to join those at Shackleford or Greenford. Complete runs of seventeen periodicals had been replaced by gift or purchase ; and a complete set of the Rolls Series had been bought.

Departmental changes. Teaching in Economics

Changes on the teaching staff included the appointment, during the second term, of R. Melville as a part-time Lecturer in the Department of Botany. In the Department of History, S. M. Hardy was appointed a part-time Lecturer, to begin in the coming session. In the Department of English, Marjorie Daunt was granted, for her course for Proficiency in English, means for getting help ; and she was subsequently aided by Mrs. M. Foster and Miss F. Ellison. In view of the pressure in the Department of Classics caused by the exceptional increase in the number of students, combined with the absence of R. P. Winnington-Ingram and A. Way on war-service, Dr. J. L. Whiteley, a post-graduate of the college, was appointed a part-time Lecturer in Classics beginning with the session 1943-44. It was decided to recall Dr. Fox, seconded at the beginning of the war to a firm engaged on important war-production, to his full-time duties in session 1943-44 in the Department of Mathematics, since he had now become available once more. During the past two sessions, successful courses at the college had been given for External[1] candidates for the Intermediate examination in studies for the Degree of Bachelor of Science (Economics) to meet the demand caused by the absence of the London School of Economics in Cambridge. Twenty applications had now been received from students who wished

[1] See p. 108, note.

to prepare for the Final examination. Since the School of Economics found it difficult to provide a teacher who would be sent to Birkbeck College to undertake the work, the Governors of Birkbeck College decided to arrange that instruction for Parts I and II of the final examination for the Degree of Bachelor of Science (Economics)[1] be given by our existing staff with the help of J. K. Horsefield, who was in charge of our Department of Economics earlier in the war, but was seconded ; and to obtain if possible on loan from the Library of the School of Economics such books as might be required by students. The question of Part III was left over until session 1943-44 in case the London School of Economics returned[2].

Some guests of the college

The college was able during the session to offer a meeting-place, as before, for the Committee of its Court of Electors, and Boards of Studies and Boards of Examiners of the University ; also for the Fire Brigade Union ; the Theatre-School of Morley College; for committees of the National Union of Students; and for St. Albans Church School. Users of our sportsground at Greenford included the Home Guard and the Imperial College Cricket Club.

Rising hopes in the War. The Germans' secret weapons

It is no wonder that the Committee of the College's Court of Electors had begin to discuss the future policy of the college, and the National Union of Students the possibility of a fourth term in University sessions, with special intentness. News of the war was infusing a kind of smothered yet rising excitement in our minds, though we knew that the end was not yet at hand. We learned of a great drive of the Russians over one thousand miles from the Caucasus to the Carpathians ; of the juncture of our forces of North Africa with Anglo-American forces in Tunis during April[3] ; of their final victory in Africa in mid-May;

[1] See below, p. 135.

[2] This School did not then return.

[3] Professor Bernal made studies of past bombing and current bombing in Tripoli.

of their attack on Sicily in July and their subsequent invasion of Italy (destined to surrender on the 8th of September, though all the northern part of Italy, including Rome, came under German control); and of the steady progress of the United States in the Pacific. Whereas air-raids on Britain were now very few, the air-raids on Germany were reaching an appalling intensity, such as Britain never suffered. About the huge mass of material being produced in the factories of Britain and America most of us could but guess and wonder.

The war had also another side about which none save the experts knew: the Germans were making ready some secret weapons to be used against us. Following on experiments made at Peenemünde before the war, they intended to begin, on the 20th of October 1943, an attack on London with rockets of long range; in the summer too of this year we found evidence from the air that a different sort of missiles[1] also was being prepared in France. The Government of Britain made plans for moving certain kinds of people, and even everyone, from London; and for bringing thousands of table-shelters into London for use in houses. The onslaught by means of these weapons did not take place in 1943—the various reasons for the delay are of much interest but must not find a place in this narrative—; yet the Germans' plans for both sorts of weapon went ahead; and our experts judged rightly that the objects seen in France were inclined ramps; and by December 1943 it was clear to them that those in Somme and the Pas de Calais pointed towards London, and some of those in the area of Cherbourg, towards Bristol. They were made for flying bombs.

Resignation of John Maud

The narrative of this further session of recovery and success at the college shall end with a record of the Master, John Maud, because the summer term was by his own choice the last in which he was Master of the College, and the story of the session to come begins well with the important result which

[1] Flying bombs; they were to begin on 15th December 1943. See pages 146 ff., 164 ff.

followed on his decision. John Maud, as United Kingdom delegate, had made a successful visit to America in connection with the International (Allied Nations) Conference on Food held at Hot Springs in California in May and June, and had broadcast from the United States on the 6th of June, on the objects of the Conference. On the 30th of August he wrote to the Governors a letter of resignation from his headship of Birkbeck College. He felt that the other work[1] on which he was engaged was taking too much of his time. The Governors at a special meeting held on the 16th of September passed a unanimous resolution "that the resignation of J. P. R. Maud, C.B.E., as Master of the College . . . . . be accepted as from the 31st of July[2], 1943, with the greatest regret ; and that he be informed that the Governors desire to express their grateful appreciation of all that he has accomplished for the college during the four years he has occupied the office, and their warmest good wishes for the success of the very important work on which he is engaged and of the even more important post-war duties to which he will be called."[3] Maud was co-opted to be a Governor of the college as from the 1st of August 1943.

[1] He had been made Deputy Secretary to the Ministry of Food in 1941, and later became Second Secretary. In 1944-45 he was Second Secretary in the Office of the Minister of Reconstruction, and in 1945 was made Secretary in the Office of the Lord President of the Council.

[2] This was the customary date for the regular ending of appointments on the Administrative and Teaching Staff of the college, where these appointments could be taken as ending with the end of a session, 1st August being the first day of such new appointments as could be taken as beginning with a new session.

[3] Quoted from Governors' Minutes, 16th September 1943, Minute 3.

CHAPTER FIVE

PROGRESS AND SHOCK

SESSION 1943-1944

Professor H. Jackson becomes Master

THE resignation of John Maud led to another prompt and important decision. At a meeting held on the 21st of October the Governors unanimously appointed Professor H. Gordon Jackson to be Master of Birkbeck College as from the 1st of August 1943, for a period of five years. This choice, of a man who had given the college good leadership for some time, met with hearty welcome, and was destined to become permanent until his grievous death in a road accident on the 5th of August 1950.[1]

The college is again full

At the beginning of the session a religious service for all believers was held at the Church of St. Dunstan-in-the-West, Fleet Street (through the kindness of the Rector, Dr. A. J. Macdonald), which was regarded as our Chapel. The address was given by the Very Reverend the Dean of St. Paul's (Dr. W. R. Matthews). The Deans of the Faculties at the college were again Dr. R. McClean (Arts) and Dr. F. Barrow (Science). Soon after the opening of the first term (10th September—20th December), the number of students was 1,029—in Arts, 599 (of which 397 were women), in Science, 430 (of which 160 were women). Some departments had been filled in advance even in July ; and at the beginning of October all regular departments in the Faculty of Arts were full, except for post-graduate research, and for Matriculation Latin. All the courses of the

[1] The frontispiece of this book is a photograph of Professor Jackson taken during the war when he was Air Raid Warden at Hadley Green where he lived.

preceding session, including those in the History of Art, in Norwegian, in Dutch, and in Radio-Physics, were continued. There was some crowding not only in departments of Science, but also in departments of Arts in Field House. Thus, even though Field House[1] was still available and we were granted an additional room in it, the college was forced to look for yet more working-space. I remember going round Field House, with another member of the staff ; when we gently opened the door in a partition between two rooms, two students at a lecture fell out at our feet. It was found possible to ease such conditions and other discomforts, but we were most certainly cramped and crowded, though there was no sign that life at college was unhealthy. The college also kept proper foresight towards the chance of air raids. As will be seen, in no month of this session, except May 1944, was London wholly free from action by the enemy in the air during night-time ; and one could never be sure that some onslaught would not come by day on a full college. Therefore, in view of the very great number of our inmates, the college took thought of using the Chancery Lane tube-shelter by its entrance in Furnival Street. All rules governing alerts were kept seriously in mind and were to be observed strictly if need arose.

Psychology at King's College and at Birkbeck College

Further, in October, a letter came from Dr. W. R. Halliday, later Sir William Halliday, the Principal of King's College, which had just completed its return to London, stating a proposal that as soon as possible practically all the part-time, that is evening, teaching that had hitherto been conducted in the Faculty of Arts in King's College be handed over to Birkbeck College[2] ; and that, in this connection, the Department of Psychology at King's College be transferred to Birkbeck

[1] When the Hulton Press became owners of Field House late in the session 1943-44, our position there was not altered during the remainder of the war.

[2] This did not apply to Geography, Portuguese, Spanish and Modern Greek. Spanish in the end became a permanent subject at Birkbeck College also.

College when suitable arrangements could be made[1]; the Delegacy of King's College, in view of the difficulties which might arise for Birkbeck College because of damage done during the war, until the college should move to its new building, would be most willing to allow the use of accommodation at King's College during evenings by classes belonging to Birkbeck. "The Delegacy would be most anxious to do anything that was feasible to help Birkbeck College out of any post-war difficulties of accommodation, and I think they would wish me to say that they would welcome such an opportunity of repaying some of the help and kindness which King's College has received from Birkbeck College during the difficult period of the war".[2] The Governors of Birkbeck College asked the Master to convey to the Delegacy of King's College their appreciation of the terms of the Principal's letter, and in due course determined to implement the transfer[3] of the Psychological Department of King's College permanently to Birkbeck College by the beginning of the session 1944-45.

Provision of more space

There was one other problem long outstanding at the beginning of the session 1943-44; this was the provision for the time being of space, at the back of the Theatre, for about 7,000 volumes of the Library, and the roofing of a portion of what was once the lower Library at Greystoke Place with a view to its adaptation later on for use as a laboratory; application was now made to the University Grants Committee for permission to put the work in hand. By the beginning of the second term of the session the college had rented two large

[1] The teachers and students in Psychology of King's College had worked at Birkbeck since the early part of 1940 (see p. 40), but there had been no transfer of the Department as such to Birkbeck; the teachers and students still belonged to King's College, where in peace-time Psychology, though open to both day and evening students, had been in practice taken almost wholly by evening students only.

[2] Quoted in the Minutes of the Governors of Birkbeck College, 21st October 1943, Minute 25.

[3] Because of this transfer the college was enabled later to add another floor to its new building.

rooms for the Faculty of Arts at the Royal Scottish Corporation's building[1] in Fetter Lane, where at times an obbligato of bagpipes might swell the lecturer's voice. In November and December the Governors had considered an offer from the Ministry of Works to complete our new building in Bloomsbury, except the north-east wing, forthwith at its own expense, to a point sufficient for its use during three years as an office-building for a Government Department. This naturally caused much interest and further discussion amongst the staff and students, but the Ministry did not after all find the proposition immediately worth while, and, when air attacks became severe again in June 1944, the project lapsed.

Departmental changes. Public lectures

On the Academic side everything went ahead with steady success. The Governors appointed a new Policy Committee of which the object was to keep in close touch with opinions about future developments in education and to advise accordingly. In November the numbers of students rose to 1,077 (in Arts 604, including 404 women, in Science 473, including 199 women). Alastair Graham was appointed Acting Head of the Department of Zoology in place of Professor Jackson, now Master of the College. In Geography, Miss E. M. J. Campbell, a Demonstrator in the Department, was made a part-time lecturer. In order to offer at Birkbeck College instruction which would include the teaching needed for students now reading[2] for the Final Examination for the Degree of Bachelor of Science (Economics), for whom the London School of Economics could not provide, the college called on S. M. Hardy, D. Smith, and E. Grebenik (responsible for the whole Department), J. Horsefield (who still continued work with the Ministry of Aircraft Production), Miss B. R. Hinchliff, and K. B. Smellie. The University now recognised the instruction given as satisfying, in its Faculty of Economics, the requirements for Internal as well as External Students. The

[1] The top of this building had been badly damaged in May 1941.

[2] See above, pp. 128, 129.

Department of Botany required another part-time Lecturer during the session, and Dr. M. A. P. Madge was appointed (she continued in session 1944-45 also). Three public lectures were arranged in connection with the London Branch of the Classical Association : two by Professor E. H. Warmington on "Greek Tyrants" and on "Virgil, Poet and Prophet," and one by G. M. Young on the subject "From Roman to Saxon."

Students' activities

When H. U. Rom, President Elect of the Students' Union, was called away suddenly in connection with coal-research, A. Heron was chosen in his place to be President. When later he was posted away to the United Nations Relief and Rehabilitation Administration, B. Chibnall, the Vice-President, agreed to serve as President for the remainder of the session, with Doreen Elderton as the other representative of the students on the Governing Body. In August the Council of the Students' Union had resolved that privileges of membership of the Students' Union at Birkbeck College, except that of taking part in private business, should be accorded to the members, of the Unions of all other Universities and University Colleges, who were also members of the National Union of Students and of its Scottish counterpart. A useful link between students and staff, namely a Staff-Students Committee, became active once more. Through it a variety of matters could be settled, or referred to appropriate persons in confidence or otherwise. Much interest was henceforth taken in the newly revived University of London Union ; and relations were maintained as in previous years with the National Union of Students. In this session the Societies of Birkbeck College flourished as at no time since the war began ; and the Students' Union developed the policy of inviting well-known persons in public life to address students' meetings. Among those who accepted an invitation during the session were Sir Peter Chalmers Mitchell, R. Palme Dutt, Arnold Lunn, Viscount Hinchingbrooke, M.P., and Olaf Stapledon. At the Freshers' Social the Birkbeck Players performed "Take back your Freedom," by Winifred Holtby, arranged for general production by N. Ginsbury ; and on the 11th of December they performed Sheridan's "The Critic." An Economics Society was formed at the end of October, and held several meetings during the session. Particularly successful during the session were the Philosophical Society ; the Historical Society, which arranged visits to Greenwich Hospital, Hatfield House, the Royal Hospital in Chelsea, and St. John's Priory in Clerkenwell ; and the Geographical Society, which from the 22nd to the 29th of January, arranged a very well supported Geographical Exhibition of the British West Indies. This was opened by Lady Davson. Among the one thousand and more visitors who attended the Exhibition, including parties from schools and other colleges, were Lord Moyne (Chairman of the Royal Commission to the West Indies, 1938-39), Ben Riley, M.P., various teachers, Dr. Rita Hinden, Mr. Rogers (from the Public Relations Department of the Colonial Office), and Mr. Learie Constantine. Activities of the Société Française included a visit and performance by members of the Théatre Molière. The Science Society continued its united activities. The Choral and Operatic Society was at present unable to go beyond informal meetings and practice. A Liberal Society was begun in the third term. The Catholic Society was revived and so was added to the never-ceasing activities of the Student Christian Movement. The college's branch of the Association of Scientific Workers held several meetings. Amendments to the constitution of the Students' Union were considered by the students with great care and submitted to the Governors. Work begun last session by Helen Cottrell in connection with supporting the International Student Service was continued with special reference to the new organisation for European Student Relief. The International Student Committee was busy collecting text-books for students in prisoner-of-war camps in Germany. When one of our own former students, Flight-Lieutenant H. J. Dothie, a prisoner-of-war since the 22nd of July 1943, in German hands, after "baling out" over enemy territory, asked for books on Physics, the college sent them, through the Red Cross Society and Order of St. John of Jerusalem, in April. Some books went astray. The Students' Union's debates included a discussion on the motion " That prolonged peace is impossible within the framework of a Capitalist Economy," proposed by R. Glascock (a student, in place of Ivor Thomas, M.P.), opposed by H. Kerr, M.P. Soldiers of the United States attended dances at the college during the session and expressed their sincere thanks. Closer contact with His Majesty's Forces also was planned. On the 1st of March Professor Jackson gave a talk, with lantern slides, on our new building. By a most praiseworthy effort the Birkbeck Players produced, on the 28th and the 29th April (see below, p. 140) a third play in this one session, Shakespeare's "Much Ado About Nothing." *The Lodestone* was issued in a slightly larger format, the first part edited by S. Rennert, the other two parts by Miss Cherry Newman. Since its first beginnings the Birkbeck College Savings Group had now saved more than £11,000.

Further changes in the second and third terms. Public lectures

By mid-March 1944 the students' numbers were 1,123 (in Arts 652, including 430 women ; in Science 471, including 172 women). To fulfil a wish expressed by the students, even in the second term laboratories in the Departments of Physics and Chemistry were allowed to remain open to six in the evenings on Mondays and Fridays. At the request of the Academic Board the Governors resolved to appoint two advisers of studies, one for each Faculty ; and appointed, for one year, Mrs. L. Simons (Acting Head of the Department of French) for Arts, and Dr. Barrow (Associate Head of the Department of Chemistry) for Science. They approved the delivery of eight lectures by Mrs. M. Clarke on the Archaeological and Social Background of the Anglo-Saxons. It was resolved also that, if there were at least six applicants from students to take, in the Faculty of Arts, History of Art at the Intermediate Examination, as a subject in its own right (not in connection with any other subject), a course be provided in the next session 1944-45, and that Dr. N. Pevsner be requested to undertake the work. On a suggestion from the University the Governors resolved to ask the University to create a part-time Chair of Zoology tenable at Birkbeck College and to appoint the Master thereto with A. Graham as

Associate Head of the Department of Zoology. They also resolved to invite Dr. Vera Fretter (at Royal Holloway College, whence she had made many journeys during the war in order to help our Department of Zoology to which also she belonged) to do more teaching at Birkbeck College than hitherto. In connection with the proposed transfer of the Department of Psychology of King's College so as to become a Department at Birkbeck College, it was deemed necessary to appoint a staff consisting of a Professor, two part-time lecturers, a laboratory steward, and two student demonstrators, and the Master undertook to proceed with negotiations for the transfer. Dr. W. P. Morrel was made Acting Head of the Department of History for the session 1944-45 in view of the coming retirement of Arthur Jones.

Three public lectures were given on War-time London : one by R. S. R. Fitter, F.Z.S., M.B.O.U., on "Birds of War-time London" ; one by Dr. (later Sir) Edward Salisbury, C.B.E., F.R.S., on "Wild Flowers of War-time London" ; and one by B. H. St. J. O'Neil, M.A., F.S.A., on "Ancient Monuments of the City in War-time" ; also three in connection with the London Branch of the Classical Association : one by Professor C. Field on "Some Reflections on Greek Science" ; one by Professor E. H. Warmington on "Dictatorship in Ancient Rome," and one by H. Mattingly on "The Death-Throes of the Roman Republic." The long intended adaptation of the back of the lower part of the Theatre for a Library store was begun, and plans for a laboratory for Zoology in part of Greystoke Place were ready and put in hand. As a result of suggestions made by the Students' Union the Governors resolved to spend a good sum on the redecoration of the college's premises, and on repairs of electrical equipment, if the Ministry of Works allowed it.

The third term (21st April—19th June) began quite normally, the numbers of students reaching a total of 1,145 (in Arts 671, including 437 women ; in Science, 474, including 175 women). Even in mid-May the applications for admission for session 1944-45 numbered in Arts 639, in Science 464. It is of interest to note that in this session 1943-44, there were 162 students from other countries, which included Australia, British West Indies, Canada, India, China, Malta, South Africa, the United States of America, Panama, Gibraltar, France, Mauritius, Belgium, Holland, Norway, Austria, Germany, Hungary, Italy, Russia, Lithuania, Poland, Roumania, Czechoslovakia, Palestine, Egypt, Iraq and Turkey. In view of the large number of students it was decided to resume awards of prizes which had been discontinued after the summer of 1940.

The 13th Haldane Memorial Lecture was postponed until next term ; but the 120th Anniversary of the Foundation of the College was celebrated on the 29th of April by the delivery, before a large audience, of a Foundation Oration on "The Common Good," by the Right Honourable Herbert S. Morrison, M.P., Home Secretary and Minister of Home Security ; the President of the College, the Archbishop of Canterbury (Dr. W. Temple) presiding. The oration was followed by a performance of Shakespeare's "Much Ado about Nothing" (cf. p. 138 above).

In connection with the London Branch of the Classical Association three public lectures were given ; one by W. F. J. Knight on "The Classics and Psychology" ; one by Dr. G. M. Trevelyan, O.M., C.B.E., on "Life in Roman Britain" (Chairman : Sir Walter Moberly) ; and one by Professor G. F. Forsey on "Ancient Towns and Town Planning." Other single public lectures during the session were : "Demand and Supply," by the Right Honourable Lord Sempill, and "The Art of Argument," by Dr. C. Joad. Four lectures were given by Dr. N. Pevsner on "The Pattern of London."

Progress of the Library

In June, the Librarian, in her annual report, announced that during the session the Library had acquired about 2,310 volumes, of which 1,058 had been given ; and had been helped by the Guildhall Library, The London County Council, the Royal Institution, the Seafarers' Education Service, Trinity House Library (Hull), and the Trustees of the British Museum, and by gifts of money. The interest on a fund established in memory of the late Professor Tanquerey would henceforth be used for buying in his name books for the section devoted to studies in French. More lost periodicals were replaced. More books on Psychology had been added on loan, to those already lent to Birkbeck College. It was still intended that the portion of the College's Theatre separated off to be a Library store would be put to use when all danger from attack from the air had ceased. This danger was not at all a remote one, as will be seen.

Retirements and resignation

As lectures ceased in June, at a time when the elation roused by our invasion of France was merging into strain of body and mind brought on by the enemy's new weapons, as will be described below, the College found itself bidding farewell to some of its senior and most renowned members of the teaching staff, on their leaving the college at the end of the session:—(i) Professor Dame Helen Gwynne-Vaughan, G.B.E., LL.D., D.Sc., F.L.S., Head of the Department of Botany since 1909, Professor of Botany since 1921, and now retiring, for whose devotion and wisdom and enthusiasm both as teacher and Governor the college was deeply grateful[1]; (ii) Professor Eva G. R. Taylor, D.Sc., LL.D., F.R.G.S., F.R.Hist.Soc., Head of the Department of Geography, who joined the staff as part-time Lecturer in 1921, and became Professor[2] of Geography in 1930, and was now retiring after doing work which, combined with the achievement of her predecessor Professor J. F. Unstead, was the making of her Department at the college ; (iii) Arthur Jones, M.A., F.R.Hist.Soc., Reader and Head of the Department of History, now retiring after a period of imperfect health ; and (iv) Professor J. Sutherland, Head of the Department of English, who was departing to become Professor at Queen Mary College.

[1] Dame Helen was made Chief Controller, Queen Mary's A.A.C., in 1917, and Commandant of the W.R.A.F. in 1918. For her appointment during the present war see above, p. 21. Later she was granted the title of Professor Emeritus by the University of London.

[2] The University later granted to her also the title of Professor Emeritus. In 1940 she had been appointed to Lord Reith's Panel of Reconstruction ; and later, to the Consultative Panel of the Ministry of Works and Buildings.

Departmental changes

On the 1st of May, G. L. Schwartz, of the Staff of the London School of Economics, succeeded, as Lecturer in the Theory and Principles of Economics, and as supervisor of our Department of Economics, E. Grebenik, who had resigned and joined the Royal Navy. In June, in view of the recall of H. Kestelman to University College, it was resolved to make a new full-time Lectureship in the Department of Mathematics. It was decided also to ask the Royal Air Force to release Squadron Leader D. Dakin (who had been serving in the Middle East), in order to resume his work as a Lecturer in History. After negotiations by the Master with the Provost of University College and the Principal of Bedford College, about intercollegiate teaching of Dutch in the University, it was agreed that Dr. T. Weevers should continue to lecture in Dutch to part-time students at Birkbeck College.[1]

Repairs; and other matters

Restoration and preparation of Greystoke Place, chiefly for the better housing of the Department of Zoology there, were in good progress ; the work included the adaptation, in Greystoke Place, for the Department of Psychology, of the remaining part of what had been the Upper Library, the Librarian's Room and the Periodicals Room, and the adaptation for the Department of Zoology of all the rest of the basement, and of five other small rooms in the remains of the "tower." During the session the college was as before a meeting-place for people not specially connected with the college, for example, Boards of Studies and Boards of Examiners of the University ; the Workers' Travel Association Fellowship ; the Historical Association of Britain (for an annual general meeting) ; committees of the National Union of Students ; the London Schools and Colleges Dining-Club (to which the Master gave a talk on the plans of our new building, and the Department of Physics gave demonstrations and an exhibition) ; and the London Conservative Association. As usual

[1] Dutch became an established Department at the college.

also the Committee of our Court of Electors met at the college. Among those who used our sports-ground at Greenford were members of Imperial College, and number 6 Central Workshops, Royal Electrical and Mechanical Engineers.

The College's fire-guard during the first and second terms of this session. Records of air-raids

During the first two terms of our academic session the Germans had made, with ordinary aeroplanes, air-raids on London at intervals, rarely however reaching great weight in their strokes, though their activities, when they did come, tended to last over several nights in succession; and in October 1943, again in late January and in February, and in springtime of 1944 England received some swift attacks. These new onslaughts were named the "Scalded Cat" raids. The college's fire-guard, which now belonged to Block F in Sector CL 529 of Division B in the Corporation of London City Fire Guard, and was under the able control of E. Smale (Block Commander), consisted of at least four persons on duty every night; and maintained unremitting watch over the college, carrying out now and again, when times were quiet, exercises in union with other fire-guards in the same block. A log-book kept by our guard records, in terse style, various sounds of air raids that occurred during the nights of the 6th—8th and from the 17th to the 23rd of October 1943; on the 25th [1]; on the 31st of October; from the 2nd to the 8th of November; on the 20th, 25th, 26th and the 29th of November; on the 1st and the 10th and from the 18th to the 21st of December, and on the 30th December 1943; then, in 1944, on the 2nd-3rd, and 4th-5th, and from the 13th to the 15th, and on the 21st-22nd[2] and on the 29th of January; on the 3rd-4th, the 6th, and from the 11th to the 13th, and from the 19th to the 24th of February;

[1] The records for October include on 7th October: "D(*elayed*) A(*ction bomb*) or ? dud shell fell about 800 yds. N.E. 22.14" (*that is, at* 10.14 *p.m.*); 17th October: "Bombs to N(*orth*). ? K's +" (*that is, King's Cross*). Fire to E.N.E."; 18th October: "Bomb (?) fell to E(*ast*). Activity over Estuary till 23.20" (*that is* 11.20 *p.m.*); 20th: "Heavy gunfire; ? 3 bombs S., 1 E."; 21st: "Local activity—fighters overhead 03.03 to 03.28 (*that is, from* 3.3 *to* 3.28 *a.m. on the 22nd.*)" Words, letters and figures in italics here spell out or explain the records.

[2] On this night London suffered its heaviest raid since 1941.

on the 29th of February; on the 2nd and 8th of March; from the 14th to the 17th of March, and from the 22nd to the 25th, and on the 31st of March. Very early in the morning of the 22nd of February some damage was done in long ago ruined Nevill's Court, where a water-main was broken. During the session so far, only on this night and on the night of the 24th and 25th of March was the college in some danger, when some incendiary bombs fell along Fetter Lane. For the 24th-25th of March the log-book reads as follows:—

(Signatures of the members of the guard, confirming that they had been on duty at the college from 1700 hours, that is five in the evening of the 24th of March, to at least 0700 hours, that is seven in the morning of the 25th of March :)

G. F. Troup Horne; N. Pevsner; H. G. Bell; B. Fishel

Narrative	Alert		All Clear
	23.25[1]		00.59[2]
	Local activity[3]		
	23.30	23.35	
	23.47	00.27	
	00.36	00.41	

Rocket-case[4] fell on roof of coll(*ege*) workshop.
Incendiaries on premises adjacent to Greystoke Place building.
Fire 23.52-01.10.
Absentees—none.

Unknown to our fire-guard until daylight, a fierce fire near the southern end of Fetter Lane, during the raid of which this is a record, seriously threatened the church of St. Dunstan-in-the-West, Fleet Street. This and other things[5] brought back sharply the memories of all that had happened to the college in

[1] That is 11.25 p.m.

[2] 12.59 a.m.

[3] That is, periods each marked at the beginning by receipt of the overhead "Divo" signal (see p. 71), whereupon all members of the guard were normally to be in the shelter afforded by the Senior Common room until the "overhead past" was given. During the three periods here given at least one German aeroplane was passing over near.

[4] Probably of one of our rockets, called, for secrecy's sake, "unrotated projectiles," shot at the raiders ; not a shell containing a "proximity-fuse."

[5] Our area had a lucky escape when a German aeroplane dropped a large bomb-container holding about 120 explosive incendiary bombs ; the container, having failed to open in mid-air so as to scatter its bombs, fell through the roof of a printing works, belonging to the Solicitors' Law Stationery Society, opposite Dean Lane, and caused one fierce fire which was put out before it spread. The one bomb which on 24th March hit St. Dunstan's Church—our College Chapel during the war—did not cause disastrous damage.

May 1941 ; but, needless to say, they gave no clue to anything that was to come in new shapes during the months of summer and autumn ; and the second term ended without very deep anxiety for the future.

Landing of the British and the Americans in France; "D Day"

In other fields of war we had been aware of slow and hard progress in Italy and of heavy air-raids on Germany, but the great preparations for our re-entry into France were secret, though shrewdly guessed at and hoped for. At last the latter part of the term (21st of April—19th of June) brought a sudden awakening of renewed excitement in the landing of the British and Americans in France on the 6th of June, followed by a period of very hard mental strain for parts of our country when the Germans used new weapons against it. The preparations for the invasion of France by the British and Americans have a special interest for the college. Professor J. Bernal, Head of our Department of Physics, was attached as scientific adviser to the planning staff of the operations, first in relation to floating harbours and then for general topographic intelligence connected with landings in France. In this he was given important help by Dr. H. Henderson and Mr. A. O'Dell, both[1] of our Department of Geography, and both on secondment from the college for National Service. Bernal studied in particular the distribution of mud and of the enemy's mines, to detect which, scouting expeditions were sent across. On the day of the invasion he went across himself, to check the accuracy of his forecasts, which, he modestly says, seemed to him to be fairly good.

The flying bombs, V.1 ("Diver"); their nature and effects

Within the next three months Hitler revealed his much vaunted secret weapons. During the early part of 1944 we had planned counter-measures against the missiles which the

[1] I regretfully omit the various good services which these two rendered to our allied cause beyond stating here that Henderson was the originator of a unit which in June 1944 became known as the Inter-Service Central Index, being available to all Government and Service Departments and all Intelligence Services, British and Allied.

Germans had long been preparing in France (see p. 130). When we bombed the very many launching sites heavily, the Germans made others which were disguised better, and about fifty survived to be used against us. No onslaughts of the kind which we expected took place before the landing of the British and American Forces. But our observations of the enemy's preparations were now proved to be accurate ; for, one week later, on the 13th of June, when a part of our session was uncompleted and preparation for some imminent examinations was still in progress, the Germans across the Channel began to send towards London their very destructive "flying bombs" called V.1.[1] They were small pilotless monoplanes, launched usually in salvos, from ramps on the ground, travelling fast with speed increasing to three or four hundred miles an hour when they were over London, between four thousand and two thousand feet from the ground, though I saw some over and north of London moving lower than that ; each carried about 1,870 pounds weight of high explosive and, driven by a ram-jet motor, was steered by gyroscopic means, but otherwise uncontrolled. They were, it seems, aimed at Tower Bridge. There were local successions of the usual signals for "alert," and "all clear," or one long-lasting alert at a time. After an "alert," one often heard nothing more in one's own neighbourhood except the "all clear" later ; often one heard the raucous grinding buzz of these plane-bombs in the distance, or nearby if they passed overhead or over to one side, fully visible in daylight. The blare of our klaxon horns along the bomb's route of approach might be added to the sound. If the noise of the bomb ceased suddenly, it meant the fall of the missile ; then would follow the great crash of the explosion near or distant, and a cloud of smoke drifting away. Sometimes the all clear came very soon after the explosion ; often the attack lasted for a long time, even hours or a whole day or night. Much harm and grievous loss of life and

[1] And also variously in common English speech buzz-bombs, doodle-bombs, and doodle-bugs. V.1 meant Vergeltungswaffe Ein—"Weapon of Retaliation One." Only four of these missiles were sent over on the 13th; the real onslaught began on the 15th of June. Most of the bombs sent crossed our coasts between Cuckmere Haven and St. Margaret's Bay.

great distress was wrought in London and in several counties of south-eastern Britain by this latest but not last of the Germans' weapons ; and, quite apart from the damage, injury, and death so often caused when the "flying bombs" fell, there was widespread loss of sleep by night and interruption of work by day. The attacks brought as serious a threat to members of Birkbeck College, to the work of the college, and to the existence of the college's buildings, as any previous acts of the enemy had done. Of the flying bombs which fell on Central London, including seventeen in the City of London, this narrative will mention seven ; of which six fell in the four-sided area bounded by Fleet Street, Farringdon Street, Holborn and Kingsway, and one fell just outside this area. It is known that the City of London received a greater intensity of flying-bombs on its acreage than any other part of London's far-spread mass (except Penge) and any other portion of England ; and it can be well believed that the burden laid on the people who lived and worked within the scope of these weapons was in places heavier than all that they had endured in the years 1940 and 1941.

The flying bombs begin

In April no activity had been recorded at the college, except a little on the 14th and also on the 19th and 26th and 27th ; in May, none at all[1] ; nor any during the first fourteen days of June, except two alerts between 3.45 and 4.35 a.m. on the 13th. These marked the coming of two out of the first four flying bombs which the Germans sent over. Then suddenly the fire-guard's records are very plentiful from late on the 15th of June onwards, and give signs of the strain under which south-eastern England laboured while the flying bombs were coming over by day and by night ; and, from our special point of view, the hardships which faced all students taking examinations at this time. On the 15th-16th June more than two hundred bombs came over England, of which seventy-three reached "greater London", eleven falling in built-up areas ; and they were followed by about one hundred a day, and above three thousand

[1] On the 13th we have in the fire-guard's book "siren heard 21.38, presumably accidental."

during the next five weeks, more than half reaching London. Our fire-guard recorded in their book, for the 17th and early 18th of June four alerts and fifteen overhead warnings, as flying bombs passed over near, and between 03.29 and 03.39 hours on the 18th "some damage[1]" to the college "from blast from Fleetway House" (a note added in the log-book later). On one occasion there were seventeen overhead signals during nine hours. Early on the 19th a flying bomb fell at the Royal Courts of Justice near our area. Records of the whole of daylight hours were not kept, but the guard recorded three alerts and five "overheads" during daylight on the 26th of June, and noted similar things on later days. Often to the actual times recorded of alerts, overheads, and explosions was added a remark saying that there were "numerous" or "various alerts and overheads." The "frequent alerts and overheads throughout the day until 21.00" (9 p.m.), recorded in the preamble on the 5th of July, marked the day after the end of examinations on the 4th. No single period of twenty-four hours was free from alert or something worse between the 14th of June and the 10th of August ; but meanwhile, as our methods of vigorous defence were meeting with success, the pressure on London was not so unremittingly severe. At the end of the first week in July the daily rate of arrivals in England fell to about seventy bombs. By the fifteenth nearly three thousand had reached our defences, and one thousand two hundred and eighty had fallen in the area of London. Just about half were brought down in various ways at various places, about forty a day reaching "greater London." So far about three thousand people had been killed, ten thousand badly hurt ; and thirteen thousand houses had been destroyed or ruined.

The members of our guard had fixed instructions as to what must be done if fire should break out, especially with reference to the Library ; but in the case of flying-bombs, of which the damaging power was much more explosive than incendiary, there was little that the guard could do. It was

[1] Done in the Theatre and to some windows—see below, p. 151. It was caused by a flying bomb which fell in Farringdon Street between Farringdon Avenue and Stonecutter Street.

decided therefore that, while all other normal precautions must be most strictly obeyed, only the member on ready duty need be awake even if an overhead had been sounded. He was required to repeat, on the college's bell, *The Daily Mirror's* signal—three short rings for "Raiders Approach[1]" and one long ring for "Raiders Past."

Effect on classes and examinations

Birkbeck College suffered with the rest of south-eastern England, though it was spared loss of life on the premises. Damage or destruction was however done to the houses[2] of members of all classes of people connected at that time or in the past with the college, and, as will be related, to the buildings used by the college itself. From the college's viewpoint, the first effects were mental. Distress and discomfort of mind were specially acute in those students whose lectures had finished shortly after the first onslaughts were made, and took their examinations on the appointed days. This of course applies to all students of London University whose examinations were held in London; for the University as a whole the difficulties in holding examinations were greater than they were in the session 1940-1941, because, since then, some colleges had come back to London. The main troubles were loss of sleep through the raids, including air-raid duties; inability to apply the whole mind on work in examination-rooms; loss of time and concentration through taking shelter during some raid; and withdrawal from examination before this was completed. After the first week of the Final examinations all the difficulties mentioned here were in existence. The University decided that candidates for the examinations held in June and July should have the choice of postponing[3] their entries, until the next examination, with no disadvantage beyond loss of time;

[1] By these words was meant the signal for "danger overhead."

[2] Few of these had any rooms strengthened into shelters; but there were other defences, notably the table-shelter beneath which, as a bomb came near, we would take a nose-dive, thereby offering to the foe a fitting end—in one sense—which he could not appreciate.

[3] Some candidates did in fact omit to take their examination on this occasion.

and that, during period of alerts, candidates could continue work or go to shelter without penalty, being put on their honour not to discuss the examinations meanwhile. At Birkbeck College, on the earliest days of the attacks, students and teachers at classes went at once to the shelters on hearing the local alert, but after a little the same process was followed as that which held good during the raids by ordinary bombing planes according to the rule laid down in September 1940, and resort to shelter was taken only when, after an alert, the " Divo "[1] was also sounded. To make surer that this danger signal, transmitted to us from *The Daily Mirror's* premises, should reach the ears of everybody at the college, an alarm bell was now fitted to the front of 20 Breams Buildings, above the main entrance, so that its ringing, controlled from within the college, could be heard by people not only in Breams Buildings, but also in Greystoke and Field House. Often enough did the "danger overhead" signal sound, at first during lectures, then, for many students, during examinations, whereat everyone took shelter. On some days, students taking examinations could hand in only incomplete scripts. Now and again a student made apology on his or her script saying, for example, that it was hard to concentrate after so many sleepless nights. With the exception of those which were to have taken place on the morning of Friday, 16th June, the examinations held at Birkbeck, and spreading over a wider period than usual because of the flying bombs, and lasting throughout June to the 4th of July, finished without serious break.[2] So far as the written examinations were concerned, now and again the candidates were forced to leave the place of examination, the Theatre, but the interruptions lasted only for a few minutes. The practical examinations were disturbed more frequently but again only during short intervals. The reason why, in the Special Intermediate Examination for Geography, the sitting for the seond paper (Regional Geography), appointed to be held on the morning of Friday, the 16th of June, was postponed, was that

[1] See above, p. 71.

[2] During all the examinations of London University no one was killed thereat; and there was but slight injury.

an attack by flying bombs was in progress and too many candidates were involved to make it possible to clear the Theatre quickly if need should arise. The wisdom of the decision was shown when a flying bomb, falling on the 18th after 3.30 in the morning[1], about 400 yards away, covered the floor of the Theatre with lumps of shattered rubbish from the newly built wall of the library-store, and caused some damage to the windows. The postponed examination was held on the afternoon of Saturday, the 24th June. There were 358 candidates taking examinations at Birkbeck College ; but in the later part of the examinations, numbers were sufficiently small to be contained in that portion of the Theatre which was safeguarded by the balcony and gallery, and, towards the end of the examinations, in the basement. Nothing was left undone throughout this time. On the 27th of June, during a meeting of a Board of Advisers of the University held in Bloomsbury[2] to interview the candidates for the Professorship in English tenable at Birkbeck College, an "alert" was sounded before the first candidate was called in. I was present there, and remember how, just after the Board had recommended that G. Tillotson be appointed to the vacancy, an "all-clear" was, one might say, opportunely heard.

The college is severely damaged by a flying bomb, 19th July, 1944

On 30th June the college was shocked to learn about the sad slaughter of people at Aldwych brought by day on a busy street by the flying bomb whose buzz and burst were clearly heard, whose foul smoke was clearly seen, in our area ; then, nearly three weeks later, itself came near to crippling disaster. On the 8th of July some flying bombs, launched by the Germans, at night only, from aeroplanes starting from Holland, began to reach London from the east; and then continued to come from that direction until the 5th of September, four-and-a-half days after the last came from France (see pp. 163, 164). It seemed

[1] See above, p. 148.

[2] In fact at the School of Hygiene and Tropical Medicine, a place having no connection with the appointment or the candidates.

to us at college as if a line followed by flying bombs coming from the south, and another followed by bombs coming from the east, crossed over our area and tended to finish in it, or else near it. At 3.7 a.m., British double summer-time, on Wednesday, the 19th, after a number of "alerts" and "all clears," a flying-bomb fell in Fetter Lane just north of the point where the street Breams Buildings meets it, and destroyed, but without causing death or injury to anybody, premises which had survived the great fire of May 1941, and were occupied by Messrs. Wyman and Sons Ltd., at the north-eastern corner of the street Breams Buildings about thirty-five yards north-east from the main entrance of Birkbeck College ; and did great harm to the college itself. By the bomb's blast every window in the college's main building was shattered ; the ceilings and roof were badly damaged and the whole fabric in parts was seriously weakened, an alarming crack appearing in the east wall. The walls however and roof stood.[1] The apparatus and other equipment in the Departments of Chemistry, Physics, Botany and Zoology was broken or thrown into utter confusion ; cabinets were burst open, neat holes were drilled through glass fronts, and fireplaces were dislodged ; our Administration's rooms were completely wrecked inside, and losses included some important documents. The Theatre was partly wrecked, desks and chairs in it, where students had sat lately as candidates in an examination, were smashed to matchwood, and the part separated off to become a store for the Library was, as an entity, destroyed. Greystoke Place also, except the walls, was also almost completely blasted, so that the Departments of Zoology and Psychology were still to remain without their promised rooms. In Field House also the partition-walls were thrown down.

Descriptions of the explosion and of its effects

Not long after the explosion, the fire-guard (Dr., later Professor, A. Graham, T. S. Jackson, A. J. Massey, G. F.

[1] At its opening in 1885, Number 20 Breams Buildings had been called "a noble structure" which was "spacious and convenient" ; and it was provided with "the most approved system of ventilation." On this 19th of July 1944, its noble sturdiness at least was proved and its ventilation vastly increased.

Troup Horne) were clearing up the masses of wreckage, helped later by members of the Establishment Staff and others. The havoc wrought now was much like the effects of other flying bombs which fell and exploded in other parts of London's solid built-up mass. Detailed accounts[1] by two members of our guard show something of what our damage was. Professor Graham writes : "I happened to be on fire watch with T. S. Jackson and Massey on the night of 18th-19th July 1944. It was a somewhat misty night and there seemed to be rather a lot of flying-bombs coming over . . . . Somebody said because they couldn't be seen[2] in mist over the Channel, although we thought everything was radar-controlled by then. Massey had the 11 p.m. to 1 a.m. watch, and I did the next. I wakened Jackson to do the 3—5 a.m. spell, and Jackson was about to begin his watch. We were saying a few words to one another when we heard *The Daily Mirror* alarm go. Suddenly the bomb, which had merely been a near one until that second, (I suppose) dived without its engine stopping. Its noise increased enormously ; Jackson and I looked at one another in silence ; and I remember wondering what was going to happen next. What did happen was all over before we realised it had happened . . . . a gigantic roar from the engine of the bomb, no noise of an explosion[3], but a vast clattering of material falling and breaking, a great puff of blast and soot all over the room,[4] and then utter quiet. Massey raised his head from the bed where he had been asleep and asked what all that was ; I grabbed a torch. In the basement all seemed normal, but when I went upstairs to the ground floor I discovered the door of Mr. Troup Horne's room standing wide open, and him, half up from his bed, wiping off from himself, with a downward brushing motion of his hands, an assorted collection of broken objects which had been hurled at him from the direction of the office. He assured me that he was all right and I went on to the front door to see if

[1] The footnotes are added by me.—E. H. W.

[2] In mist they could not be brought down by methods which were in use, unless any struck a barrage-balloon.

[3] Such was the impression which both Graham and T. S. Jackson had at the moment. There was in fact of course a great crash.

[4] The Senior Common Room, which was the fire-guard's room.

there were anything I could do there. The first thing I did was to crash into the outer metal doors which the blast had flung through the wooden swing doors on to the floor of the hall, but I climbed over them and went on to the street. Some of the watchers of the Solicitors' Law Stationery Society[1] were climbing out of their shelter, and we gave one another mutual assurances that we were all, fortunately, unhurt. As we did so a policeman came running along Breams Buildings from the direction of Chancery Lane ; when he got up to the level of Birkbeck and saw that the bomb had crashed still nearer Fetter Lane, he called backwards into the darkness . . . 'It's all right, George, it's in the City'. [2] But he did assure himself that all was right with us, at least, before retiring to the right side of the frontier.

"Next we made a rapid survey of the College. The main building was indeed a lamentable sight with doors blown off. their hinges lying on the floor, window frames smashed, and glass flung over the rooms, and the contents of cupboards all mixed in disorder and thrown on to the floor. When we got up to the Chemistry floor, we found broken water pipes and a small fire, but Jackson said that he would deal with these while I went across to Greystoke. Here the same tale repeated itself, perhaps the worst casualty being Steward's laboratory, which had been altogether smashed. Water was escaping from several broken pipes in the building so I crawled into the débris of this laboratory to get at the main water tap which was in a recess in its floor—a rather foolhardy thing to do as I had no real knowledge that the whole thing might not collapse on top of me. However it went all right. The next thing that I discovered was a fire in the cupboard in the passage way outside the room ; this turned out to be due to a bottle of phosphorus which Steward kept there. The bottle had broken, the water

[1] The building which they were guarding, between Greystoke Place and the empty space whence the shop occupied by Wyman and Sons had just now disappeared, was a ruined shell.

[2] That is, within the official western boundary line of the City of London ; it runs through Number 20 Breams Buildings (the main building of the college) which thus lies partly in the City of London, and partly in the City of Westminster.

drained away, and there were the makings of a tidy little fire. Very fortunately, however, members of the National Fire Service arrived almost at this moment to see if they were needed for anything, so I led them to this and let them deal with it. We had some tea ; but there was no sleep for anybody during the remainder of that night. Members of the Women's Volunteer Services arrived and fed us with more tea and buns ; and in between these events we started to sweep out of the building some of the enormous quantities of rubbish that had suddenly been made for us."

Writing about the same event, Thomas Jackson, our Accountant, gives the following narrative:—"Having recovered from the blast and shock caused by this infernal machine, we managed after a while to scramble to our feet. It was some time before we were able to see what had actually happened to our good Fire Guard Room. Owing to the density of soot and dust which were disturbed by blast, it was far worse than any London fog I had ever experienced. We first proceeded to ascertain what damage the old building had suffered. On our way up the stairs, of course our first thought was to satisfy ourselves as to the safety of Mr. Troup Horne. As we were entering his room, we were presented with a spectacle which I shall never forget. Our colleague was at that moment rising from his divan looking somewhat like the local sweep (only worse), for he was covered from head to foot with soot, dust, and thousands of fragments of broken glass and other bits scattered from the partition which separated the general office from his room. We all had a thorough laugh, and were assured that he was quite all right and certainly felt none the worse for the shower and experience. Then for a peep at the general office which, not surprisingly, looked a shambles—front windows shattered, furniture smashed, cupboards upturned and records of the past century scattered all over the place. How fortunate that this all happened in the early hours of the morning ! For I fear that otherwise the consequences would have been serious for the staff. The next port of call for Massey and myself was across the way to Greystoke. Here the destruction was much the same as that which we had already seen in the main building. Leaving Greystoke looking in a very sorry state, we then decided to make our way back into the main building to investigate the damage done to the floors above the ground floor, but when we reached the steps at the entrance, a thought for the safety of the Fire Guard on duty in the Solicitors' Law Stationery Society's building (which incidentally received a very fair share of the bomb) flashed across my mind; and at this point I decided to turn back, leaving Massey to investigate on his own. I turned half-right across the road, made my way to the spot where I believed their entrance was. Suddenly to my astonishment and relief, the four men on duty emerged through the dust and rubble. They cheerfully assured me that they were quite all right after what must have been a very unpleasant experience. Now feeling very comforted at what I had just witnessed, I continued my journey alone to the upper regions of the main buildings. Damage and destruction was similar all the way up. When eventually I arrived on the fourth floor (Department of Chemistry), I was greeted with very strong doses of chemical fumes which were flowing from the broken bottles on to the floor below[1]. Feeling fairly overcome from these gases I was determined to complete my researches, when to my surprise a flame of fire suddenly appeared. Being single-handed you can imagine I felt scared for the moment, but in a flash I thought of the sand which was placed on each floor as a precaution against such an eventuality; "here goes," I said to myself; ran back, grabbed one of the sand-buckets, returned and smothered the flames with the contents until finally with great satisfaction I decided that all was well."

Mr. Troup Horne records as follows: "Not being on duty until 05.00, I was asleep in my room. At 03.06 I was awakened by a doodle overhead. Thinking we were for it, I pulled a sheet over my head to keep the plaster out of my remaining hairs; and five seconds later the damned thing went pop. After waiting for half-a-minute, I sat up. There was a knock at the door. and Mrs. Costello, who had been sleeping on the staircase,

[1] When Massey also went upstairs in the main building, he was met with a steady flow of liquid acid which was descending the stone steps. It came not only from those bottles but also from the large accumulator set in the little battery-room between the second and third floors.

said: 'Are you all right?' Legend records that I shouted 'Cancel the window-cleaning contract!' Switching on the light, I found myself looking into the street, the windows in the front of the office having been blown in, and the partition, made of glass and wood, separating my room, completely demolished, A voice from the road shouted, 'Put out that light!'; and having made a suitable response, I surveyed the damage. Graham and Jackson having arrived, we all got busy."

Mrs. Phyllis Costello, who had joined our administrative staff in 1940 and was now Troup Horne's chief assistant, had been occupying, in Chancery Lane, a "flatlet" in a bomb-damaged building where, at night, she was the only person present. When the flying bombs began, she preferred to be on the roof; but after a very bad night Troup Horne insisted that she must stay at the college.[1] She thus became, like him, permanently available for the college's fire-guard, and had a bed on a staircase. On the night of the 18th and the 19th of July she was therefore present at the college, though not on guard-duty. She says: "Troup *did* say 'Cancel the window-cleaning contract.' I think that it was when I entered the room. It doesn't take a woman long to dress in an emergency; I knocked at his door before things had finished falling, and found him with a sheet over his head to catch the glass. He said something about someone making a lot of unnecessary noise in the night. When fire broke out in the basement of Greystoke, I was most interested to see how the firemen smashed their way in, and I remember the Women's Volunteer Services van outside and having a welcome cup of tea. I also remember Troup opening bottles of beer for the boys; and I had my share." For some time the college had a sort of watchword stating that "We have no panes, dear mother, now." But this precious stone of humour was not of our cutting; it was a notice which appeared in Fleet Street during the air-raids of 1940.

Repairs and replacements

For the third time Troup Horne was leading the task of restoring the college to a state in which it could continue, as

[1] He was right, for the bomb which fell later at Staple Inn (see page 161) ruined her room in Chancery Lane.

required, its normal work. Vigorous action was taken by the Master. Mr. Mayhew, the City Surveyor, after inspecting the college with a representative of Messrs. Widnell and Trollope, Quantity Surveyors, was confident that structural repairs could be made successfully. With a view to effecting such repairs as would enable the college to open in a working condition at the beginning of the next session, applications for which from students had by early July completely filled the departments of Science and very nearly the departments of Arts and Economics, the Architects and Contractors of the new building of the college were consulted, and the worst problems seemed to be solved. Special fabric was obtained to take the place of the absent windows. In due course, besides working equipment for the damaged departments, a large quantity of new china and cutlery was ordered, and other furniture, including a hundred lecture-chairs, seventy-five ordinary chairs, thirty tables, one office-table, and one kitchen-table, all to replace losses through the attacks from flying-bombs.

Thus the session ended in yet another onset of stress and strain ; and more was to come as a prelude to the next session —the last of the period of the war.

CHAPTER SIX

STRESS AND SURVIVAL

SESSION 1944-1945

The college is damaged again, 13*th August*, 1944

DURING most of the vacation between the session 1943-1944 just passed and the session 1944-1945, the method of attack by flying-bombs on south-eastern England continued[1]. On the 28th of July, one which fell at Essex Street, south-west of the college just beyond Fleet Street, about 9.48 in the evening, loosened still further the already weakened roof-sheeting on the college. During all August there was constant coming and explosion of bombs in England, chiefly after dark. The fire-guard's record of the 2nd of August gives some idea of what London and some parts of Britain were still undergoing on a bad night.

[On Duty]

G. F. Troup Horne ; F. Barrow ; W. Fried ; W. O. Mortimer Gibson.

Narrative	Alert	All Clear	Locals[2]
	23.25	06.26	23.32—23.45
	06.46	09.22	23.40[3]
Normal Day			00.49—01.01[4]
			01.11—01.21
			01.11[3]
			01.12
			01.19
			01.50
Absentees : Nemo			02.21

(more follows in the log-book.)

[1] We were mastering the menace. For, whereas during six days from 17th July 204 bombs, out of about 473 that came within our defences, reached the area of London, on 28th August, of 97 sent against England, 90 were brought down and only 4 reached London.

[2] That is, signals of "danger overhead."

[3] That is, time when an explosion was heard.

[4] That is, "danger overhead" signal was given at eleven minutes to 1 a.m., and the "overhead off" was given at one minute past 1 a.m.

The record (not given complete here) shows that, during the whole period of this single night's watch, ten "overhead" signals and seventeen explosions were heard.

On the calm sunny morning of Sunday, the 13th of August, after an undisturbed night, the alert sounded while the present writer, one of the guard (the others being R. Siday, W. Fried, G. R. Green, W. Smith, and W. O. M. Gibson), was watching a family of London's new birds, black redstarts, on the ruined space east of the college, and brought me back into the main building ; then the familiar buzz of a flying-bomb was heard ; the "overhead" signal united all the members of the guard in the Senior Common Room, our shelter ; over sped the bomb ; then the noise stopped, which meant that the missile was falling ; we dropped to the floor ; heard a whistle of air as the bomb swooped near ; we raised our bodies a little off the floor on forearms and knees ; then came a great crash as the bomb exploded on contact at Cursitor Street about 150 yards north-west of the college. Our main building audibly shook ; more soot (some was left in the chimneys even after the effects of the bomb which fell so near on the 19th of July) puffed out of the fireplace into the room. My soot-soiled hand wrote in the log-book the time—07.56. We then all ran up and out to see the cloud of smoke drifting by, and having found Mrs. Costello safe, inspected the whole college, after finding that our help was not needed elsewhere because so far as we could learn only one person had been hurt, and that but slightly, by the explosion. In spite of the barrier formed by Field House, which suffered much superficial damage on one side, some similar damage was caused to our main building also, and our recent makeshift repairs were all undone. We were again anxious about the east wall, but then, because it looked solid, told the Master by telephone what had happened and that he need not come in from his home at Hadley Green. However, come he did. Outside the college all was calm again, and the black redstarts were behaving as if nothing unusual had happened.

The college is damaged yet again, 24th August, 1944

Conditions were much quieter as regards bomb-attacks during the days which followed.[1] But on the 24th of August the college was again damaged. The fire-guard's log-book includes the following on that date:—

[On Duty]			
			Narrative
19.00—08.00	J. W. Fox		
17.00—08.45	G. M. Davies		
17.30—08.00	L. Simons	19.23	Bomb on Staple Inn, next to site of original coll. building.
00.30*—09.00	G. F. Troup Horne		

*Bomb damage on Southern Railway. 5 hrs. delay.

Alert	All Clear	Locals On	Locals Off	B[2]
17.50	20.35			
21.10	21.54	18.23	18.25	
07.15	07.31	18.36	18.48	18.37
		18.55	18.57	
		19.23	19.26	19.23
		19.36	19.39	
		19.54	19.56	
		20.13	20.27	

Absentees : Nemo

The bomb which fell, as here recorded, at 19.23 hours, that is 7.23 p.m., and which destroyed the old hall of Staple Inn, was about 250 yards north-north-west of the college, but since there were a number of buildings standing between, damage to the college by shock and blast was not severe.

Difficulty about repairs; opening of the session postponed; fall of a chimney stack

Yet the cumulative effects of all three bomb-explosions (19th of July, 13th of August, 24th of August) caused the opening of the Session 1944-1945, fixed for the 15th of September, to be impossible. We were grateful for the personal interest of Sir Hugh Beaver, Director-General and Controller General of the Ministry of Works, and there were several discussions with the Architects, Contractors and the City Surveyors, but it was very hard, because of shortage of labour and materials, to get even first-aid repairs done. Further rooms were hoped for in Field

[1] By the end of August no more than one bomb in every seven passed through our defences and reached the area of London.

[2] That is, explosion of bomb was heard.

House ; but here also the Hulton Press had its difficulties, in spite of quick progress in repairs to roof and windows and other parts. Early in September a number of our students offered to help, during week-ends, in restoring windows there ; from some of these the frames were gone, or had fallen away from the structure. It was felt however that such a task was too dangerous for students, for they were not covered by the Workmen's Compensation Act. Therefore, at a special meeting of the Academic Board held on the 9th of September, it was decided to put off the opening of the college to the 6th of October, in order that the Faculties, especially the Faculty of Science, could adapt their plans. The destruction which had taken place had made it even more necessary than before to choose carefully from the many applicants for admission, and to consider closely every applicant's claim to be accepted as a part-time student. Except for a few vacancies in Arts subjects, the applications already received had filled the capacities of both faculties ; and in Science alone more than one hundred applications had had to be refused. Well over one thousand letters had to be sent to inform students of the delay in opening.

To make matters worse[1], on the 17th of September, which would have been the Sunday of the opening week-end had not the date of opening been postponed, a very high wind dislodged one of the weakened chimney-stacks on the western end of the main building, so that about four tons of masonry came plunging through the roof of the lecture theatre in the Department of Chemistry (a theatre which could hold about eighty students, and would have been occupied by them at the time but for the postponement of opening), smashed benches there, and damaged the ceiling of the room below where two students were dusting some apparatus belonging to the Department of Physics but were not hurt. One week before the newly fixed date for beginning the session the City Surveyor reported that the west wall was unsafe, thus threatening the lecture-theatre in the Department of Physics. Part of it was taken down at once and efforts were made to prevent further harm to the College's Theatre, of which only the stage could now be used.

[1] For the coming of the first rocket-bombs, see below, pp. 164, 165.

For a time also were laid open the kitchen and portions of the Departments of Chemistry and Botany to the air until, during the term, repairs to the main building's weakened east wall, and the restoration of part of Greystoke Place, were put in hand.

The session opens. Rooms and repairs

The college meanwhile opened as arranged, the Deans being, of the Faculty of Arts, Mrs. L. Simons, of the Faculty of Science, Dr. P. Dienes. Because of the renewed wreck and ruin of Greystoke Place, lectures and "practicals" in the Department of Zoology were held partly in the Department of Botany, partly at Mercers' School, partly in the long vacant Zoological rooms at University College, which courteously allowed us to continue to use them after it had made partial return to London by the beginning of the second term ; and for lectures in Psychology a mutual arrangement was made with Bedford College. Two rooms in the Scottish Corporation's premises were retained, and a room at St. Dunstan's Girls' School was hired. In Field House, of the two floors used by the college, one floor was ready early in October, and the second not long afterwards. Two further rooms in it were made available for our use. Thus, through the vigorous efforts made by the Master, the Clerk, the staffs of every grade in the affected departments, by students and by people engaged in repairs ; through prompt help and wise advice given by the Architects, Surveyors and Contractors ; and through the courtesy of the Headmaster of Mercers' School, the Provost of University College, and of the Principal of Bedford College, Birkbeck College was at full work again at week-ends in early October.

The "rocket-bombs," V.2 ("Big Ben")

Happily the strain caused by sleepless or broken nights was now very much less because the attacks by flying-bombs slackened off greatly. But the enemy was trying another weapon. Just after the Germans' chief launching sites in Europe for the flying bombs had been put out of action in the first week of

September by the British and Canadian armies, the enemy substituted, without entirely giving up the flying-bombs,[1] attacks by destructive rocket-bombs, which the German government called A-4 but published as V.2. These, launched from the ground, and carrying about one ton of high explosive—more than the flying bombs—travelled in an immense parabola and fell unseen at an angle, from a height of fifty miles or more, at a final velocity of about four thousand miles an hour—much quicker than that of sound[2], so that the crash of the explosion, of which there was no warning of any sort, except at night if any rocket became red hot in parts as it sped down, was followed by the long and belated roar of the already completed fall through the air, the fall being heard in reverse. The target was London[3], but many fell far wide of it. There was much damage and loss of life[4]; but otherwise the startling effect of this last weapon was less of a strain than the flying-bombs had been; no "alerts" or "overheads" or any other signal preceded the explosion of the bomb. The fire-guard's log-book has in its column of narrative for Friday, the 8th of September (members: G. F. Troup Horne, H. G. Bell, F. Barrow, N. Pevsner):

> Day. Nil report. Night. Explosion (heavy) S.W. from college—probably on river (? ammunition barge) circa 18.45 hrs.

A pencilled note added later says :

> 400 yards from the B.C. allotment !

[1] Henceforth the Germans launched about 500 of these, from travelling aeroplanes, and from ramps on the ground in Holland. The last flying bombs sent against us came between the 3rd and the 29th, inclusive, of March, 1945.

[2] As a result of this, two heavy bangs were often heard in rather quick succession, by people who were east of a line drawn north and south through the place of the fall. The first was caused by the "bow-wave" of sound from the missile near the end of its rush, the second, following closely on the other, was that of the explosion. Because of the angle of the fall and the consequent direction of shock upwards into the air, people west of a line drawn north and south through the place of the fall heard the second bang only. The rocket's journey lasted only three or four minutes. Each one was 46 feet long and weighed 14 tons when it was launched.

[3] For a short time the target was Norwich.

[4] To the explosive power of the rockets' warheads was added the kinetic energy of their rushing mass. On an average, the explosion of a rocket-bomb killed or wounded twice as many people as did the explosion of a flying bomb.

Different reasons were given for this and for other heavy explosions. For the 11th, the guard's book has :

> Day. Nil report. Night. Explosion at 06.14. Various explanations.

In fact however the explosion heard at the college on the 8th of September was that of the first rocket-bomb sent against this country ; the bomb fell in Chiswick at 6.43[1] in the evening. During the next ten days there came about two a day, it seemed mostly from the areas of The Hague and Leiden ; some from Walcheren Island also. For the 13th of September (members : W. Fried, L. Simons, C. Fox, Phyllis Costello) the book has :

> Day. Nil report. Night. Explosion 04.54. Direction east. Subsequent information—Walthamstow.

Likewise a pencilled note on the explosion heard by the guard at 04.08 on the 15th reads:

> Subsequent information—Sunbury-on-Thames.

And so the records go on. London was free from attack between the 25th of September and the 3rd of October, while a few were being aimed at Norwich only. Then up to the 18th of November came about two or three a day from The Hague, then about four a day for three weeks, then for a week six a day. A particularly noisy night of the term was that of the 14th-15th November, when both kinds of "pilotless" bomb were sent over in numbers by the Germans, London getting six rockets on the 15th. Once more from the log-book we get, for the 14th-15th : (members : E. H. Warmington, Thomas Jackson) :

> Alert 19.07[2]. All clear 19.25. Alert 00.11. Overhead on 00.22. Explosion 00.23. Overhead off about 00.25. All clear 01.00. Alert 05.42. Overhead on and explosion 05.43. Overhead off and all clear 05.55[3]. Explosions 22.25, 00.05.[4]

London had four rockets on the 17th. At first it looked as if the reduction of the guard to two members after the 12th of November was an overbold step. In fact, however it was justified, and many days and nights followed on which nothing

[1] The uncertainty of the time as recorded by Troup Horne in the log-book may have been caused by confusion with the explosion of the second rocket-bomb ; this fell at Epping sixteen seconds after the first.

[2] British ordinary summer-time (double summer-time had ended on Sunday, 17th September).

[3] These were all caused by flying-bombs.

[4] That is, five minutes after midnight. These two were very distant rocket-bombs.

was recorded by the guard. From the 19th of November to the end of the year the attack on London slackened, and not much came by day.

The rocket-bombs came at any time of the day or night—about two hundred of them every month—during the first two terms of the session. Now and again their explosions were heard near or in the distance by the college even during lectures to students and during public lectures. Some were very near our area. On the morning of Sunday, the 5th of November, for example, when a rocket-bomb was heard during classes, some nervous effects in some students were perhaps dispelled by humour from the lecturer when he said, "Oh, of course, it's November the 5th." I was discussing a matter with Mrs. Costello in the college's office on the fine sunny morning of Saturday, the 25th of November, when a rocket-bomb fell at Warwick Court, south of Gray's Inn near Chancery Lane Station. On going outside we could see a large cloud of dark and dirty smoke drifting away over buildings and over ruins caused by raids of the past. Then, back in the office, she said "What were we saying when we were interrupted?" Lectures were not stopped even by this bomb. In one class on this occasion a student, forgetting that no dive for safety could be of any avail to her after the explosion of a rocket-bomb, unless the buildings began to fall, crouched under a desk and became somehow wedged there until the lecturer, who had not ceased from speaking, heard some time later a voice utter plaintively "I can't get out." After a very simple rescue, the lecture continued. These were good ways of taking such things, when we were not near enough to any scene of horror to be of help; but we knew well how dreadful the effects could be—witness the deaths caused by the rocket which fell at Warwick Court, and very much more disastrous rockets which we knew about. However, people in the act of attending Birkbeck College remained unharmed, and the buildings used by the college escaped further disaster from this form of weapon, though half-a-dozen temporary windows of "windolite" were lost on the 25th of November, and later a few similar windows were broken, for example, by the explosion at half past five in the evening of the 14th of February 1945;[1] and slight other damage was done chiefly in early March, when, on the 8th, most horrible slaughter and mutilation of people took place, on the fall of a rocket-bomb near noonday in the crowded market at Farringdon Road, just outside our area. Our damage was trifling, but it led to the hurried taking down of one of our remaining chimney-stacks.

Four new Professors. Other departmental changes

The college welcomed at the beginning of the session four new Professors, each to be Head of a Department: of English, Professor G. Tillotson, M.A., B.Litt. (formerly Reader in English Literature at University College, London); of Geography, Professor S. W. Wooldridge, D.Sc. (formerly Reader in Geography at King's College, London); of Botany, Professor C. T. Ingold, D.Sc., F.L.S. (formerly Lecturer in Botany and Head of the Department of Botany at University College, Leicester); and, of the Department of Psychology, transferred from King's College, Professor C. A. Mace, M.A., D.Litt. He, while Reader in Psychology at Bedford College (housed at Cambridge) had lectured at Birkbeck College also to students of King's College, who had not gone to Bristol, and was now finally established at Birkbeck College, a University Chair of Psychology having been vacant since the death of Professor F. Aveling. Other experts in Psychology now at Birkbeck College, instead of belonging to another college, were R. J. Bartlett, Dr. J. Hadfield, Dr. May Smith and Adele Frankenstein (part-time lecturers), and Dr. A. Caws, L. Cooper, G. Adcock, and Dr. Grace Calver (demonstrators). Acting Heads of Departments were reappointed, and Dr. W. P. Morrell became acting Head of the Department of History. In the Department of Mathematics Dr. P. Dienes during the session was made Professor and Head of the Department; Dr. F. V. Cantalamessa and Dr. J. L. Cooper were appointed full-time Lecturers. Professor S. Mandelbrojt, of the Sorbonne, Paris, gave lectures on the Theory of Functions. In Classics, H. G. Rawlinson, M.A., F.R.Hist.Soc., was unable to continue

[1] In November 1944, the rocket-bomb which burst in the air or in the river Thames (no trace of it was ever found), damaging King's College's building, shook us also.

his part-time lectureship because of illness, and Dr. J. L. Whiteley and Mr. E. C. Kennedy took his place. In Economics G. L. Schwartz had resigned his appointment as Lecturer in Economic Theory, and his work was now undertaken by J. Horsefield, who as Lecturer resumed supervision of the Department until the London School of Economics should return. To this Department came also : to lecture in Economics, Dr. T. Wilson ; from Dundee Technical College, J. K. Eastham, and from the London School of Economics, A. Radomysler. Further, Professor C. A. Manning, from the School, began a whole session's course of lectures on International Relations ; R. C. FitzGerald again gave instruction on the British Constitution, and also on the Elements of English Law, and from University College came J. Unger, LL.M., to lecture on International Law. In Geography, G. Gray was appointed part-time Lecturer and demonstrator, and A. Moodie continued to help although he had also accepted a post at Bedford College. In English, the proper courses for proficiency in English had ended, but Marjorie Daunt continued instruction in it during the session 1944-1945. Dr. Joyce Tompkins was employed to give six lectures on Jacobean Drama ; in History, R. C. Latham, of King's College, to lecture one hour a week ; and in Physics, E. P. George, hitherto part-time Lecturer in Radio-Physics only, was made part-time Lecturer in Physics. Several members of the staff served as advisers and inspected courses of instruction at the Canadian Khaki University near Watford, whither they went at times when classes were not being held at Birkbeck College.

Public lectures

The opening of the session was marked as in session 1943-1944 by a religious service at the church of St. Dunstan-in-the-West on the 1st of October, a few days before the first term began, the address being given by Canon V. A. Demant, D.Litt., of St. Paul's; and on the 19th of October, the thirteenth Haldane Memorial Lecture, postponed from the previous session, was given by the Right Honourable Lord Greene, O.B.E., M.C., Master of the Rolls, in the Old Hall of Lincoln's Inn, kindly lent by the Treasurer and Benchers because our Theatre was insecure. The subject of the lecture was "Law and Progress" ; and the Lord Mayor of London, Sir Frank Newson-Smith, presided. A public lecture was given on Ancient Greek Democracy by Professor E. H. Warmington in connection with the London Branch of the Classical Association.

Death of the President of the College

The college was grieved to learn of the death of its President, Dr. W. Temple, Archbishop of Canterbury, 26th October 1944. Record of the interest which he showed in the activities and welfare of the college has found a place in this history.

Donation from the Queen

On December the 16th the college received with gratitude a further Special Donation from Her Majesty the Queen who was again informed of the condition of the college and of its activities.

Students' activities

The number of students half-way through the term was 1,055 (in Arts 616, including 411 women ; in Science 439, including 169 women). The President of the Students' Union was D. G. Arnott, with B. H. Chibnall as the other representative student on the Governing Body. Although the rocket-bombs and at times flying bombs were a source of anxiety, the worry caused to students was not to be compared with the strain of the past summer-term. A new Society was now active, namely, the Rowing Club, which had enjoyed itself even during the past vacation, having facilities at the University Boat House at Chiswick. A Psychology Society was begun ; and efforts were continued to form a Liberal Society. There was some renewed activity also in the Natural History Society, and in the Classics Society. The Geographical Society and the Historical Society made plans for expeditions. Other activities of the students included a sensible discussion about the apparent growth of "Fascism" in Greece and Belgium newly liberated from the Germans, and a tightening of discipline with reference not only to single persons, but also to a College Society which did not keep the reasonable rules of procedure. Other colleges, for example, University College and the Imperial College of Science, were allowed to use our sports ground at Greenford as in previous sessions.

The second term. End of air-attacks. Rooms and repairs

During the second term of the session, which began on the 12th of January 1945, when hopes of final victory were rising higher and higher, after the united onslaught on Germany began in January 1945, the attacks on this country by rocket-bombs and occasionally by flying bombs were continued. The new year saw heavy blows again with rockets. More than eight rockets a day on an average fell on England in the first half of January, then a little less ; there was another increase early in February, about ten a day in mid-February. The three rocket bombs heard by myself during fire-guard duty at the college on the 14th of February, some blast from the first of which broke a few windows at the college, as mentioned above (pp. 166, 167), were some of more than seventy that fell on England in seven days. Whereas during this term only such slight damage by rocket-bombs was done to our buildings, on the 14th of January Peter Hayward, a student of the college working for the B.A. Honours Degree in History, was killed by one at his lodgings. At the end of March, when the allied forces against Hitler were closing in on Germany, the attacks[1] by both weapons ceased. On the night of the 26th and 27th of March the fire-guard at the college made its last detailed records—one "alert" and "all clear," and three explosions heard, all on 27th. The time of the college's last record of explosions was 7.20 in the morning; of eleven hundred and fifteen rocket-bombs which fell in England, or in the sea near,

[1] Of institutions in London University, King's College, Richmond College and the London School of Medicine for Women, besides Birkbeck College, had been damaged by them. It has been estimated that in England 200,000 houses were destroyed or badly damaged and more than 1,000,000 others damaged by the combined action of these two weapons.

between early September 1944, and the time when we liberated The Hague whence most of the missiles had come, the last fell at Orpington in the afternoon of the 27th of March 1945.[1] The last flying bomb came on the 29th of March.[2] Our guard ceased to serve after the 1st of August.[3] Repair of the main building up to February proved slow and difficult, through conditions of weather, and Greystoke Place remained unusable ; but repairs of the rooms occupied in Field House had been completed earlier, and the whole of its third floor and more than hitherto of the second floor were available, so that in Field House twenty-one rooms were in use by the Faculty of Arts. In February the College suggested to the Court of the University that the derelict house, number 21 Torrington Square, University of London, Bloomsbury, immediately north-east of the incomplete new building of the college, might be made available for research conducted by Professor J. Bernal in Physics. Later on this proposal brought important results. In March application was made for priority licences to provide working-space in the remains of Greystoke Place, for Zoology (in the basement), and Psychology (on a reconstructed first floor) ; to repair in the main building the upper part of the Theatre, and the fourth floor which was above it, and to provide a book-store on its ground floor ; and to build huts in the forecourt of Greystoke Place.[4]

[1] About five hundred had fallen on or near London. It seems that at least 2,850 civilian people were killed and at least 6,260 badly injured by these missiles in England. In London more than 2,500 people were killed, more than 5,860 badly hurt.

[2] Of the very many flying bombs sent against England—killing more than 6,130 civilian people and seriously wounding at least 17,230, destroying also and damaging about 750,000 buildings—, about 2,400 had reached London, which was the greatest sufferer in Britain. Belgium also suffered greatly, especially Antwerp and Liége, from deliberate attack with both these and rocket-bombs.

[3] People may be interested to know that on the City alone of London had fallen, besides countless incendiary bombs, 417 explosive bombs and 13 mines ; and that the sirens had sounded there 715 times—415 times during the last five months of the year 1940.

[4] The project to build huts was not carried out in the way planned. See page 179. But the work for Zoology and Psychology in Greystoke was completed later and held good until the college left Bloomsbury in 1951.

Departmental changes. Intercollegiate fees

The number of students had risen in March to 1,112 (in Arts 656, including 420 women, in Science 456, including 175 women). In History the part-time Lectureship held by Dr. S. M. Hardy was converted into a full-time Assistant Lectureship. It was resolved to ask the University to create a Chair in History tenable at the college ; and to fill the vacant Chair in French. In Geography it was resolved to appoint Miss E. M. J. Campbell, who had been promoted from demonstrator to part-time Lecturer during this session, to a full-time Assistant Lectureship to begin next session. In the United States of America, the University of Chicago, having learnt that the laboratory and apparatus provided by the Rockefeller Institute, to enable Dr. F. C. Steward, in our Department of Botany, to carry on his research in Physiological Botany, had been destroyed through action by the enemy, had invited Dr. Steward to continue his research in its laboratories in Chicago for three years. The Governors of the Birkbeck College granted him leave of absence for that period and later resolved to appoint a full-time assistant Lecturer to take his place until his return. In Zoology, N. Barnicot, from University College, was appointed to give lectures with particular reference to Comparative Physiology. In Chemistry, R. W. Pittman was appointed a full-time Lecturer as from the 9th of February. The Governors expressed full agreement with a recommendation contained in a letter from Dr. W. R. Halliday, Principal of King's College, about intercollegiate fees : "That the Governing Bodies of Bedford College, Birkbeck College, Imperial College, Queen Mary College and University College, be informed that the Delegacy" (of King's College) "would welcome the abolition, in all Faculties other than the Faculty of Laws, of the system of payment of intercollegiate fees between the college" (that is, King's College) "and each or any of them in respect of any subject for which provision is made at both institutions for the students so attending, and would be prepared to enter into reciprocal arrangements to this effect for a period of five years in the first instance."[1]

[1] Birkbeck College Governors' Minutes, 15th Feb. 1945, Minute 304.

The students. Decision to revert to evening classes

The Students' Union, under the plan of the National Union of Students for exchange of hospitality between colleges and universities, extended the freedom of its common-room to all students in Britain. It became very anxious, in view of the now assured victory in the war, about the decision of the college to give up week-end classes altogether and to revert to evening classes from Mondays to Fridays inclusive, as the college was bound to do if peace came again, since it is an evening college, not a week-end college, of the University of London. The students held a referendum among themselves in which 69% of the voters desired week-end courses ; 42% would be unable to attend in the evenings ; 24% desired evening courses not at week-ends ; 56% would be unaffected by change to evenings ; 3% expressed uncertainty ; 2% said it would not matter.

On the one hand, our present students had become used to week-ends of work at college, and their whole courses had been planned on this arrangement ; many students came in from parts which were at some distance from London, and thus could attend during week-ends only, spending at least two days in the city ; most of them felt that two successive days spent at college formed some approach to full-time education at a University ; others, who could indeed attend on evenings of mid-week, yet did not like the prospect of exchanging four or five evenings for two whole days ; they looked with foreboding on the prospect of fatigue caused by an evening's lectures after a day's other work ; the college's social activities would have to be put very late ; and many students would prefer to go home than to partake in them. On the other hand, week-end work at college, despite the use of whole days, was hardly enough for the needs of internal students ; and moreover it now caused serious over-crowding, especially in departments of Science where the various kinds of workers were crammed together in laboratories, often without a chance of proper setting out and adjustment of all equipment and apparatus for each class. When work was spread out over several evenings weekly, such conditions could be made vastly better ; week-ends could then be devoted, as in the time before the war, partly to private study, partly to healthful exercise in open air on our sports ground or in the country, and in other forms of recreation and rest. Again, most members of the staffs of the college, not being transient like students, would, unless the college went back to its methods of peace-time, face a life of over-strain at week-ends, and might feel chary of taking leisure during mid-weeks while others worked ; many of the teaching staff earnestly desired a spread of their labours over several days. The Governors, though sympathetic towards the students, were of course unable to go back on the inevitable decision ; but it was resolved to take care that all difficulties be overcome according to the necessities of the students concerned.

In the course of the term two new societies were formed—the Conservative Society and the Table Tennis Club. In March the Science Society revived an activity of the days before the war—a conversazione which was attended by about a thousand visitors ; and the Birkbeck Players produced Shaw's "Arms and the Man." In the Easter vacation Abingdon was the place where the Student Christian Movement held its annual conference ;[1] in the same vacation the Departments of Geography, Botany and Zoology resumed their Vacation Field Courses which had been in abeyance since the war began.

Victory in the War

In Europe our forces crossed the Rhine early in March ; about a million men pushed on towards Emden, Bremen and Hamburg, and in April joined with the Russians who entered ruined Berlin on the 23rd of April. Before the end of the month both Hitler and Mussolini were dead. In April also came the certainty that Japan would, like Germany, be overwhelmed. It was grievous that Roosevelt was prevented by his death from sharing in the coming triumph of his country and its allies. Partial surrender of Germany to Field-Marshal Montgomery on the 4th of May was followed by complete surrender which, made on the 7th, was confirmed on the 9th.[2]

[1] In 1943 and 1944 no annual conference had been held.

[2] Japan surrendered on the 10th of August, accepting terms later. Professor Bernal, transferred to the South-East Asia Command, had been connected with plans for landings which had proved unnecessary because the Japanese had already left the area concerned.

Thus, early in the third term (which began on the 20th of April) of our academic session came the end of the long and fearful struggle in which the college had shared ; and an end, not of our problems or worries, but of the special sense of strain which had never been entirely absent for six or rather seven years.

Message to the King. Foundation Oration. Other matters

On the 10th of May a message was sent to His Majesty the King, after the end of the fighting : "The Governors, the Master, the Staff and the Graduates and Undergraduates of Birkbeck College, University of London, Your Majesties' most loyal and devoted subjects, tender their humble duty and beg to offer their respectful congratulations on the brilliant and overwhelming victory achieved by your Majesty's forces. Whilst rejoicing in the successful issue of all aspects of the war, it is a special honour for the college to have remained in London with your Majesties throughout these recent years." The reply from the King's private secretary was : "Please convey His Majesty's sincere thanks to all those associated with you in your loyal message on the victorious conclusion of the War against Germany.[1]" On the 11th of May the 121st anniversary of the foundation of the college was celebrated by the delivery of a Foundation Oration, on the subject of Education, by the Right Honourable R. A. Butler, M.P., Minister of Education, in the Theatre, with the Lord Mayor of London, Alderman Sir Frank Alexander, in the Chair. On the 13th of May, the Rev. A. J. Macdonald, Rector of the church of St. Dunstan-in-the-West, conducted for the College a Thanksgiving Service, well attended by students and members of the staff. On the 17th of May the Governors at a meeting replied with cordial thanks and good wishes to a telegram :—"Victory Greetings from ex-student to staff and students," just received from J. Eiduss, a student at the college from 1938 to 1942, one of the fire-guard on the night of the 10th and 11th of May 1941,[2] member of the Russian Forces and wounded during service, and now doing research at the University of Riga.

[1] Governors' Minutes, 17th May, 1945, Minutes 479, 480.
[2] See above, pp. 87, 88. Governors' Minutes, 17th May, 1945, Minutes 585, 586.

Departmental changes

As regards the teaching staff it was resolved to appoint, for the session 1945-46, Mrs. L. Simons to be Adviser of Studies in the Faculty of Arts, and Dr. Barrow as Adviser of Studies in the Faculty of Science ; to promote Rosemary Freeman to a Lectureship in the Department of English ; to create an Assistant Lectureship in the same Department, and to appoint H. F. Brooks as its first holder ; furthermore to appoint P. F. J. Sewell an Assistant Lecturer in Zoology ; Dr. W. Rigby, a Lecturer in Chemistry, Dr. K. J. Dormer, a temporary Assistant Lecturer in Botany, Ruth Saw, a full-time Lecturer in the Department of Logic, Philosophy and Ethics ; to create a new part-time Lectureship in the same Department ; to establish a course by Dr. N. Pevsner for a Final Examination in the History of Art, to be delivered in the session 1945-1946 ; to accept the resignations of Dr. F. J. Llewellyn, of the Department of Chemistry, who was leaving the college to take up a Research Fellowship offered by Imperial Chemical Industries and tenable at the University of Birmingham, and of A. C. O'Dell of the Department of Geography who had accepted a Lectureship in Geography at Aberdeen ; and to ask the University to appoint a Reader in Mathematics. The return to the college of members of the staffs who had been absent, wholly or partly, from the college on other work, was expected with gratification.

Public lectures

A public lecture was given by Walter De La Mare on "Nonsense and Lewis Carroll" ; and, in connection with the London Branch of the Classical Association, Professor G. Forsey gave a public lecture, the last of the war-time lectures[1] which had kept the Branch alive, on "Dreams and Oracles in the Ancient World."

[1] Two more were given in the session 1945-1946, after which the Branch revived its activities of peace-time.

Progress of the Library

The report on the Library, made in June, showed that, during the session, 1,805 books had been acquired, of which 643 were given. The college was indebted to the British Academy, the Carnegie Trust, the London University Library, King's College Library, University College Library, the Trustees of the British Museum, the Royal Geographical Society, the Early English Text Society, the Institute of Historical Research, the Oxford and Cambridge University Club, and the Seafarers' Education Service. In April, runs in eighteen periodicals dealing with Psychology were transferred permanently to the college from King's College, which in July formally transferred all books previously deposited at Birkbeck College on loan. There were in the Library 2,548 bound periodicals and 409 pamphlets, the total of the other books being 18,102. About 650 were not yet catalogued, and a number of unbound periodicals were still housed elsewhere. Issues to readers numbered 8,849, of which 168 were books borrowed from other Libraries. A small room in Field House was being provided with shelves for books at present housed away from the college, but since the part of the Theatre separated off for a Library store had been destroyed, much of the Library still had to be kept elsewhere. The Library gratefully accepted about 2,000 volumes left by the late Professor Tanquerey.[1] At present these were housed at Greenford.

Students' activities

The decision of the Governors to renew the awards of all college studentships, exhibitions, scholarships, and prizes was welcomed. The numbers of students in June was 1,130 (in Arts 667, including 425 women ; in Science, 463, including 177 women). The students were now giving increased support to Student Relief schemes and to International Student Organisations. Recognition by the Governors was given to the Mountaineering Club and to the Table Tennis Club. The Cricket Club revived, and a group of the Youth Hostels Association

[1] See above, pages 113, 114.

was formed at the college. On the 28th of April and the 5th of May, the Birkbeck Players achieved a most able and interesting production in the Theatre, of Shakespeare's "Two Gentlemen of Verona," for which W. Taylor, one of the actors, composed music for "Who is Sylvia ?" The Music Society, which provided the singer and a string quartet for Shakespeare's play, also performed Stainer's *Crucifixion* at a joint meeting with the Literary Society and the Student Christian Movement. Two issues of *The Lodestone* during the session were edited by Elizabeth Gundrey ; the third was edited by R. Glascock.

The college continued to afford a meeting-place to other bodies, offering, for example, room for a meeting of the British Geographical Association and one for the British Aeronautical Association, and, as in previous sessions, the Theatre on several days for St. Albans Church School.

The College's problems on the coming of peace. Working space and teachers

Before the end of the session the college was considering most carefully several related problems : (i) the expected increase in the number of applications for entry to the college, as a result of the return of large numbers of men and women from the Forces, and of the slackening in pressure of work upon many people engaged on occupations in civil life. There were also the claims of former students returning to interrupted studies, and requests of Governments of Dominions and Allies for admission of students from overseas. Applications for admission to the college numbered more than 1,100 in mid-July.[1] (ii) The provision of enough room for our present students and for as many as possible of the new applicants. (iii) Provision of further teaching-staff in addition to those[2] employed at present both by the college itself and those[3] employed by the University in posts tenable at the College. It was felt that the number of students in the near future might have to reach 1,500,

[1] Because of the damage done during the war, it was still hard to provide any facilities for post-graduates in departments of Science even for the session 1945-1946.

[2] Teachers below the rank of Reader.

[3] Professors and Readers.

but it was also deemed desirable that the college should not become permanently larger than it was in the years before the war; and that the principle be adhered to that only students who were taking full degree courses and were also in full-time employment during the ordinary day-time should be admitted, without insisting on such full-time employment in the case of applicants for a post-graduate course.

Some subjects cease at the college

When the London School of Economics returned from Cambridge, students of Economics at Birkbeck College were transferred, though in the first part of the session some day students of the school were admitted to Field House. The end of the war brought also the discontinuance of Norwegian at the college; and also Radio-Physics as an alternative study in Physics; and of Spanish, which was, however, renewed permanently, as a subject taught at the college to its own students, in session 1948-49. Meanwhile these changes did not do much to solve our difficulties.

Housing of Zoology, Psychology, and Geography

In July the Master reported to the Governors that licences asked for in February had been granted, and work at Greystoke Place for the housing of Zoology and Psychology was in progress. It was not however permissible to build, on the forecourt also of Greystoke Place, huts large enough for our purposes, because of the Disused Burial Ground Act. In Greystoke Place workable housing for Zoology was in fact achieved; and arrangements were made for two huts—one for Geography and one for Psychology—to be built on the vacant site adjoining the main building on its eastern side; and these were completed and occupied by the end of June 1946.

Offer from the Institute of Education

The problem of working space was indeed giving much anxiety, especially since we would not be able to use Field

House after March 1946, and it would take a long time to complete the new building at Bloomsbury, however soon work on it might be resumed. But already in June it became known that Professor G. B. Jeffery, Director-Elect of the Institute of Education (University of London), having heard of the difficulty which would arise in housing our Faculty of Arts, had kindly suggested that the reciprocal use of accommodation between Birkbeck College and the Institute, arranged before the war to begin whenever the college's new building should first come into use, should be put into practice by the Institute on its own side at once. Birkbeck College would be allowed to use the Institute in the evenings as soon as there was need[1]. This suggestion was gratefully accepted, and began a line of policy which when carried into effect stamped a special character on the life of the college during the next six years until it entered its new building late in the summer of 1951. By this arrangement about six hundred students in the Faculty of Arts were housed for class-work in Bloomsbury at the Institute forthwith and at the School of Oriental and African Studies, by the courtesy of the Director, both institutions being next to the site where the new building of Birkbeck College was awaiting completion. Members of the staff of the Institute of Education most kindly allowed members of the staff of Birkbeck College to share their private rooms. Moreover the University of London[2] gave the college permission to occupy the house 29 Russell Square near by, and, after some difficulties were overcome, adaptation went ahead to house there the general Library and a refectory, and to provide common rooms and some private rooms for departments in the Faculty of Arts. Thus the session 1945-46 was not only the first of peace after war, but also an academic year of passing to a new stage in the history of the college ; for the college was split into two parts, the Administration and the Faculty of Science remaining in the old building

[1] Governors' Minutes, 21st June 1945, Minute 598.

[2] The central administration of the University returned to its home in Bloomsbury in December 1945 and during 1946, progressively according to the gradual departure of the Ministry of Information which had been in occupation there.

at Breams Buildings with Greystoke Place, whither the Department of Zoology returned in September, 1945, and in new huts housing Geography and Psychology which are common to both Faculties ; while the Faculty of Arts moved to Bloomsbury. Such division caused great difficulties for the Students' Union until the whole college entered its new building in 1951. This and other problems which the college had to face in the half-decade which followed the end of the war arose out of the war itself ; but these sessions 1945-1951 form another period in the life of the college, and lie outside the scope of this present work.

Retrospect. Omissions from this History

When this history is considered, two things should be clear even to persons who are without experience of the college, whether during the war or at other times. First, the actual intensity of the hardships encountered by the college was much less than the sufferings of people elsewhere in the British Isles and even quite close to the college; and very much less than the sufferings of people in other lands including Germany itself—throughout this narrative the main foe—where the loss of life and destruction of property caused by fearful air-raids during most of 1943, 1944 and the first part of 1945, were appalling. It seems that, by the end of the war, attacks by air against London had killed nearly twenty-nine thousand nine hundred people and had badly injured about fifty thousand five hundred, besides countless who were slightly hurt ; and had destroyed some one hundred and seven thousand houses and badly damaged one hundred and seventy thousand others; and had done less harm to countless others. At the old site itself of Birkbeck College loss of life was none ; hurts were slight ; and damage done did not make all our buildings fall. Yet of persons connected with the college some had lost their lives ; some had been hurt ; some had lost their kin ; some had had their homes destroyed or damaged. Second, the narrative omits various details about (i) finance connected with salaries, superannuation—even when these details were not confidential—and with general upkeep and working of the college ; (ii) the various departments and subjects of academic studies, and branches of the college's administration ; (iii) students' troubles and their difficulties in supporting their own organisations, societies and clubs ; (iv) individual persons. Further, the weaker side of human beings would make no ugly showing. Examples of bad discipline or more serious wrongdoing, which found written record or can be remembered from experience, were very few indeed. The war did not visibly increase wrong behaviour ; and two cases among students, successfully dealt with by other students, to the benefit of all concerned, show clearly enough the soundness of our college-life. We were all human ; there were fears, complaints, grumbles and groans against events and conditions and against each other, when we were more annoying, or less patient, or both, than we might have been. But these and other shortcomings are hardly worth any mention. In this history there is no claim to perfection, but there is a revelation of much persistence and even some greatness. It is these lasting qualities, and not the small or momentary lapses, forgotten or hardly remembered, that, tested during a time of hardship and danger, make memorable the story of the college during the long war. On the 30th of May the Committee of the Court of Electors of the college said that it "places on record its admiration of the manner in which the staff of Birkbeck College, administrative, academic, and establishment, has carried on its work during the many trials of war-time conditions." The same sort of praise is due to the students for whom life in London was sometimes hard, for whom the teaching which they received at college was sadly hampered by troubles of various kinds: and to all those people on whom so many vital decisions depended.

Governors

The labours of the Governors of the college during the war can be surmised from the narrative of this history, even in places where this ruling council of the college is not mentioned. There was no aspect of college life with which they did not deal ; no grade or person connected with the working of the college was unrepresented among them, because the Establishment staff, as well as part of the Administrative, found a permanent acting representative in the person of the Clerk to the Governors, G. F. Troup Horne, their employer. In no way was the democratic constitution and spirit of this governing body thrust aside even under the pressure of war and its very unusual conditions. There is no need to dwell on these points further here. To one man among our Governors the College owes very special gratitude—E. J. Syer, who was Chairman of the Governors' Finance and General Purposes Committee, and also Deputy-Chairman of the whole Governing Body throughout the war, after the death of W. L. Hichens, in October 1940, until his retirement at the end of 1944[1].

Changes in the membership of Governors

In January 1941, in order to reduce the number of meetings of committees during a most difficult time, the work of certain committees (College Societies, Library, New Buildings) was transferred to the Finance and General Purposes Committee ; and that of the Publications Committee was transferred to the Academic Board, which has permanently retained the duty of deciding about assistance for publications by members of the college. Alterations in the membership of the Governors other than changes in the representation of the students recorded in the course of the narrative, were as follows. After the resignation in December 1939, of A. L. Bostock, the Court of Electors chose H. D. G. Trew to represent them with H. W. Cornes. In the autumn of 1940 Professor H. G. Jackson succeeded, as representative of the Academic Board, Professor Dame Helen Gwynne-Vaughan when she resigned her membership ; and when she returned in 1941 Professor Jackson retained his membership. In October 1941, Professor J. Sutherland took the place of Professor E. H. Warmington as the other representative of the Academic Board. In place of the Right Honourable Lord Stamp of Shortlands, killed in an air-raid in April 1941, the University elected Sir Ernest H. Pooley, M.A., LL.B., as a representative. In 1942, on the resignation of membership

[1] He died in 1951.

by Professor S. Sugden, J. B. Reed was chosen by the Court of Electors in his place. In July, the resignation of the Right Honourable Lord Justice Sir Henry Slesser, K.C., J.P., co-optative governor, was accepted with much regret. In session 1943-1944, John Maud, C.B.E., M.A., and T. R. G. Bennett were made co-optative governors ; when O. W. Moss resigned in February 1944, the Court of Electors chose T. Dewar in his place. At the beginning of session 1944-1945, Dr. R. J. McClean and Professor W. Wardlaw succeeded Professor J. Sutherland and Dame Helen Gwynne-Vaughan as representatives of the Academic Board ; on the retirement of H. Cornes, Professor Lillian Penson[1] was elected by the Court of Electors in his place. Lastly, with reluctance the Governors accepted the resignation, in December 1944, of E. J. Syer, as mentioned above, and in June 1945, of the Dowager Viscountess Harcourt, representative of the City Parochial Foundation.

* * * * *

[1] See below, p. 187.

Afterword

The students and the members of the staff who worked at Birkbeck College during the whole or part of the war[1] remember with pleasure the presence at the college of foreign exiles who belonged to several nations and came from friends and foes, and were surpassed by nobody in their fortitude and humanity; and of nuns who helped to brighten dull and dreary times with their cheerfulness and grace—for they were part of us and shared our troubles and our pleasures. We thank the Reverend A. J. Macdonald, Rector of the Church of St. Dunstan-in-the-West, for the spiritual care and hospitality which he gave to all such members of the college as chose to accept them; our neighbours, the owners of Field House—the Field Press and then the Hulton Press—for courteous provision of indispensable rooms to suit our requirements, and the Directors of *The Daily Mirror Newspapers* for co-operation[2] in guarding our premises; other good friends in our area such as The Mercers' School, Lincoln's Inn, Clifford's Inn Club; local services of London and Essex for strong support in the midst of attacks by the enemy; contractors for structural repairs and caterers for provision of food; the Senate, Court, and officials of the University of London for constant aid and counsel; colleges and schools of the University who helped us by lending teachers for instruction, and housing for our departments of Science; all persons and institutions that aided the recovery of our Library; and all persons who spent time and trouble in coming from other places to deliver at the college public lectures on special and other occasions. Of such readers of this history as were part of the college during the war, there are students who said that all owe thanks to the teaching staff; and I say that the teaching staff

[1] The present tense used in this and other parts of my narrative might well be taken as lapsing in the passing of time. But if 'the Birkbeck Spirit', mentioned at the end of the third chapter, lives on, so also may the feeling of gratitude live on, towards people who are dead, in the minds of the living.

[2] See especially pp. 70, 71, 72, 78, 79.

feel grateful to students ; and both kinds to the chief administrative officers ; and all to the Governors and their Committees ; the administrative assistants and the establishment staff should likewise get their tribute of gratitude from all the rest of the college. Our survival in a living college at our own place has caused many of us not only to look back with gladness on all these and other memories of good fellowship, but to think even of the ugly buildings with some affection. When we left them in 1951 we knew well that they had done us no mean service.

Appendix

SPECIAL DISTINCTIONS AND APPOINTMENTS

(i) Governors and Members of the Teaching or Administrative Staff

*Sir Ernest Pooley, M.A., LL.B., created a Knight Commander of the Royal Victorian Order, 1944.

*A. King-Hamilton, C.C., appointed by the Alderman of the Ward of Cornhill to be his Deputy, June 1941.

*Professor G. F. J. Temple, Ph.D., D.Sc., elected a Fellow of the Royal Society, 1943.

*‡Professor S. Sugden, D.Sc., F.R.S., appointed by the University of London to be its representative on the Governing Body of the Guildford Technical College and School of Arts, 1940 : appointed Superintendent of Explosives Research to the Ministry of Supply, 1942.

*†Professor Dame Helen Gwynne-Vaughan, G.B.E., LL.D., D.Sc., F.L.S., granted the honorary rank of Chief Controller of the Auxiliary Territorial Service on her retirement from the post of Chief Controller 1941. Professor Emeritus 1945.

*W. R. Wooldridge, Ph.D., M.Sc., M.R.C.V.S., F.R.I.C., elected President of the National Veterinary Medical Association of Great Britain and Ireland for 1941-42 and 1942-43.

*J. P. R. Maud, M.A., Master of the College, created Commander of the Order of the British Empire, 1942 ; K.C.B., 1946.

*†Professor H. G. Jackson, D.Sc., F.Z.S., appointed by the University to be its representative on the Governing Body of the South-Eastern Agricultural College, Wye, Kent, 1941-2 ; appointed by Birkbeck College to be a representative on the Governing Body of Southlands Training College, 1941 ; appointed a Governor of William Ellis School, 1942.

*‡Professor Lillian M. Penson, Ph.D., F.R.Hist.Soc., one-time student at the college ; lecturer in the college's Department of History 1921-30; Chairman of the Court of Electors 1931-32; elected representative of the University's Faculty of Arts (of which she was Dean 1938-44) on the Senate of the University 1940. She became a Governor of the College in 1944.

†Professor Eva G. R. Taylor, D.Sc., LL.D., appointed to be member of Lord Reith's Panel of Reconstruction 1940; appointed a member of the Consultative Panel of the Ministry of Works and Buildings, 1941-42. Professor Emeritus, 1945.

*†Professor J. R. Sutherland, M.A., B.Litt., appointed by Birkbeck College to be a representative on the Governing Body of Southlands Training College.

†Marjorie Daunt, elected a Member of the Council of the Philological Society for 1942-43 ; appointed by Birkbeck College as a representative on the Governing Body of Gipsy Hill Training College, 1941.

*†Professor E. H. Warmington, M.A., F.R.Hist.Soc., appointed by Birkbeck College member of the Appointments Board of the University of London for the years 1939-44 ; appointed by Birkbeck College a representative on the Governing Body of Gipsy Hill Training College, 1941.

†A. Jones, M.A., F.R.Hist.Soc., elected a member of the Society of Antiquaries, 1940.

†L. F. Spath, D.Sc., F.G.S., elected a Fellow of the Royal Society, 1940 ; awarded the Lyell Medal of the Geological Society ; elected Vice-President of the Palaeontological Society, 1944-45.

†F. J. Llewellyn, B.Sc., Ph.D., A.I.C., elected Fellow of the Royal Institute of Chemistry, 1944.

†May Smith, M.A., D.Sc., created an officer of the Order of the British Empire, 1945.

(ii) Former Governors or Members of the College

Sir T. Franklin Sibly, LL.D., D.Sc., Vice-Chancellor of the University of Reading ; Governor representing the University of London, 1926-29 : created a Knight Commander of the Order of the British Empire, 1943.

M. F. Lindley, C.B., B.Sc., LL.D., Comptroller-General of His Majesty's Patent Office : one-time student and Governor. Created a Knight Bachelor.

Professor P. M. S. Blackett, M.A., F.R.S., Professor of Physics in the University of Manchester, formerly Professor of Physics at Birkbeck College ; granted one of the two Royal Medals awarded by the Royal Society for 1940.

* Governor.
† Member of the Teaching Staff.
‡ Formerly member of the Teaching Staff.

DR. H. N. RYDON, D.Sc., Ph.D., A.R.C.Sc., D.I.C., Demonstrator in the Department of Chemistry, 1934-37 ; awarded the Meldola Medal (which is given every two years), by the Institute of Chemistry for the most distinguished research by chemists under 30 years of age, 1939 ; awarded the Harrison Memorial Prize of the Chemical Society for 1941.

AGNES MURE MACKENZIE, M.A., D.Litt., Lecturer in the Department of English, 1920-24 ; appointed a Commander of the Order of the British Empire, 1945.

ROLL OF HONOUR, 1939-45

CECIL V. ANDREWS. An undergraduate in the Faculty of Science, 1937-39. Killed in action whilst a member of the magazine crew on board H.M.S. *Hood*, 24th May 1941.

RAYMOND G. BATES. An undergraduate in the Faculty of Science (Special Chemistry), 1937-39. R.A.F. Killed in an air crash, 7th July 1943.

FRANK BLYTHEN, B.Sc. A graduate (Phys. 2, 1933), and member of the Court of Electors. Killed in an accident at the Munitions Factory where he was employed, 7th June 1942.

CHARLES A. CAMBURN. An undergraduate in the Faculty of Science, 1928-32. Killed by enemy action whilst on duty as a Customs Officer at London Docks, 1941.

LEONARD P. COX. An undergraduate in the Faculty of Science, 1939-42. Killed on active service, 28th June 1945.

J. CURCHIN, D.F.C. Flight-Lieutenant, R.A.F. Missing, presumed killed in action, 4th June 1941.

SYLVAINE J. E. DEACON, B.A. A graduate (French 1, 1943), and member of the Court of Electors. Awarded a University Postgraduate Studentship of £150 for one year, 1943. Member of W.A.A.F. Accidentally drowned on active service, 19th August 1944.

ALFRED ROY DRAKE. President of the Students' Union, 1932-33 ; Student Representative Governor, 1932-34. Accidentally killed whilst on A.R.P. duty in October 1940.

GORDON D. H. DUTTON, an undergraduate in the Faculty of Science in 1938-39 ; was a Sergeant Pilot in the R.A.F., commanding a Wellington bomber. After many operational flights over enemy territory, he was killed in a crash on 11th November 1941, shortly after qualifying for a commission.

WILLIAM J. B. ELLIOTT, an undergraduate in the Faculty of Science (Special Physics), 1926-29, was a Wing Commander in the R.A.F. Killed in action.

Frederick S. Fisher, an undergraduate in the Faculty of Science in the Session 1940-41 ; was a Sergeant Observer in the R.A.F. Killed in an aircraft crash whilst engaged on a night operational flight on 14th November 1942.

Alfred R. Forster, Captain, R.A., an undergraduate in the Faculty of Science, 1936-38, and a member of the College Company of the University O.T.C.

Peter S. Gumbrell, an undergraduate in the Faculty of Science, 1937-39, was a Flying Officer in the R.A.F., and was killed in an air crash on 29th December 1943.

Dennis N. L. Harwood, an undergraduate in the Faculty of Arts in 1934-35 ; was a Sergeant in the R.A.F.V.R. He was called up in 1940, and after considerable service was killed in an air crash whilst proceeding to the East on 6th June 1942.

Peter V. S. Hayward, an undergraduate in the Faculty of Arts, killed by enemy action on 14th January 1945.

Geoffrey S. Hensby, B.Sc., a graduate (Phys. 1, 1938) and distinguished student of his Faculty ; was a civilian technical expert and was killed in an aircraft crash whilst on an experimental flight on 19th July 1940.

W. Lionel Hichens. A Governor of the College for eighteen years, and Chairman from 1927 until his death by enemy action on 14th October 1940.

Patrick J. Irwin, M.A., Ph.D. A distinguished graduate (B.A. Eng. 2, 1929 ; M.A. Eng. with distinction, 1931 ; Ph.D. Eng., 1935) and member of the Court of Electors. Died as the result of a street accident whilst on duty as a member of the Home Guard, 23rd January 1942.

Phadric W. Kerry, an undergraduate in the Faculty of Science in the Session 1939-40. Volunteering for the R.A.F., he joined the Force in July 1940, becoming later a Pilot Officer Observer. Throughout his operational career he was engaged on lone "Mosquito" daylight flights over Germany, and it was whilst so employed that he was killed on 1st August 1942.

Gladys M. Knowelden, B.Sc. Graduated 1st Division, 1916 ; Science Mistress at Catford Central Girls' School. Killed at her post when the school received a direct hit in an enemy air raid on 20th January 1943.

Roy C. J. McClumpha. Pilot Officer, R.A.F.V.R. Missing, believed killed in action.

Donovan J. Mammen, an undergraduate in the Faculty of Arts in 1938-39, was killed in action near Tobruk in the advance on 19th November 1941. He was a Wireless Operator in a forward tank of the 3rd County of London Yeomanry, R.A.C.

HORACE A. MATTHEWS, B.A., graduated Ph.D. from the College in 1930, Senior Lecturer in the Department of Geography from 1928-37. Flight-Lieutenant, R.A.F., died whilst on active service, 2nd March 1943.

HENRY D. J. METTEN, B.Sc., Ph.D., an undergraduate in the Faculty of Science, 1926-28. Civilian casualty in a war industry accident.

FREDERICK R. POVEY, an undergraduate in the Faculty of Science in 1938-39, was a Flight-Lieutenant in the R.A.F., commanding a Radio Station in Malta, and was killed whilst salvaging radio gear from a crashed plane, 1st April 1942.

JOHN R. POWELL, B.A. Graduated 1939 (History 2). Died on active service in West Africa, 18th April 1943.

PETER J. RIDDLE, an undergraduate in the Faculty of Science (Special Physics), 1937-39, Major, Dorsetshire Regiment attached Worcestershire Regiment. Killed in action in Normandy, 27th June 1944.

GEOFFREY G. SHALJEAN, an undergraduate in the Faculty of Science, 1942-43, trooper, 1st Fife and Forfar Yeomanry. Killed in action on the Belgium-Holland frontier, 21st October 1944.

A. F. D. SMITH, College Contingent of the University O.T.C. Major, Royal Berkshire Regiment. Died of wounds, Western Europe.

THE RIGHT HON. LORD STAMP OF SHORTLANDS, G.C.B., G.B.E. A Governor from 1925 until his death on 17th April 1941, by enemy action.

HEDLEY C. SWIFT, B.A. Lieut. R.H.A. Killed in North African Campaign, April, 1943.

DOUGLAS W. B. TAYLOR, B.Sc., an undergraduate in the Faculty of Science, 1934-35. Flying Officer, R.A.F.V.R. Missing, presumed killed in action, August, 1943.

JOHN C. VINES, an undergraduate in the Faculty of Science, 1931-36. Major, Royal Berkshire Regiment. Died of wounds, Western Europe.

ARTHUR J. WENSLEY, M.Com. Former lecturer in Economics, was posted as "missing" at Dunkirk in June 1940; officially presumed killed.

GERALD A. WHYTE, an undergraduate in the Faculty of Arts, 1939-40, serving as a Lieutenant in the Essex Regiment, was killed in action in Italy, November 1943.

P. S. WOODHAM, T./Sub-Lieutenant, (A)R.N.V.R. Missing, presumed killed in H.M. Aircraft Carrier *Avenger*.

OBITUARY

Here are recorded deaths other than those given in the Roll of Honour.

PROFESSOR SIR HAROLD CARPENTER, M.A., Ph.D., D.Met., A.R.S.M., F.R.S. Professor of Metallurgy at the Royal School of Mines, in the Imperial College of Science and Technology. Accidentally drowned 13th September 1940. Governor representing the University of London, 1922-25.

PROFESSOR (Emeritus) E. A. GARDNER. Governor 1924-26. Died 27th November 1939.

DR. GEORGE D. LANDER, D.Sc. Former student ; Governor 1914-21. Died 25th October 1939.

BERNARD M. NEVILLE, B.Sc., F.Inst.P. President of the Students' Union, 1910-11 ; Governor 1912-26. Died 11th April 1942.

G. WORRALL. Student and Governor, 189 -1902. Died 1942.

H. J. TOZER, M.A. Governor, 1907-11. Died 31st October 1943.

ROGER T. SMITH, B.Sc., M.Inst.C.E., M.I.Mech.E., M.I.E.E., M.Inst.T. Governor 1930-39. Died 28th April 1940.

F. GOSSLING, B.Sc., F.C.S., F.G.S. Distinguished student at the College 1883-1887. Joint Head of the Department of Chemistry 1888-97. Governor 1898-1921 and 1923-27. Died 21st June 1945.

THE BARON ALBERT PROFUMO, K.C., LL.M., F.R.A.M. Generous donor to the New Buildings Fund in 1935. Died 27th March 1940.

SIR DANIEL STEVENSON, Bt., D.L., LL.D. Chancellor of the University of Glasgow, Lord Provost of Glasgow, 1911-14. Generous donor to the New Buildings Fund. Died 11th July 1944.

HENRY BIRKBECK. Grandson of the Founder of the College. Died 29th June 1942.

MAJOR ARTHUR BIRKBECK. Grandson of the Founder of the College. Died 24th June 1945.

A. C. CUMMING, O.B.E., D.Sc. Lecturer in Chemistry 1907-09. Died 28th September 1940.

J. W. KILNER, M.A. Senior Lecturer in Classics, 1913-19. Died 2nd April 1940.

COLONEL J. M. MITCHELL, C.B.E., M.C., M.A., LL.D. Lecturer in Classics, 1913-15. Died 24th December 1940.

SIR D'ARCY POWER, K.B.E., M.A., M.B., F.R.C.S., F.R.F.P.S., F.S.A. Lecturer 1890-98. Died 18th May 1941.

Mrs. Marjorie E. Robinson, M.A. Part-time lecturer in Economics 1930-36. Died December 1939.

Professor F. A. P. Aveling, M.C., D.Lit., D.Sc., D.D., Ph.D. Head of the Department of Psychology at King's College, accommodated at Birkbeck College since January 1940. Died 6th March 1941.

George Senter, D.Sc., Ph.D., F.I.C. Head of the Department of Chemistry 1914-18. Principal of the College 1918-39. Governor 1920-39. Died 14th March 1942.

Professor F. J. M. Tanquerey, D. ès Lettres, B. ès Sc., O.A. Since 1925 Head of the Department of French. Governor 1935-37. Died 24th March 1942.

A. W. Baker Welford, M.A. Barrister-at-Law. Lecturer from 1920 until the discontinuance in 1938 at Birkbeck of the Faculty of Laws, of which he became Head in 1924. Died after an accident on 1st February 1942.

C. Delisle Burns, M.A., D.Lit. Lecturer in Logic, Philosophy and Psychology, 1921-27. Author in 1924 of "A Short History of Birkbeck College." Died 22nd January 1942.

Professor (Emeritus) H. G. Atkins, D.Lit., M.A. Formerly Professor of German at King's College, and for some time lecturer in German at Birkbeck College. Died after an accident, 13th August 1942.

Sir Allen Mawer, M.A., Litt.D., D.C.S., F.B.A. Provost of University College, London. Lectured in English at Birkbeck College, 1904-05. Died 22nd July 1942.

G. W. Clough, D.Sc. Late Head of the Department of Chemistry at the Royal Veterinary College. Senior Lecturer in Chemistry at Birkbeck College, 1902-17. Died 20th February 1944.

G. V. Coates, M.A., A.R.Ae.S. Senior Lecturer in Mathematics 1905-29. Died after an accident 30th March 1944.

The Most Rev. and
Right Hon. William Temple, P.C.
Archbishop of Canterbury

President of Birkbeck College since 1942
Died 26th October 1944

FINANCE

The recurrent Maintenance Grant made by the Court of the University of London was £36,700 in session 1939-40, £37,700 in 1940-41, 1941-42, 1942-43, and 1943-44 ; and, in view of the transfer of the Department of Psychology from King's College, £41,000 in 1944-45, when there was also a special grant of £4,594. Receipts from appropriated and unappropriated City Parochial Foundation endowments remained unchanged throughout the war, as did also grants from local authorities outside the Administrative County of London remitted through the Court of the University. Income from other sources varied, especially that from course-fees and examination-fees ; it was, to the nearest pound, in session 1939-40, £5,657 ; 1940-41, £2,297 ; 1941-42, £4,490 ; 1942-43, £7,187 ; 1943-44, £9,944 ; 1944-45, £11,432. The college showed on the year's working a surplus, to the nearest pound, of £2,007 in 1939-40 ; £148 in 1940-41 ; £130 in 1941-42 ; £102 in 1942-43 ; and £186 in 1943-44 ; and a deficit of £299 in 1944-45.

STUDENTS' OCCUPATIONS AND AGES

Study of the different kinds of daily occupations of our students, so far as these were ascertained when they attended at the college, reveals that, in war-time as in peace, the profession most largely represented in every year was that of Teachers, whose occupation was on the list of "Reserved" during the war—nearer one-fourth than one-third of the total in session 1939-40, 1940-41, and 1941-42 ; over one-fourth in 1942-43 ; nearly one-third in 1943-44, more than one-third in 1944-45, as in following years. In all years of the war the categories of Chemists and of Technical and Research Assistants, taken as one class, come next, then Clerical Assistants and Accountants, then Civil Servants (Clerical and Technical). The numbers in any other kinds of employment were very small. The Navy, the Army, and the Air Force, with the Women's Services contributed at least 7 in 1941-42, 26 in 1942-43, 33 in 1943-44, 37 in 1944-45. There were in every year more students of ages 19, 20, 21 and 22, than there were of any other age, though in 1943-44 there were larger proportions than usual of students aged 18 and 23, than in other years, and, in 1944-45, of students aged 24. In the "lean" sessions also 1939-40 and 1940-41, there were a good number aged 18. A smaller proportion of the whole number in every year were of ages between 26 and 30 inclusive, and a smaller again than this were of ages between 31 and 35 inclusive. Persons older than 35 were about one-seventh of the whole number, in all except the "lean" sessions. This proportion increased somewhat in the years 1945-1950.

SUMMARY OF EXAMINATION RESULTS

		1939-40
TOTAL NUMBER OF GRADUATIONS		75
Faculty of Arts—		
D.Lit.		—
Ph.D.		5
M.A.		4
B.A.—Honours	19	
General	1	
	—	20
Faculty of Science—		
D.Sc.		1
Ph.D.		5
M.Sc.		3
B.Sc.—Special	24	
General	13	
	—	37
Faculty of Laws—		
LL.B.		—
UNIVERSITY DIPLOMAS, CERTIFICATES AND PRIZES		
Academic Diploma in Geography		2
University Certificate in English		2
Prizes		1
TOTAL NUMBER OF PRELIMINARY EXAMINATION PASSES		84
Intermediate Arts		24
Intermediate Arts in part		11
Intermediate Science		37
Intermediate Science in part		11
First Examination for Medical Degrees		—
First Examination in Veterinary Science		1
INSTITUTE OF CHEMISTRY		
Associateship (A.I.C.)		3

		1940-41
TOTAL NUMBER OF GRADUATIONS		56
Faculty of Arts—		
D.Lit.		1
Ph.D.		2
M.A.		1
B.A.—Honours	18	
General	7	
	—	25

Faculty of Science—		
D.Sc.		—
Ph.D.		6
M.Sc.		5
B.Sc.—Special	14	
General	1	
	—	15
Faculty of Laws—		
LL.B.		1
UNIVERSITY DIPLOMAS, CERTIFICATES ABD PRIZES		
Academic Diploma in Geography		1
University Certificate in English		4
Prizes		1
TOTAL NUMBER OF PRELIMINARY EXAMINATION PASSES		41
Intermediate Arts		17
Intermediate Arts in part		3
Intermediate Science		14
Intermediate Science in part		6
First Examination for Medical Degrees		1
First Examination in Veterinary Science		—
INSTITUTE OF CHEMISTRY		
Associateship (A.I.C.)		1
		1941-42
TOTAL NUMBER OF GRADUATIONS		43
Faculty of Arts—		
Ph.D.		1
M.A.		1
B.A.—Honours	11	
General	9	
	—	20
Faculty of Science—		
D.Sc.		1
Ph.D.		2
B.Sc.—Special	16	
General	2	
	—	18
UNIVERSITY CERTIFICATES		
Proficiency in English	2	
Proficiency in English, Part I	3	
	—	5
Proficiency in Radio-Physics		5

TOTAL NUMBER OF PRELIMINARY EXAMINATION PASSES ..		98
Intermediate Arts		48
Intermediate Arts in part		9
Intermediate Science		32
Intermediate Science in part		6
Intermediate Science (Econ.)	1	
Intermediate Science (Econ.), Part II ..	2	
	—	3
INSTITUTE OF CHEMISTRY		
Associateship (A.I.C.)		1

		1942-43
TOTAL NUMBER OF GRADUATIONS		39
Faculty of Arts—		
Ph.D.		2
B.A.—Honours	11	
General	2	
	—	13
Faculty of Science—		
Ph.D.		1
B.Sc. Special		21
Faculty of Economics—		
B.Sc. Honours		2
UNIVERSITY DIPLOMAS AND CERTIFICATES		
Academic Diploma in Geography		2
Proficiency in English	6	
Proficiency in English, Part I	1	
Proficiency in English, Part II	1	
	—	8
Proficiency in Radio-Physics		9
TOTAL NUMBER OF PRELIMINARY EXAMINATION PASSES ..		139
Intermediate Arts		46
Intermediate Arts in part		23
Intermediate Laws		1
Intermediate Science		45
Intermediate Science in part		12
Intermediate Science (Econ.)	9	
Intermediate Science (Econ.), Part II ..	2	
	—	11
Qualifying for B.Sc. (Econ.) Examination		1
INSTITUTE OF CHEMISTRY		
Associateship (A.I.C.)		5

		1943-44
TOTAL NUMBER OF GRADUATIONS		65
Faculty of Arts—		
Ph.D.		2
M.A.		1
B.A.—Honours	18	
General	11	
	—	29
Faculty of Science—		
D.Sc.		1
Ph.D.		1
M.Sc.		1
B.Sc.—Special	24	
General	5	
	—	29
Faculty of Economics—		
B.Sc. Honours		1
UNIVERSITY DIPLOMAS AND CERTIFICATES		
Academic Diploma in Geography		3
Proficiency in English, Scheme A ..	4	
Proficiency in English, Part I	2	
	—	6
Proficiency in Radio-Physics		1
SCHOLARSHIPS, STUDENTSHIPS, PRIZES		
The "Granville" University Postgraduate Studentship in Physics : £100 for 1 year		1
TOTAL NUMBER OF PRELIMINARY EXAMINATION PASSES ..		166
Intermediate Arts		40
Intermediate Arts in part		31
Intermediate Science (1 Engineering)		58
Intermediate Science in part		10
Intermediate Science (Econ.)		12
Intermediate Science (Econ.), Part I		5
Intermediate Science (Econ.), Part II		7
Intermediate Science (Econ.) in part completing ..		3
INSTITUTE OF CHEMISTRY		
Fellowship (F.I.C.)		1
Associateship (A.I.C.)		5

		1944-45
TOTAL NUMBER OF GRADUATIONS		123
Faculty of Arts—		
M.A.		5
B.A.—Honours	31	
General	10	
Aegrotat	1	
	—	42
Faculty of Science—		
D.Sc.		3
Ph.D.		2
M.Sc.		2
B.Sc.—Special	40	
General	17	
	—	57
Faculty of Economics—		
B.Sc. (Econ.) Honours		7
Qualified to proceed to a Higher Degree		5
UNIVERSITY DIPLOMAS AND CERTIFICATES		
Academic Postgraduate Diploma in Psychology—		
Complete		14
Part I only		3
Part II only		1
SCHOLARSHIPS, STUDENTSHIPS, PRIZES		
The George Smith Studentship (£150) and Prize (£5 in Books)		1
TOTAL NUMBER OF PRELIMINARY EXAMINATION PASSES		196
Intermediate Arts		66
Intermediate Arts in part		22
Intermediate Science		61
Intermediate Science in part		9
Intermediate Science (Econ.) complete		21
Intermediate Science (Econ.), Part I		6
Intermediate Science (Econ.), Part II		4
Intermediate Science (Econ.), in part completing		7
INSTITUTE OF CHEMISTRY		
Associateship (A.R.I.C.)		4

Index

THE RAMIREZ BRIDE

THE RAMIREZ BRIDE

BY

EMMA DARCY

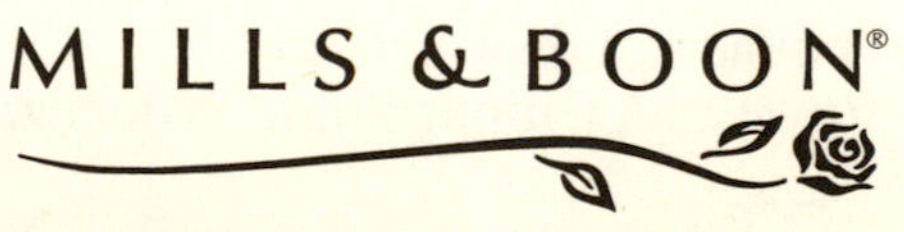

All the characters in this book have no existence outside the imagination of the author, and have no relation whatsoever to anyone bearing the same name or names. They are not even distantly inspired by any individual known or unknown to the author, and all the incidents are pure invention.

First published in Great Britain 2005
Large Print edition 2006
Harlequin Mills & Boon Limited,
Eton House, 18-24 Paradise Road,
Richmond, Surrey TW9 1SR

ISBN 0 263 18923 6

Set in Times Roman 16½ on 18 pt.
16-0106-49294

Printed and bound in Great Britain
by Antony Rowe Ltd, Chippenham, Wiltshire

CHAPTER ONE

A PACKET from Brazil...delivered by a courier fulfilling instructions to have Nick Ramirez himself sign for it so that delivery to him personally was assured, no chance of it being mislaid and not reaching him...this packet from Brazil.

Nick watched the courier leave his office, his gaze fixed on the man's back, on the door closing behind him. He didn't want to look at the packet now lying on his desk, didn't want to open it. The hand that had directed it to him had to be the hand of his father, his biological father, who had not earned the right to touch his life in any way whatsoever, let alone force an entry to it. That door had been closed sixteen years ago.

No. Earlier than that.

Much earlier.

Nick was thirty-four now and he'd only been seven when the sense of rejection had hit

him full force from all sides. The
himself as a young schoolboy not
ing anything, stirred Nick out of h
angry shot of adrenaline energisi
away from the packet from Brazi
he'd been a complete innocent,
web of adult deceptions, trying
where he fitted, and the brutal
been…he didn't fit.

Anywhere.

So he'd learnt to make his own

And this office was part of hi
driving centre of the advertising c
occupied two floors of this prestigi
at Circular Quay with its comman
Sydney Harbour. It was Nick's co
alone. He'd built it up, pursuing hi
what the market would respond
been proved right. Spectacularly ri

As he stood at the window, lo
the opera house and the huge coat
of the bridge behind it, Nick sar
flected that everyone knew sex so
glamour. But he knew it very pe
much so he had the knack of pack

CHAPTER ONE

A PACKET from Brazil…delivered by a courier fulfilling instructions to have Nick Ramirez himself sign for it so that delivery to him personally was assured, no chance of it being mislaid and not reaching him…this packet from Brazil.

Nick watched the courier leave his office, his gaze fixed on the man's back, on the door closing behind him. He didn't want to look at the packet now lying on his desk, didn't want to open it. The hand that had directed it to him had to be the hand of his father, his biological father, who had not earned the right to touch his life in any way whatsoever, let alone force an entry to it. That door had been closed sixteen years ago.

No. Earlier than that.

Much earlier.

Nick was thirty-four now and he'd only been seven when the sense of rejection had hit him full force from all sides. The memory of himself as a young schoolboy not understanding anything, stirred Nick out of his chair, an angry shot of adrenaline energising a move away from the packet from Brazil. At seven he'd been a complete innocent, caught in a web of adult deceptions, trying to find out where he fitted, and the brutal truth had been…he didn't fit.

Anywhere.

So he'd learnt to make his own place.

And this office was part of *his place*, the driving centre of the advertising company that occupied two floors of this prestigious building at Circular Quay with its commanding view of Sydney Harbour. It was Nick's company. His alone. He'd built it up, pursuing his concept of what the market would respond to and he'd been proved right. Spectacularly right.

As he stood at the window, looking out at the opera house and the huge coathanger span of the bridge behind it, Nick sardonically reflected that everyone knew sex sold. Sex and glamour. But he knew it very personally, so much so he had the knack of packaging it better than anyone else, constructing impact shots that were highly memorable, fixing the target product in people's minds. His style of advertising had made him a very wealthy man, well able to afford this million-dollar view, both in his work-place and the penthouse apartment he owned at Woolloomooloo.

Here he was, standing on top of his world, totally self-sufficient, a successful man in his own right. He didn't need anything from any of his *fathers*—the rich, powerful men his mother had attracted, drawing from them whatever her covetous heart desired.

Over the years of his boyhood and adolescence they'd shelled out a lot to him, as well, wanting to please her. He'd used the money to fund his aims and ambition. Why not? He'd earned it by not being a pest in their lives.

But he didn't *take* anything from any one any more.

Didn't need to.

Didn't want to.

And it was far too late for Enrique Ramirez to offer him anything. The Brazilian had had two chances to make a difference in Nick's life. He'd walked away from the first. As for the second, when Nick had turned up in Rio de Janeiro—an eighteen-year-old youth seeking to acquaint himself with a father he'd never known—he'd been met with furious resentment at the sheer impudence of presenting himself as Enrique's son in the man's own home.

'What do you want from me? What do you imagine you can get out of me?'

The jeering contempt from the highly placed Brazilian had stung Nick into replying, 'Nothing. I just wanted to meet you in person. But I *will* take your name. I can see now it belongs to me.'

There was no denying the genetic pattern that had clearly been passed on to him—the same thick black hair and distinctive hairline, dark olive skin, deeply set green eyes with double-thick lashes, a long aristocratic nose, high angular cheekbones, hard squarish jawline broken by a central cleft that probably should have weakened the forceful impression of aggressive masculinity but perversely enough lent a rakish power to it, a mouth that was carved for sensuality, and the tall muscular physique combining both strength and athleticism.

Oh yes, he was his father's son all right. And when he'd returned home to Australia he had claimed the name, Ramirez, by deed-poll. At least, that wasn't a lie. But whatever the packet from Brazil contained…Nick was already rebelling against any effect Enrique might think he could have on him.

His desk telephone rang.

A few strides back from the window and he snatched up the receiver.

'Mrs Condor is on the line, wanting to speak to you,' his PA informed.

His mother. Which made two unwelcome parental intrusions this morning. A sense of black irony tipped Nick into saying, 'Put her through.' A click, then his dry invitation to converse, 'Mother?'

'Darling! Something extraordinary has happened. We must speak.'

'We are speaking.'

'I mean get together. Can you fit me in this morning? I'm on my way into the city now. It is important, Nick. I've received a packet from Brazil.'

Nick's jaw tightened at this news. 'So did I,' he bit out.

'Oh!' The sound of surprise and disappointment. 'Well, I was going to break it to you gently since he was your father, but I guess I don't need to now.' A dramatic sigh. 'Such a waste! Enrique could only have been in his sixties. Far too young for a man like him to die. He was so virile, so indomitable…'

A weird pain shafted Nick's heart.

His mind recoiled from the knowledge that Enrique Ramirez was dead.

Gone.

Never to be known as a son should know his father.

No more chances.

He stared at the packet on his desk—the last contact!

'He has gifted me the most magnificent emerald necklace…'

Pleasure in her voice as she proceeded to gloatingly describe every detail of it. His mother adored beautiful things. And she had certainly taught Nick the worth of sexy glamour. Every man who'd shared her bed—husband or lover—had paid for the privilege very handsomely indeed.

She was on her fifth marriage now, and if some more challenging mega-rich guy came along, Nick had little doubt her beautiful and highly acquisitive golden eyes would rove again. Though she hadn't snagged Enrique Ramirez as a husband.

In actual fact, she probably hadn't wanted to marry a Brazilian and settle in a very foreign country, anyway. It had undoubtedly been enough that the international polo-player had happened to be a judge in the Miss Universe contest, held in Rio de Janeiro the year Nadia Kilman had won that title.

Of course, she hadn't meant to get pregnant by him. That had been an unfortunate accident, especially when she was planning to marry Brian Steele, the son and heir of Australian mining magnate, Andrew Steele. But, easy enough for a woman of her persuasive charms to let the husband of her choice think he was the father of the child in her womb. It had certainly nailed a wedding to the targeted home-grown billionaire bridegroom.

Marriage had meant she had to give up her year as Miss Universe, but having won the title, his mother had never relinquished it and always—still—lived up to it.

The whole history of their mother-son relationship marched through Nick's mind as she raved on about the Ramirez emerald mines in Bolivia as though he had some legitimate claim on them. His mother specialised in making convenient claims.

Nick wondered if he would have remained Brian Steele's son if she had not been caught out in the lie. Even after the divorce and with both his parents remarried, Nick had still believed Brian Steele was his natural father, finally fronting up to him to demand why he didn't visit him at school, attending sporting events as other divorced fathers did.

'Ask your mother,' had been his harshly dismissive reply.

'It's not my fault you don't love my mother any more,' Nick had argued with a fierce sense of injustice. 'I'm not only her son. I'm *yours*, too.'

'No, you're not.'

Shocked, hurt, angry, Nick had fought against such an unfair and outright rejection. 'You can't divorce children. You're my father. Just because you've started another family doesn't mean…'

'I'm not your father.' The denial had been thundered back at Nick in red-faced rage. 'I was never your father. For God's sake, boy! Look at yourself in a mirror. There's not a trace of me in you.'

This further punch of shock had been countered by a rush of disbelief. It was true he didn't have red hair, fair skin or blue eyes, but he'd simply assumed he'd inherited his mother's darker colouring, and that was what his father hated in him—the constant reminder of her.

'You just don't want me, do you?' he'd flung out, tasting the bitterness of being the victim of a broken marriage, yet still intent on making his father face up to being his father.

'No, I don't. Why would I want another man's bastard as my son? Your real father's name is Enrique Ramirez and when he's not playing international polo, he lives in Brazil. I doubt *he* will ever visit your school to watch you play sport but you can try asking your mother to get in touch with him on your behalf.'

Having absorbed this new parentage and with seven-year-old determination, Nick had tried.

'Darling, I'm sorry you're upset about Brian not being your father.' His mother's brilliantly sympathetic smile had glossed over the dark wound he'd been nursing, as did her next words. 'But you have a perfectly good stepfather in Harry who's much more fun to have around...'

'I want to know about my real father,' he had bored in stubbornly.

'Well, he's married, dear. No chance at all of a divorce, I'm afraid. All wrapped up in the religion and politics of his country.' Her graceful hands had fluttered appealingly. 'So we can never form a family even if we wanted to.'

'Does he know about me?'

'Yes, he does.' A rueful sigh. 'One of those unlucky coincidences in life. He came out to Australia to play polo and your grandfather—well, he's not really your grandfather as you obviously realise now—invited him to play on his country property near Singleton, having built himself a private polo ground and fancying himself quite an accomplished player. It was a huge festive weekend. Impossible to get out of going. And I did think Enrique would be discreet and pretend not to know me.' Another sigh. 'It was seeing you that caught him off-guard.'

'He recognised me as his son?'

'Well, there was the matter of timing. Your age, as well as how you look, dear. The two things together… I had to admit it to him…and he used the secret to…uh…'

Blackmail her into bed with him.

And that was all Nick had meant to his biological father—a handy by-blow who'd given him the leverage to have his way with the ex-Miss Universe again. Though Nick suspected the arrogantly handsome and charismatic

Brazilian had not needed much leverage. Never mind the risk of scandal they'd both run. Never mind the fall-out for Nick when both their old and current affairs had been discovered.

'Your mother was as hot for me as I was for her,' Enrique had blithely excused when Nick had eventually laid out to him the consequences of his actions. Not a twinge of guilt to be seen. He'd thrown out elegantly dismissive hands. 'She could have said no. I have never made love to an unwilling woman. It was her choice. Her life.'

'And *my* life was irrelevant to you,' Nick had shot at him accusingly.

Enrique had snapped his fingers at what he considered a stupid complaint. 'I gave you life. Get on with finding pleasure in it. This dragging through the past will bring you no joy whatsoever.'

Good advice.

Nick had taken it.

Which was why he still didn't want to touch the packet from Brazil.

'What did he gift to you, darling?' his mother finally queried, her honeyed voice lilting with avid curiosity. The emerald necklace had certainly whetted her appetite for more treasure from Brazil.

'I'd say most of my physical features,' Nick mocked.

'True, dear, but that's not what I meant and you know it. Don't be tiresome. He wrote me that the necklace was a token of gratitude for having borne him such an impressive son. Obviously, if Enrique was pleased with you, he'd leave you much more than a necklace.'

'I haven't opened the packet yet.'

'Well, do get on with it, Nick. I expect to hear all when I get to your office. This is so exciting I can hardly wait. Your father was fabulously wealthy, you know.'

Yes, he knew, having seen the incredible riches displayed in Enrique's home—a veritable treasure trove everywhere one looked—old, old wealth, the kind that belonged to aristocracy and was kept in the family, passed on from father to son.

But Nick didn't want it. His whole body burned to reject everything attached to the life that had meant so much more to his father than getting to know or playing any part in the life of his bastard son.

'I should be there in fifteen minutes,' his mother archly warned, clearly anticipating a happy sharing time together. 'Isn't it wonderful to be remembered like this after all these years?'

As always, she was totally self-centred in her view of the world and every situation in it. Nick was niggled into drawling, 'No, it isn't *wonderful*, Mother. I actually find it grossly insulting for my father to wait until he's dead before granting me some acknowledgement.'

'Oh, don't be stuffy, Nick. What's gone is gone. You should always make the most of what you've got.'

The rock-like principle on which Nadia Kilman / Steele / Manning / Lloyd / Hardwick / Condor had built her life. No shifting it. No changing it.

'Of course, Mother. I look forward to seeing you and your necklace.'

Which would be shamelessly displayed around her neck the moment an opportune occasion presented itself. Since it was already mid-November, she didn't have long to wait for the festive season to be in full swing.

Nick set the telephone receiver down and once more stared at the packet on his desk. Part of him wanted to drop it in the litter bin unopened, yet another part of him wanted to know what his father thought he was worth. With a sense of very dark cynicism, he decided it was best to know the finishing line so he could put it completely behind him.

He opened the packet.

It contained two letters.

Predictably enough, one was from a lawyer, Javier Estes, now handling the Ramirez estate. The other, surprisingly, was handwritten by Enrique and addressed very personally to Nick. Its content was stunning in its intimate knowledge of almost every detail of Nick's life and the big punchline at the end of it put a seductively new and challenging spin on his world.

His mind was still intensely engaged with it when his PA opened the door between their offices and his mother made her entrance.

It was always *an entrance.*

Even at fifty-five…looking not a day over thirty-five, if that—she was the ultimate display of female beauty, with a lushly curved body that screamed sexy woman, and she certainly made the most of all she had.

Wherever she went in public, eyes swivelled to look and were instantly trapped into keeping on watching her because she was so very watchable, everything and everyone in her vicinity simply fading into insignificance. Miss Universe was still strutting her stuff with no encroachment whatsoever from the years that had passed since she'd won that title.

Her thick, wonderfully lustrous, long wavy hair looked like a rippling stream of dark brown silk, temptingly touchable. Her large, amber eyes had a hypnotic quality. Whenever she focused them on a man, he seemed to drown in them. Her nose was perfect. Her full-lipped sexy mouth was positively mesmerising, as were the flash of her gleaming white teeth.

And, of course, her long graceful neck was invariably adorned by dazzling jewellery which complemented her dazzling beauty and dazzling, up-to-the-minute, designer clothes. Today she was in black and white with just the right dramatic touches of red.

The moment the door behind her was closed, her hands were reaching out, gesturing for him to give her what she wanted. 'Well…?' It was a prod, delivered with a provocatively appealing smile.

Nick strolled around to the front of his desk and casually propped himself against it, viewing his mother with considerable cynical amusement as he delivered some news that might wilt her monstrous vanity.

'I don't think you're the only woman who received an emerald necklace from Enrique Ramirez this morning.'

Her perfectly smooth brow defied its many Botox treatments and frowned. 'What do you mean?'

'Apparently oats were being sown all around the world in my father's polo-playing years. I have a half-brother in England, and another in the USA, both of whom have impressed my dear dead Dad every bit as much as I have, despite all three of us being his bastard sons. Which undoubtedly means he felt a debt of gratitude to their mothers, as well.'

'Oh!' She shrugged. Her mouth twisted into a wistful smile. 'He really was quite irresistible. I have no doubt any woman would fall for him. But not so good for you, Nick. I guess this means Enrique has cut any inheritance for you three ways.'

The inheritance was irrelevant. Nick wanted to meet his half-brothers. And to do that, he had to fulfil a dead man's crazy fantasy of reliving a different life through his illegitimate son...a life filled with real love and commitment, fidelity and fatherhood. It was either marry and have his wife at least pregnant within the next twelve months, or never learn anything more about his half-brothers.

That was the bare bones of Enrique's wishes...his challenge to Nick.

Forget the rest.

Nick didn't believe in love and marriage and happy families, but he could and would outwardly comply with those terms in order to get to a meeting with his half-brothers—his real blood family however fragmented it was, not step-siblings who came and went with his mother's marriages. He wanted to meet Enrique Ramirez's other by-blows, wanted to know if they were anything like himself, wanted to feel he was not alone.

'There is no inheritance to be had,' he lied, aware that his mother couldn't help herself from plotting for it if he told her the truth. He smiled sardonically as he added, 'My father has graciously granted me some knowledge of a family I went seeking when I was eighteen. What you might call too little, too late.'

'Half-brothers…' The Botox got another workout. 'Are you going to go looking for them now?'

'I don't have any key to finding them. Unlike me they haven't been aware that Enrique fathered them so the Ramirez name would mean nothing to them. I've been told their identities will be revealed to me when the estate is settled. I can wait. In the meantime, I'm going to get on with my business. If you'll leave me to it…'

He strolled over to the door and opened it for her. 'Thank you for your visit. I'm glad you're happy with your necklace.'

'You're not disappointed, Nick?'

He shrugged. 'He who expects nothing cannot be disappointed.'

'Oh, you…' She tapped his cheek in mock exasperation, her golden amber eyes looking for some chink in his cynical armour. 'You should have fought Enrique for some recognition while he was still alive. You've always been too proud, Nick. Too independent.'

'The product of my circumstances. Goodbye, Mother.'

With nothing to get her pretty teeth into, she accepted the exit line, undoubtedly eager now to get the emerald necklace valued to see how much she'd been worth to Enrique Ramirez. His mother was incredibly good at maths when it came to totting up the profit from each connection she'd made.

Left to himself again, Nick concentrated on formulating how best to get to the end he wanted without paying too much for it. He simply didn't have enough information—no names, no descriptions, no ages—to try finding his half-brothers himself. The only guarantee of meeting them was to go down the route Enrique had laid down.

No way was he going to lose out on seeing if he could connect with some *real* family, so that meant he had to face marriage and fatherhood first. The trick was to create a situation he could live with. He didn't want any child of his suffering through divorce, getting screwed up from feeling unwanted. If he had to have a child, he needed to set up a stable environment for it.

His mind kept zapping to one woman.

He'd trust Tess to do right by him—right by their child.

He was almost sure he'd be able to work out an agreement with her—a sensible legal agreement that protected all parties. Tess wasn't like any of the other women he knew—the women who'd jump at marrying him because of who and what he was. Tess didn't want anything from him, didn't want anything from any man.

But she might want a child.

And she knew where Nick was coming from.

Tessa Steele came from the same place.

It didn't matter that she was Brian Steele's daughter—real daughter—she had a mind of her own and had made a life of her own, just like Nick.

The big question was…would she be interested in forging a life in partnership with him, given the incentive of having a child together?

CHAPTER TWO

'THERE'S nothing of you in him, Tessa,' her father growled, a disgruntled look on his face as he studied her two-month-old son.

Nothing of *him*, he meant. Tess knew she was her father's favourite child because he could see his genes in her red hair, fair skin and blue eyes. She'd never been sure if this was a natural hang-up with him—some male primitive need to see the imprint of himself repeated—or a reaction against having another man's child passed off as his. Nick's mother had left a lot of emotional havoc in the wake of her marriage to Brian Steele.

Undoubtedly it had been wounded pride that had driven her father to plunge straight into marriage with another spectacular woman—the blonde and beautiful star of stage and screen, Livvy Curtin. This unlikely coupling had only lasted two years, but at least a child of his own had come out of it and after the divorce had been settled, Livvy had been happy for Brian to have the major share of custody, leaving herself less burdened in pursuing her acting career.

Tess had always known she was loved by her father. Even after his third and still current marriage had produced two sons of whom he was extremely proud, he'd kept a very soft spot for his one and only daughter—a softness which was considerably resented by his third wife who'd taken every opportunity to shunt Tess off to her *real* mother, who much preferred to ignore that reality. Livvy—*you are not to call me Mummy*—had no interest whatsoever in even acting out a maternal role.

Tess's own life experience fed her determination to keep a very simple family line for her child. No marriages. No divorces. No messy extended relationships. Above all, her son was going to know he was loved by his mother. And his genetic pattern was irrelevant. She'd given birth to this baby and he was hers. All hers.

'He does have curly hair,' she pointed out, though her own curls were inherited from Livvy, not her father.

Brian Steele's hair was dead straight, like a wire-brush, and the red was all white now. The blue eyes, however, hadn't faded one whit with age and were as sharp as ever as they swung to his daughter, wanting to pin her down on a few matters which she'd been successfully evading.

They were sitting in the sunny courtyard at the Steele family's Singleton property, both of them taking time out from their individual business interests. This securely secluded country home provided the privacy Tess had wanted for having her baby, and since this was her father's first grandchild, he'd readily granted her the occupation of it for a few months while he and his wife were currently winging between the Steele family residences in Sydney and Melbourne, keeping up their social engagements.

'Are you going to tell me who the father is?'

'It doesn't matter who, Dad.' She smiled her own deep maternal love at the black-haired, green-eyed baby in the rocker at her feet. 'He's mine.'

And thank God his olive skin was never going to have a problem with being out in the Australian sun. No rigid restrictions for *his* childhood. No fear of disfiguring freckles rammed into him. Her own mother's brainwashing edict—'You'll turn out ugly, ugly, ugly, if you don't cover up and wear a big hat'—would never be a part of his life.

'Tessa, I understand you didn't want to marry the guy…'

'He wouldn't have wanted to marry me, either,' tripped off her tongue before she could think better of revealing that piece of information.

'Why not?' Her father sounded affronted, as though any man should feel enormously honoured to be her husband. After all, she was a Steele, daughter of a billionaire, heiress to a fair chunk of the family mining fortune, and not without physical attraction when Tess bothered to play up her natural assets.

She shook her head, not wanting to give away any clues to the identity of her son's other parent. Her father would be even more affronted to know it was Nick Ramirez he could thank for this grandchild.

'Does he even know about your having his child?'

'No. I didn't tell him. Things would only get messy if I did.'

'Is he already married?'

'No.' Her own vivid blue eyes lasered his. 'It was just a once only thing, Dad. A big mistake in hindsight. Wrong for both of us. Okay?'

Wrong for Nick, anyway. He'd made that perfectly clear to her afterwards, showing how appalled he was at having been caught up in the spontaneous combustion that had ended in wild hot sex with Brian Steele's daughter.

'Don't you think he might guess when he sees you with a baby?' her father nagged.

'That's very unlikely,' Tess figured that having sex with her was now a sealed compartment in Nick's memory, never to be reopened. 'On the whole, we don't mix socially,' she explained. 'And by the time it's generally known I have a child, the date of birth will be blurred, so there won't be any ready connection to him.'

'You don't *want* him to know,' her father shrewdly concluded.

It was all too complicated, Tess thought. Apart from the family entanglements, on a purely personal level she was not the kind of woman Nick normally chased and bedded, and given his own background, he would absolutely hate the fact of having been involved in an accidental pregnancy. Especially with her!

He was anti-marriage and totally cynical about any *love* relationship lasting. Fatherhood was an extremely sore point with him and if control of his life was taken out of his hands by having fatherhood thrust upon him… Tess mentally shuddered at his possible reaction. Fierce resentment would be the least of it and she was not about to let that touch her son.

Better for Nick that he didn't know. Better for herself, too. Nick Ramirez was like forbidden fruit. She couldn't stop wanting him even though she knew being near him was poisonous to any peace or happiness in her life. It had been like breaking an addiction to give up dealing with him professionally when she could no longer hide her pregnancy. To invite a lifelong tie with him by telling him about their child… Tess knew that could only bring her continuous torment.

'Keeping secrets…' Her father's breath hissed out from between his teeth, a sure sign of unease. 'It's a recipe for future grief. Time will come when the boy will want to know who his father is.' His shaggy white eyebrows beetled down. 'Are you going to tell him lies? Say his father's dead?'

'I don't know. I haven't thought that far ahead.'

'Well, start thinking about it, Tessa,' he sternly advised. 'Best get things straight with the father now because your son has the right to know who he is and shocks aren't good further down the road.'

She looked askance at him, trying to gauge if she dared bring up the sensitive past. Only recently Livvy had told her what had happened all those years ago between her father and Nick. As Brian's new second wife, she'd heard all about *the boy's* visit from her angry husband, how Miss Centre of her own Bloody Universe, Nadia Kilman/Steele/Manning, hadn't bothered to tell her Brazilian lover's bastard son that he wasn't Brian's son.

'Like…with Nick Ramirez, Dad?' she asked hesitantly.

He grimaced at the reminder, then glanced sharply at her. 'Who told you about that?'

'Livvy.'

He snorted. 'No doubt your mother recounted it as a piece of high drama.'

'Actually she thought I should be aware of the family background since I was doing business with him.'

'Business…' His eyes openly mocked that motivation. 'Just a line for Livvy to hang her tittle-tattle onto. Business is business. A man as successful as Nick Ramirez is at what he does, would never let who you are get in the way of what's working for him. Besides, he eventually took his real father's name and you have the right to mine. He'd respect that.'

'But it was a shock to him…back then?' Tess prompted, wanting to continue this thread of their conversation.

'Hell of a shock!' Her father winced over the memory. 'I didn't deal kindly with him. Something I'll always regret. I was so mad at Nadia, so mad at being tricked into thinking he was my son, I took it out on him. And none of it was his fault. He was just a boy, fighting for what he believed was his rights.'

'So in a way…you admired him?' she probed.

A wry laugh. 'No, I hated his guts because I kept seeing that blasted Brazilian popinjay in him. But afterwards I felt ashamed of how I broke the truth to him. I was furious with Nadia at not having done it herself.' A rueful sigh. 'He was only seven years old yet he stood his ground, defying me until I smashed his belief in me as his father. And then…it was like I'd killed something in him.'

He shook his head at her. 'I wouldn't like you to put your son—my grandchild—in that kind of position, Tessa. I don't care about the father. Just don't do it to your boy. He has the right to know. Know from the very beginning.'

It was a sobering piece of advice, cutting through the emotional turmoil that always swirled around Tess's thinking about Nick. To her it was totally unforgettable that he'd been *embarrassed* about having sex with her, that he couldn't put it behind him fast enough, careful never to even slightly refer to it after they'd agreed that one intimate flashpoint shouldn't affect their work relationship.

He frequently used her services as a casting agent to get the right people acting in the TV commercials he created. In the months of face to face business discussions with him during the early stages of her pregnancy, Tess had waited for—yearned for—some sign that he might feel drawn towards having more than a work relationship with her.

A stupid wish, she knew. And, of course, no sign had come. In fact, it hadn't taken him long to start a hot affair with another one of the models who streamed through his life. And bed.

Once Livvy had told her the background, Tess had realised that Nick Ramirez would never seek an intimate connection with Brian Steele's daughter. It had probably amused him to use *her* casting agency, although after she'd proved her worth to his business, he'd come to respect her judgement.

They'd even reached a kind of platonic friendship in their mutual understanding of each other's backgrounds. But the desire that had flared up one night…to Nick it had been highly *undesirable* in hindsight, never to be allowed to slip past his guard again.

Common sense had forced her to adopt the same attitude whenever they'd met professionally, and each meeting had hammered home the point he wanted no consequences from what he obviously considered a moment of madness. Business, as before, was strictly adhered to.

However, Tess now realised her father was right. Her own feelings and Nick's feelings were irrelevant. It wasn't their baby's fault that he was *a consequence*. They'd made a child and every child had the right to know its biological parents. She was going to have to tell Nick, but not until she was feeling less raw about it, more able to adopt and hold onto a totally convincing independent stance.

Her mobile phone played its call tune.

She smiled at her father as she picked up the personal communicator and stood to move away for some privacy. 'Keep an eye on Zack for me while I deal with this?'

He nodded while grumbling, 'Don't know why you had to call him Zack. What kind of name is that? Some fancy idea from your mother, I'll bet…'

This was undoubtedly her father's way of letting her know he was well aware of the media's spotlight on her mother's arrival in Sydney yesterday, and he was assuming the call was from Livvy who had recently earned his disapproval by attaching herself to a toyboy.

Tess had made the same assumption which was why she was moving out of earshot, knowing that any conversation with her mother would draw an acid side commentary from her father. She was already opening the gate out of the enclosed courtyard as she accepted the call and identified herself.

'Tess, it's Nick. Nick Ramirez.'

The shock of hearing so directly from the man who'd just been the focus of considerable mental and emotional conflict, robbed Tess of any ready reply. It also jolted her feet into a dead halt until she recovered sense enough to realise she didn't want this conversation overheard, either.

'Where are you right now?' Nick ran on, apparently too impatient to wait for a normal greeting.

Facing the polo field where your father played with my father, setting off the train of events which has led to the situation we now have between us.

Tess checked the wild drift of her mind and the headlong rush of her feet to wide open spaces, took a deep breath, and with as calm a voice as she could manage, asked, 'What is the problem, Nick?'

It had to be something to do with the casting agency. Had her personal assistant messed up *his* business in some critical way?

'There's no problem,' he hastily assured her.

'Then why are you calling me?'

'I want to meet with you.'

'What for?'

Silence.

A wave of electric fear shot through every nerve in Tess's body, leaving them at rigid attention. Had he somehow heard about the baby? Did he think he might be the father?

'Can we get together for lunch?' he pressed. 'You must be back in Sydney. Livvy's here.'

'No, I'm not in Sydney, Nick.'

'Didn't you tell me your mother needed you with her as a people manager while she directed her first movie? Wasn't that why I've had to deal through your PA and not with you personally for the past six months? Because you were away with your mother?'

'Yes,' Tess acknowledged, her stomach contracting as she realised how easily Nick could uncover her lies if he put his mind to it.

'Well, Livvy flew in from LA yesterday,' he went on. 'Since you're answering this call, you're obviously back in Australia, as well. So where are you now?'

'I'm at Singleton, visiting with my father.' That, at least, was the truth, and no way in the world would Nick Ramirez front up here.

His sigh seethed with frustration. 'Tess, I need to get together with you.'

The driving purpose in his voice sent a quiver through her heart. 'What for, Nick?'

He ignored the question, seizing on an event where her presence was certainly expected. 'The premiere of *Waking Up* next Thursday night…'

It was a teen horror movie, its release timed for the end of the school year, hoping to draw big audiences once the Christmas vacation started. Tess had planned to return to Sydney tomorrow, settle back into her home at Randwick, catch up with her mother, buy something suitable to wear to the premiere…

'I remember you did the casting for that movie,' Nick said with considerable satisfaction in having connected her to a definite time and place. 'If you don't have an escort lined up for the red carpet, I'll fill in. Okay?'

Shocked by what could not, by any stretch of the imagination, be called a *business* arrangement, Tess could not contain her astonishment at this suggestion. 'Why?' tripped straight off her tongue.

'Why not?' came shooting back at her. 'Have you finally found a guy you care about? A guy who'd object to your being with me?'

The terse tone of his voice implied he didn't care for any such hitch in his plans. Tess was goaded into saying, 'Isn't there a woman hanging around your neck who'd object to me sharing a premiere spotlight with you?'

'Not a factor,' he claimed.

'I can't believe you don't have someone on your string.'

'That string will be cut before next Thursday.'

An emphatically decisive note there.

Tess wondered if it was an ominous note for her. It wasn't unusual for women to come and go very quickly in Nick's life, but linking the current lady's exit to this out-of-character public date with her...was Nick wiping his slate clean to deal with fatherhood?

This meeting could not be about business. Yet how could he know about the baby when she had literally dropped out of circulation in Sydney before her pregnancy showed?

She took a deep breath and confronted the issue. 'What's this about, Nick?'

'I'll tell you when I see you, Tess. Where and when do I pick you up for the premiere?'

He was arrogantly assuming she didn't have an escort lined up. Or she'd just mentally jettisoned any prior arrangement to be with him instead. Fair enough, she supposed, given his belief that she'd been in Los Angeles for the past six months and definitely not deeply engaged with any hometown guy. Nick Ramirez was an important client who did warrant some indulgence and he was demanding it.

Besides, with her father's very recent advice still weighing heavily on her mind, this was clearly an opportunity for her to get personal with Nick on her son's behalf, if the circumstances felt reasonably favourable. Better not to protest too much when she had her own agenda. And no man in tow, anyway.

On the other hand, until such time as she felt right about telling him of their child, she didn't want Nick seeing Zack, or even knowing about him.

'I'll be staying at The Regent Hotel that night.' Completely neutral ground. 'The after-show party is to be held there,' she went on. 'I'm not sure when the limousines will start rolling to the theatre…'

'Meet me in the lobby of the hotel for drinks at six.'

A public place was fine. 'Okay. Six it is.'

'Thanks, Tess.'

Was that a tinge of relief in his voice? Tess was intrigued by the idea of Nick Ramirez needing her for something personal.

'You know, I've actually missed you while you've been away,' he added, and she could hear him smiling through the words, the dry mocking smile he attached to any expression of emotion. 'I look forward to being with you, Tess.'

Connection cut.

She stood in stunned stillness.

This call couldn't possibly have been related to any suspicion she'd had a baby—*his* baby. Clearly Nick still believed her LA cover story which explained her lengthy absence from normal business. The most curious and nerve-tingling part was…his saying that he'd missed her, which had to mean *her, the person,* because this movie premiere had nothing to do with business and he had offered her his arm for it.

In the context of his previous strongly negative attitude towards any personal involvement with her, this didn't make sense.

None of it made sense.

He hadn't even said goodbye to his current girlfriend yet.

The only possible answer was… Nick Ramirez wanted something from her—something urgently needed by him—something important enough to drive him into breaking his own rules to get it.

Which put a fascinating spin on this extraordinary move.

Tess decided she had nothing to fear from it.

And quite possibly much to gain.

CHAPTER THREE

NICK was smiling to himself as he entered The Regent Hotel. Brilliant move—starting off a serious personal relationship with Tess in the publicity blaze of a premiere. If Enrique's surveillance guy was on the job, reporting back to Javier Estes, he could hardly miss it.

Step one towards *love and marriage.*

Six o'clock and the lobby was abuzz with people coming in from the day, making plans for the night, waiting to be joined by others before proceeding elsewhere. Nick knew the bank of elevators was at the back of the open lounge area and he took up a position in a relatively clear space near the reception counter so Tess could easily spot him when she came down from her room. Any minute now. Unlike most women he knew, Tess had always been a stickler for punctuality.

No doubt time-keeping had been drilled into her at boarding school where bells were invariably rung to command a move from one place to another and punishments were handed out for dallying beyond an acceptable limit. It was another part of their background in common…boarding school, where many inconvenient children got dumped. It was also one thing he was sure Tess would agree on—no boarding school for their child *if* they had one.

Nick was not yet fully committed to the idea of being a father, taking on the heavy and enduring responsibility it entailed. At this point he was only playing with the factors, seeing if they could be moved into an acceptable framework. He could envisage doing the marriage part of the mission with Tess. That was mostly paperwork—a contract signed and subsequently dissolved at the parties' convenience. The child part was far more troubling.

Weirdly enough, Enrique's challenge on the fatherhood issue had certainly stirred him up on how parents should treat their children. Nick found himself brooding over an endless list of negatives coming straight out of his own life. But to carry through the positives that every child deserved was by no means an easy task. It would require some very solid planning.

If he went through with this.

It was a damnedly insidious challenge Enrique had thrown out. To get to brothers of his own, he had to beget a child of his own. But a child was a child, with much to be done for him or her. The brothers he didn't know yet had to be adults if they'd been conceived and born during Enrique's international polo-playing days—men he might not even like, let alone care about, not worth going through all this to get to them.

Nevertheless, having them arbitrarily withheld from him…

That was intolerable!

The sound buzz in the lobby changed—surprise and excited speculation lilting through it—alerting him to people turning, looking up to the head of the grand staircase which led down from the mezzanine level where the main restaurant was situated. Bound to be one of the actors starring in tonight's premiere, Nick thought, his gaze flashing up in the expectation of seeing an instantly recognisable face.

Recognition certainly hit him but for a few stunned moments Nick couldn't quite come to grips with what he was seeing.

Tess...walking down the stairs like a movie queen?

Tess...looking so fabulous, so glowingly exquisite, she would leave both *her* mother and *his* in the shade, even on their best-foot-forward days!

Her red hair, shining with golden highlights, rippled down in long loose curls all over and around her pale pearly shoulders. Framed by this spectacular halo and with the natural prettiness of her features enhanced by artistically applied make-up, her face positively sparkled with star-power, vividly lit by her bright blue eyes and even brighter white smile.

She wore a dress that would have been a show-stopper on any red carpet in the world. Silvery beaded mauve lace barely cupped her breasts, the low decolletage caught together by swathes of mauve chiffon, hugging her small waist and tied tightly with long silver tassels that swayed over a long skirt of rows of lace and seductive frills, graduating in shades of mauve to smoky grey and deep violet. The frills played peek-a-boo with her long shapely legs and feet encased in very high-heeled sexy silver sandals.

Complementing this was the jewellery—diamond bracelet, long dangly diamond earrings and around her neck a fine chain of diamonds leading to a whopping big diamond pendant. The heiress to a mining fortune was certainly not hiding her light under any bushel tonight!

This vision of Tess did odd things to Nick's stomach.

And predictable things to his groin.

Which completely fused his thought processes.

Tess paused halfway down the staircase. She'd spotted Nick before starting this perilous descent on the sexy stilettos that had to be worn with this dress. His focus had been trained elsewhere but it certainly had a fix on her now. He was staring straight at her. But he wasn't moving, wasn't taking one step to meet her.

Tess felt an almost evil satisfaction at the stunned look on his face. Just because she'd made a point of not dressing up for him all during their professional relationship, not wanting to be viewed as another one of the herd of women dying to draw his attention, it didn't mean she couldn't lay out the bait with the best of them when she wanted to. All it took was time; time with a hair stylist, time with a beautician, time shopping. And money, of course. The old adage—fine feathers made fine birds…always held true.

If she had to rock the boat between them by telling him about their child, she'd decided she might as well rock the boat in every direction—force him to see her as not so *accidentally* desirable, make him remember how he'd felt with her the night Zack had been conceived. She wasn't sure if it was reckless pride driving her into being deliberately provocative or a savagely primitive need to knock Nick's socks off so he'd reassess what he wanted from their relationship.

It was almost a year since he'd walked away from that explosive night of wild careless sex, forcing her to set it aside, as well. Was he remembering it now? Was that why he wasn't moving to meet her? Bad Tess, stirring it up for him! Out of control Tess, not doing the sensible thing for once.

A fierce rebellion was surging against the pigeonhole Nick had put her into. He was still standing flat-footed in the reception area, not coming to her. Fine! She'd go all the way to him, force him to acknowledge he was with her tonight. At his own insistence!

She resumed her descent of the staircase, a burning anger turning her previous graceful carriage into a flaunting strut. Perhaps a sense of courtesy finally kicked through Nick's shock. He started towards the foot of the staircase, and, as was usual with him, people rolled back from his path like the Red Sea for Moses.

He had the commanding charisma of being spectacularly tall, dark and handsome, especially in formal clothes, and there was something about his Latin-lover looks that stirred a spine-tingling sense of danger, adding immeasurably to the sexual allure of the man.

When Tess had first laid eyes on him, she'd thought there wouldn't be a woman in the world who'd be immune to at least a fleeting desire to sample him in bed. The trouble was Nick knew it, and something in her had instantly wanted to be the exception, defying his power to get women virtually dropping at his feet.

But she was no exception.

She'd fallen when he'd opened the door to having sex with her. And she'd fall again, given the chance. Without a doubt, it would be much, much easier to tell Nick he was the father of her child if he was sharing a bed with her.

However, if she had lit any fire in him just now, he certainly had it under control by the time he met her at the foot of the stairs, halting her on the step above him by taking her hand and lifting it to his mouth in mocking homage.

'Pure Hollywood, Tess,' he purred through a sensuous brushing of his lips over her skin. Then he gave his twisted little smile and cocked a sardonic eyebrow. 'Getting into the spirit of a premiere?'

Electric tingles ran up her arm and shot adrenaline through her bloodstream, sharpening her mind to defence stations as her all too vulnerable heart pitter-pattered its distress at the dying hope for anything different coming from Nick. If he wanted something personal from her tonight, it was obviously not going to comprise a shift away from platonic friendship.

'I thought I'd better lift my game for the publicity limelight,' she explained, colouring all her efforts to *affect* him as something professional, not personal.

His laugh was tinged with irony. 'You didn't just lift it, Tess. You've totally outclassed any possible competition.'

'I'm not competing,' she swiftly denied, hating the thought that he suspected she might be. 'Have I overdone it? Is that why you just stood there and stared instead of coming to greet me?'

He shook his head, eyes twinkling amusement at the sudden crack in her confidence. 'You haven't overdone it, Tess. In fact, you deserve a standing ovation for a perfect production. I just wasn't expecting the grand entrance from you.'

She shrugged. 'Well, I can be my mother's daughter when I choose to be. And why not when I'm going to a premiere?'

'Why not, indeed? I simply needed a moment or two to get accustomed to *this* image of you.'

'You have seen me dressed up before,' shot out of her mouth, propelled by a rampaging need for him to acknowledge he had found her desirable the last time she'd fine-feathered herself—the night they had both attended a product launch party. Separately. And ended up intimately together.

The thick black lashes lowered, instantly veiling *his* response to the memory. His full-lipped provocative mouth moved into a teasing moue. 'Playing with fire, Tess?'

Heat whooshed up her neck and into her cheeks and she silently and violently cursed the fair translucent skin which was such a telltale barometer of her feelings. Her inner agitation seized on a counter-attack to defend herself.

'You're the one crossing the line, Nick. I didn't ask you to be with me tonight. You asked yourself, remember?'

'I did,' he agreed, but his mouth was still taunting, turning her into just another woman who fancied getting into his trousers.

'As for the *grand entrance*, you triggered that yourself,' she ran on, her fight to equalise everything gathering a fierce momentum. 'Firstly you were so stuck in a world of your own I couldn't draw your attention from the mezzanine level. Then when I started down to collect you and you did happen to look up, instead of bounding up the stairs to meet me, you stand and stare, making me come all the way down...'

'Don't tell me you didn't enjoy creating a sensation, Tess,' he slid in mockingly.

'I happen to be dressed for the occasion, Nick Ramirez, and instead of puffing up your macho ego, thinking I've done it to impress you, perhaps you'll now escort me back upstairs so we can have a bite to eat in the coffee shop before we leave for the theatre.'

'At your service.' He flashed her an openly charming grin as he took the hand he was still holding, tucked it around his arm and stepped up to do her bidding. 'And that tart tongue of yours has just reminded me why I've missed you so much.'

'Too much honey for the busy bee?' she slung at him. Her heartbeat was in major overdrive, causing her mind to zing beyond the bounds of discretion. She was viciously jealous of all his other women, but showing it with her tart tongue was not a good idea.

To her intense relief he laughed, his wicked green eyes dancing pleasure in her, and the steely pride Tess was trying to keep in her spine was in instant danger of melting. It wasn't fair that one man should be so attractive. If it was only the physical impact, it wouldn't be so difficult to set it at a distance and ignore it. But when his mind clicked with hers, which it did all too frequently on many levels, everything within her yearned to have Nick Ramirez as *her man*.

Unfortunately, knowing that was never going to happen did not diminish the desire. Tess mostly managed to counter it by being as sane and down-to-earth as she could be around Nick. She just wasn't on top of that game tonight. Probably never would be again. The six-month break from frequent practice at it left her feeling inept, and the sense that everything had to change between them anyway eroded the old need to keep it up.

Returning to the sore point of his women, Tess decided she might as well be blunt in sorting out this current situation. Pitching her voice to a light bantering tone, she invited him to be forthcoming. 'So tell me why you dumped your current bedmate to come out with me tonight.'

He shrugged. 'Purely an incidental. She was ready to move on.' A sardonic twist of his mouth as he added, 'Had another guy already lined up.'

'Having realised *you* weren't ever going to put a ring on her finger?'

'I never lead any woman to believe that, Tess.'

'Doesn't stop them from hoping for it. After all, it's part of the deal.'

'What deal?'

'You know perfectly well *what deal.* It's part and parcel of the high-flying world we were both born into. *Men go after the most attractive women they can afford; women go after the richest men they can attract.*'

Her father and his mother were prime examples of this pattern of behaviour.

'I don't buy my women,' Nick protested.

She flicked him a mocking look. 'Yes, you do. You buy them with who and what you are. You just never close the deal. They don't realise at first that you're only into visiting their bedrooms, not staying there. I bet every one of them thinks she'll be the one to keep you at her side.'

'Well, I can't control hopes but I certainly don't ever feed them.'

'Maintaining your brand of integrity?'

'I have always hated deceit, Tess.'

Which set all her nerves on edge over what she'd been keeping from him. Maybe she should blurt it out right now, throw fatherhood into his lap and watch how he dealt with it. On the other hand, he hadn't yet laid out his purpose behind being her escort tonight and there had to be one. Tess didn't believe he'd simply been *missing her tart tongue*.

The fatherhood issue could wait a bit longer. She wanted her curiosity satisfied first.

'Will a plate of fruit and cheese do it for you or do you want something more substantial?' Nick asked matter-of-factly as he steered her to a vacant padded booth in the coffee shop overlooking the lobby. 'And what would you like to drink?'

'Hmmm...a lovely rich creamy Brandy Alexander to drink and a wicked slice of Chocolate Mud cake to eat,' she rolled out with sinful relish, deciding comfort food could be forgiven tonight since she was feeling distinctly fraught. 'And I won't share, so if you're hungry, too, order something for yourself.'

At his look of surprise at her grossly non-dieting order, she dryly pointed out, 'You are not with a figure-watching model tonight and I feel like spoiling myself.'

His grin was warm this time. 'Curves are good.' His gaze dropped to her cleavage as he saw her seated, causing her wretched skin to flush again. Then to fluster her further, there was definitely a lustful simmer in his eyes when they smiled into hers. 'I'll go and order, organise quick service. Be back in a minute.'

She nodded, telling herself she was dressed to attract that kind of male response and Nick had just given it to her. Being the man he was, he probably couldn't help himself. She should feel happy about it. She wanted him to want her. But not just because her rather full breasts were being flaunted tonight. That put her in the same category as all his other women.

Tess shook her head, hopelessly confused over what she wanted from tonight with Nick. She certainly didn't want him to see how vulnerable she was to the desires he stirred. It was lucky there were beads sewn over the lace of the skimpy bodice, hiding the fact that her nipples had just become embarrassingly hard and prominent.

Really, it was highly vexing to get so messed up in a sexual sense when she wasn't getting any answers from him. Plenty of reaction to her but no reasons for his own actions. She took a few deep breaths to cool herself down, resolved to take some initiative in questioning him when he returned, and wished life could be a lot easier to figure out.

Before she could formulate a line of attack, Nick was sliding onto the seat on the other side of their table, positioning himself directly opposite her, lining up a face to face conversation, which he immediately started.

'Where do you fit into the deal, Tess?'

She looked blankly at him. 'What deal are you talking about?'

'The one where men go after the most attractive women they can afford, and women go after the richest men they can attract.'

'I don't fit.' She shrugged. 'I guess you can't separate an heiress from the fortune that comes with her. As a marriage prospect, men would inevitably be thinking more about my money than me, and I'd rather not feel they were with me because of it.'

'Is that why you remain single, Tess? You don't trust a guy to love you for the person you are?'

She frowned at him. 'Why are you trying to psychoanalyse me again? You're not very good at it, Nick. Last time you decided I'd been ripped off and hurt by so many guys I'd become an ice maiden. All because I wasn't playing your game.'

'My game?'

'Where you put out a blast of sexual magnetism and I'm supposed to turn into putty so you can squeeze me however you want.'

He rolled his eyes at her description of his modus operandi with women. 'I did not try to blast you with sexual magnetism.'

'No, in all fairness, it probably flows naturally from you. But you were peeved at my resistance to it. Why else would you cast me in ice?'

'You were also denying your femininity, Tess,' he pointed out. 'Always wearing androgynous jeans, shirts, no make-up, hair scraped back in an unflattering style…'

'I was simply going about my business which does not require me to impress anyone with my looks. As a casting agent, it's the looks of my clients that I peddle. Better that I don't distract from them.'

'Okay, so I read you wrong.' His mouth twitched into that sexy moue again. 'And you proved me wrong. It's been a long time now since I attached ice to your sexuality.'

'That was only a year ago,' she reminded him, the date being extremely pertinent to her, considering she still had to tell him about Zack.

'I know you better now,' he pressed on.

'Intimately better,' she pushed, recklessly intent on forcing him to remember what she couldn't forget. Especially when the result of their intimacy had to be revealed.

'Any objection to us getting that close again, Tess?'

It came out of nowhere.

No foreplay.

No seductive moves suggesting it might be on offer.

Just laying sex with him on the table for her to pick up or not as she pleased.

It took Tess's breath away, rendering her totally speechless. Not that her shocked mind was in any kind of working order to formulate thoughts which could be put into words. In fact, its emptiness seemed to be ringing with the echo of her thumping heart.

A waiter arrived at their table and proceeded to serve their drinks and her chocolate cake.

A timely distraction.

Nick couldn't expect her to answer him until they were alone again. He sat back…waiting. Watching her and waiting. And Tess had the weird sense of him harnessing all his dynamic energy, ready to roll right over her reply and get what he wanted any way he could.

But for what purpose?

And why *now*?

CHAPTER FOUR

NICK wondered if he should dump the sexual approach. There was no doubting Tess's shock. She hadn't been expecting it and quite possibly was recoiling from it.

He'd read her provocative strut down the staircase as being aimed at him, a deliberate sexual stir, but maybe she'd simply been doing the female thing of putting on a show, doing it because she could, revelling in being the centre of admiring and amazed attention. Her six months in Hollywood with her mother might well have made this behaviour seem absolutely normal.

Problem was...he had been stirred by it.

Stirred into a highly vivid memory of how it had felt to have nothing between them except the heat of intense and passionate pleasure. Big mistake to ever get sexually involved with a highly useful business connection, he'd told himself, but the truth was...he'd felt himself shifting onto dangerous ground with Tessa Steele and his survival instincts had screamed at him to get out fast—get out and don't revisit that scene. It raised too many ripples of consequence and he didn't want to face any of them.

Now…well, marriage was something else.

And if he was going to have a child with Tess, consequences had to be faced.

He saw having great sex with her as a bonus, and a means of persuading her into considering marriage with him. There was no denying the chemistry between them could be explosive, given free rein. Seeing her dressed to kill tonight, he'd thought she was inviting him to revisit that scene, which could have provided a smooth path into a long intimate relationship with her.

It still could, Nick reasoned, if he played his cards right. He wanted the intimacy with her. In fact, he wanted it so badly the desire was surprisingly uncomfortable.

Tess was sitting very still while the waiter unloaded his tray, setting everything out correctly on the table. Still, silent, tense, her gaze fixed on the guy's hands. Once the waiter had gone, she stared at the cake, finally picking up her fork and carving a slice of it, working the heavy chocolate mixture onto the silver prongs to lift it to her mouth. When it was arranged to her satisfaction, she lifted her gaze and directed a sharp blast of killer blue eyes right at him. It was a look designed to pin him to the wall and make him squirm.

'This doesn't make sense, Nick. Why would you suddenly fancy having another one night stand with me?'

'The experience lives in my memory as one that bears repetition, Tess.'

Hot colour rushed into her cheeks but the laser burn of her eyes did not waver from his. 'I thought you were committed to an easy come, easy go, mindset.'

'Well, that is the most sensible attitude in today's world of changing partners. Less grief all around.'

'Then we should be *gone* as an item. Why come back for seconds?'

'I don't have a one night stand in mind, this time around.'

'I think you'd better lay out what you do have in mind, Nick, because I am feeling distinctly lost on the road you've just taken.'

She shoved the chocolate cake into her mouth, leaving him to talk without any interruption from her. Her gaze was still trained on his face, eyes guarded, yet intensely watchful for every variation of expression from him.

'If we had a much closer relationship, at least you'd know it had nothing to do with your money,' he started slowly, feeling his way forward with careful respect for her feelings. 'In fact, nothing would induce me to touch a cent of the Steele fortune.'

A derisive little laugh gurgled from her throat. 'I thought that applied to me, too.'

He frowned, not understanding. 'What do you mean?'

'Well, after our unplanned...fling...you couldn't drop me fast enough. Didn't want to touch me again. It seemed to me you were appalled to find yourself *in flagrante* with Brian Steele's daughter.'

'You think I care who your father is?' He was astounded she should think it, incensed at the idea that any judgement of her would be based on her parentage. 'Fathers are totally irrelevant to me, Tess. We make our own lives, regardless of them.'

'Irrelevant…' she echoed, as though weighing that concept in her mind. She heaved a deep sigh and gestured with her fork for him to continue before digging it back into the mud cake. 'Okay, I accept that my money is no attraction to you…and you tell me you don't care who my father is, even though you once thought he was yours and got horribly rejected by him…'

'That's ancient history, Tess.'

'Is it, Nick?' She gave him an ironic look. 'I've always thought we are the sum of our past. It's all inside us, driving who and what we are. Take fathers, for instance. I happen to love mine…'

'It's fine that you do,' he swiftly assured her. 'I have no problem with Brian Steele. He had every right to deny I was his son. It was the truth. And I have no problem with you being his daughter.'

It rather amused him that his erstwhile father would end up his father-in-law if Tess married him, and Brian Steele wouldn't be able to deny that their child was his grandchild.

She shook her head, took a deep breath and said, 'Let me get this straight. The only reason that our one night stand was a one night stand for you was because we were doing business together on an ongoing basis, so it wasn't a good idea to extend it into an affair, which might have made things messy between us. Is that right, Nick?'

'Yes.'

Though the main reason had been the strong sense of falling down the same slavish pit his mother's men fell into, losing control of themselves and their lives by giving in to her sexual power over them. Just one night with Tess had demonstrated how addictive she could be—experiencing the whole package of her—and Nick instinctively shied from ceding that control to any woman. However, if he could keep things reasonable, and Tess was a very reasonable woman…

'But since my agency has done business with you...during my absence...for the past six months...' she went on, building a line of logic, '...you've reappraised the situation and decided you *can* have a harmless little affair with me. Is that where we are now, Nick?'

The incredulous note in her voice was warning enough that she'd find his proposal completely off the wall, but it had to be put on the table and the sooner it was done now, the better, giving him a platform to move forward with her.

'Not an affair, Tess. I was thinking more along the lines of us getting married. Having a child together.'

For Tess, it was like a huge shift in the fabric of her life. To say she was thunderstruck was putting it mildly. A hysterical bubble raced around her zapped brain, yelling out *we've already had a child together*. But the big incredible door of *marriage* kept blocking the wild bubble from breaking out into speech.

For the past few minutes she had been seesawing over spilling the fact of his fatherhood.

Several times she had thought the right moment had come, only to be diverted by the seductive idea of Nick positively wanting an affair with her, not just playing with the thought, actually putting it to her, which was amazing enough…

But marriage!

Marriage meant Nick would be her husband, her man, the impossible dream come true…

Except he wasn't saying she was the love of his life—which would be a totally absurd statement anyway, given their recent history. It was eleven months too late to be bringing up any feeling of deep attachment to her. No credibility at all. The fantasy of the black prince miraculously becoming her white knight in shining armour simply didn't play out in these circumstances.

In fact, the only thing he was hanging this proposal on seemed to be his desire for a repetition of his sexual experience with her, and since when did marriage have anything to do with his pursuit of bedding a woman?

Which left…*having a child together.*

Setting aside the fact they already had a child together, why would Nick suddenly want the commitment of fatherhood? Here was a man who avoided any long-term relationship commitment like the plague. What had changed his mind?

He hadn't said anything about why he wanted her to be his wife or why he wanted a wife at all! He'd always shown contempt for the institution of marriage, calling it a property trap that only fools would enter of their own free will.

She suddenly remembered he'd just assured her he wouldn't touch a cent of the Steele fortune. And, of course, being the heiress she was, he'd assume she wouldn't bother milking him of *his* assets if it came to a divorce between them. So the property trap wouldn't apply to them if they married. He'd obviously thought that through. But it didn't answer the big question...*why marry her at all?*

'This is...a surprise,' she said rather limply, needing him to bolster the idea with cogent reasons.

'Not an unpleasant one, I hope.' His magnetic smile flashed out, designed to pull her his way. His dark eyes twinkled warm confidence in their reaching a mutual and beneficial understanding. 'I think we could deal very well together, Tess.'

The persuasive purr of his voice was like a siren song, seductively calling her to set obstacles aside and just go with him, whatever he wanted, because she wanted it, too. But a bank of past hurts wouldn't let Tess plunge blindly into what would most certainly be an emotional minefield for her.

'Are you tired of tom-catting around, Nick?'

She set down the cake fork and picked up her drink, eyeing him over the rim of her glass as he constructed an acceptable reply.

'I think monogamy with the right woman could be very comfortable.'

'Mmmh…'

Tess sipped the brandy and cream, trying not to bridle with pleasure at being labelled *the right woman*. This had to be cynical flattery, she told herself. *Comfortable* was far more apt.

Her own pride had forced her into allowing him to *comfortably* continue their professional relationship after their one intimate night together, not creating any emotional drama when he'd moved on to satisfy himself sexually with another woman. But if he thought she'd continue a marriage through one infidelity after another, he could kiss any idea of that comfort zone goodbye!

'You're actually willing to try it,' she posed, gearing up to test his sincerity. '…staying wed to your wife, cleaving only to her until death do you part?'

He grimaced. 'I'm talking about a partnership, Tess, not a life sentence. Like any partnership, as long as it's working for us, fine. If it doesn't give us what we want, then we dissolve it.'

In short, he would act to suit himself. As always. Definitely no declaration of undying love coming from the lips of Nick Ramirez! They were great for kissing, great for promising the most incredible sexual pleasure and satisfaction. But love to last a lifetime? Forget it!

'Didn't you tell me two years was the maximum limit for passion?' She gave him a mocking little smile. 'Even if you've worked up a head of steam for me while I've been absent from your life, do you see us staying married for a longer period?'

He nodded.

She couldn't believe it.

Nick Ramirez offering her a commitment that went beyond the heat of sex?

'That's where the comfort part kicks in,' he explained. 'I've always enjoyed your company, Tess. I never feel bored by you and you've never given off bored vibrations with me. I don't see that changing. Do you?'

'I don't know. Our rather infrequent meetings don't exactly test that assumption, Nick. I'm amazed you're prepared to base a marriage on it. Amazed you've got marriage on your mind at all.' She arched one eyebrow in quizzical challenge. 'Want to tell me why?'

The shutters came down so fast on all his charged-up dynamic energy Tess could almost hear the clanging of steel doors closing out any possible entry to whatever was driving his mind, almost see the signs flashing up—

PRIVATE
TOP SECRET
CLASSIFIED INFORMATION

Tess suspected that Nick Ramirez would never let any woman past the barriers surrounding his heart and soul and he wasn't about to let a wife, either. But one thing she now understood very clearly. The motivation for this marriage proposal went deep and was very personal because Nick was intent on shielding it from her. For some reason he needed a wife and he'd chosen her as the most suitable candidate.

Tess—whose sex appeal had not been completely worn out on their one night stand.

Tess—who hadn't ranted and raved about his moving on from her to the next woman who took his eye.

Tess—who wouldn't take him down financially when it came time to part because she had money to burn herself.

Eminently sensible Tess who wouldn't give him too much grief once his private purpose had been served.

A fast building wave of fierce resentments swelled through her as she waited for Nick to construct a reply aimed at winning her acquiescence to his plan.

No way, she thought venomously. No way in the world was she going to be his bunny in some agenda that held no real caring for her. She was right on edge, ready to explode with a host of blistering home-truths, her nerves jumping so much her skin felt as though it was crawling as she watched him regather himself. No smile. Deadly serious. Dark green eyes locked onto hers, intensely purposeful.

'It's about having a child,' he said softly. 'It's about bringing up our child in a far more stable home than *we* were ever given. You'd be with me on that, wouldn't you, Tess? We know what it was like for us so...' The intensity in his eyes moved up a notch. '...we'd make it different. Better.'

Her heart lodged in her burning throat, choking off the tirade she'd been about to hurl at him.

He knew about Zack.

Had to.

And he'd just been cobbling together a marriage proposal because he felt it was the right thing for their child to have both parents living under the same roof, making a home…

'I think we could make a good go of it together,' he pressed.

Her mind whirled wildly around this contention. She simply hadn't expected Nick to embrace fatherhood at all, let alone take the old-fashioned honourable route of actually marrying her for the sake of their child. A horribly cynical voice in the back of her head observed that it was far too late to propose an abortion. Their son was already born. A real flesh-and-blood person. Nick's flesh and blood as well as hers. Had this fact stirred some proprietorial instinct in him?

'You don't have to marry me,' she blurted out, hating the thought of any intimate link between them based on a sense of entrapment. 'I won't mind sharing Zack with you. I'm glad you want to play a part in his life.'

'Zack?' Nick frowned heavily at her.

Gearing up to criticise her choice of name, just like her father, Tess thought. 'I don't see that you have any rights over our son as yet, Nick,' she stated somewhat belligerently. 'You weren't around when I gave birth to him two months ago, so…'

'You gave birth…to our son…two months ago?'

His voice climbed from a grated growl to a powerful punch of seething emotions. His eyes blazed with frightening intensity. His whole face tightened as though throwing up a wall of resistance to what she'd just told him. His shoulders squared into fighting rigidity.

The snap of breaking glass drew Tess's gaze down. The V-shaped goblet that had held Nick's martini was lying askew on the table, its fine stem still gripped upright in his hand. His hand was cut, oozing drops of blood.

Flesh-and-blood reality, Tess thought, her own heart thumping wildly at having faced Nick with it.

This was different to making a plan.

Different to putting forward a proposal.

Zack…their child…was real.

Right now real.

And Nick had not known about him!

The realisation of what she'd just done hit Tess like a knock-out blow.

She shut her eyes.

She shut her mouth.

Everything had just crashed out of control.

She had comprehensively lost the plot.

CHAPTER FIVE

IT WASN'T a lie.

As much as Nick wanted it to be—needed it to be—logic kept ramming it through the savagely defensive resistance in his mind that what Tess had just revealed *could not be* a lie. She had unwittingly spilled the truth, thinking he already knew it.

There had been no artfulness in what she'd said, no intent to get anything out of him, no reason at all for her to lie about having had his child. And the appalled look on her face when she'd realised his marriage proposal had not been about the baby she had secretly kept from him…impossible to even think she'd made a mistake and the child had been fathered by someone else.

Yet if he accepted this as truth, other things he didn't want to accept became truths, as well. The words from Enrique's letter began burning a hellish path through his brain…

I remember your visit to me when you were eighteen, the scorn in your eyes for the way I'd lived my life, taking my pleasure from beautiful women at no cost to myself. Do you honestly believe you haven't pursued the very same path since then, tasting as many as you can, just because you can?

You're following my footsteps…

No, I'm different to you, Nick had thought. I'd never be so irresponsible about sowing wild oats…

But he'd done precisely what his father had done.

And he'd done it to Tess.

Of all people.

Leaving her pregnant with a child he'd known nothing about.

A son…born two months ago.

A *bastard* son.

'Miss Steele, your limousine is here.'

The announcement from the bellboy broke through Nick's fierce and tumultuous introspection. 'No!' snapped off his tongue, his free hand lifting and slamming down onto the table to reinforce his command. 'Send it away. We're not going to a movie premiere.'

'Sir!' Consternation on the guy's face. 'There's been an accident with your glass? Do you need medical attention for that cut?'

Cut? Nick's gaze jerked down to the table, taking in the spilled drink, the broken glass, the stem of which was sticking out of his grasp and stained with bleeding from the fleshy part of his hand between thumb and index finger.

'I think if you'd just fetch some tissues to form a compress?' Tess quietly suggested.

Nick glanced up to see she was staring at the wound, too.

The bellboy hesitated. 'If Mr Ramirez was served with a flawed glass…'

'It's nothing,' Nick quickly declared, not wanting a fuss. 'I'll use my handkerchief.' He whipped the dressy white triangle out of his breast pocket, set down the bit of glass he'd still been holding and wrapped up the evidence of what had obviously been a moment of madness on his part. 'Sorry about the mess,' he muttered.

'It's no trouble, sir. I'll get it cleaned up for you. About the limousine, Miss Steele...'

'Tess...' Nick growled warningly, his eyes zapping hers with a bolt of ferocious determination.

She sucked in a quick breath and conceded the change of plan. 'I won't be needing it, after all. Please let the chauffeur know I've cancelled.'

The bellboy left to do her bidding and almost simultaneously a waiter arrived to clean up *the accident*.

'You should check that the cut is minor, Nick,' Tess advised, her gaze skating away from his to fix on the handkerchief, now bound around the injury.

She was nervous, he realised, frightened of dealing with a man who was so out of control he broke glasses and didn't even know it. She was sitting back on the booth seat, hands on her lap, keeping still, trying to look cool, calm and collected, but the scarlet staining her cheekbones was evidence enough of a highly heated inner agitation—a cauldron of worries boiling behind her smooth brow.

Nick checked the wound to appease any more concern. 'Needs a Band-Aid. Nothing more,' he said dismissively, then sat back himself while the clean-up waiter did his job. Adrenaline was pumping aggression through his entire body. The hands in his lap were clenched ready to fight, wanting to fight. But reason kept telling him it was Enrique he wanted to fight, not Tess.

Tess was his solution, not his problem.

He had to deal fairly with her, kindly with her, win her compliance to what he needed, and above all, he needed to prove his bed-hopping Brazilian father was wrong about him. Deeply, essentially wrong!

'Another drink, sir?'

'No. Thank you.'

This was a time to be stone-cold sober, to have all his wits about him, channelling them into treading gently, because he had no legal rights here. Tess had his child. Tess had the Steele fortune behind her to fight any claim he might make on their son should he cross what she decided was a reasonable line. The power was all hers right now.

He had to get her to marry him.

That was absolutely paramount.

It wasn't about getting to his brothers any more.

It was about getting it right for *his own son*!

The clean-up waiter left.

'So…' Nick opened up as calmly as he could. '…you met me tonight to tell me this, Tess?'

She shook her head. 'More to test the waters, find out why you suddenly wanted to meet me. It made me wonder if you had somehow discovered…' A heavy sigh acknowledged her mistake in blabbing what could still have been kept hidden.

Nick could not soften the razor edge of his voice as he cut to the core of the situation. 'Why didn't you tell me when you first found out you were going to have my child, Tess?'

The question lay between them, loaded with currents of accusation and criticism. He saw Tess bristling, calming herself, her vivid blue eyes going hot and cold. It was impossible for him to retract the question, impossible for her to evade answering it.

'I didn't want to tell you,' she finally stated—flat, unequivocal, bluntly honest.

'Why not?' he bored in again.

She shrugged, obviously reluctant to give him any further reply. Her lashes lowered to half-mast. She lifted her hands from her lap and wrapped them around her drink, probably feeling the need for a slug of brandy.

Nick frowned over her possible motives as she raised the glass to her lips. 'Did you think I'd deny the baby could be mine?'

She sipped, set the glass down, concentrated on tipping the cinnamon pattern on top of the creamy drink from side to side. 'You were using condoms that night,' she reminded him.

'They're not one hundred percent safe, Tess, and in actual fact, one broke. That's why I asked if you were on the pill.'

Her lashes lifted, her eyes shooting a blue blaze of self-derision at him. 'I lied.'

'You lied?'

'Yes. I didn't know you were worried about a condom breaking. If you'd told me I could have taken a morning-after pill.'

'But why lie about it?'

'Because I didn't want you to know I hadn't been with anyone for so long that taking a contraceptive pill was irrelevant to my life,' she threw at him with an air of exasperation. 'You'd already cast me as an ice maiden, which I wasn't. It just seemed more… *normal*…if I said I was on the pill.' She rolled her eyes mockingly. 'I'm sure every other woman you've been with has taken care of such things. I just wasn't prepared for you. Okay?'

'And that's why you didn't want to tell me we'd made a baby?' he pressed.

Her chin came up belligerently this time, eyes flashing daggers that had clearly wounded her. 'It was a one night stand for you, remember? You didn't want any *consequences* flowing from it.'

'I just didn't want sex messing up our business relationship,' he hastily excused, hearing the passion of deeply hurt feelings building in her voice, not wanting to contribute more to them, yet unable not to press his point. 'Having a baby is something else, Tess.'

Emotion exploded from her. 'Yes, having a baby is the most essential part of being a woman and you rejected me as a woman, Nick. You rejected that part of me that made our baby, so why would I share him with you?'

Why, indeed?

Rejection hurt. He knew how badly it hurt. He hadn't realised Tess had felt that way over what he'd tried to write off as a brilliant sexual experience—one worth having by both of them.

'By the time I discovered I was pregnant…' she plunged on, her volatile tone gathering an acid note, '…you'd already plunged into an affair with another woman—an affair that went on for months—beyond the time when I dropped out of your life on the business level.'

The picture was very clear to him now. Shamingly clear. He'd run from getting into a far too heavy involvement with Tess and sought a distraction from the lure of it, caring only about what he felt, what he wanted. He'd been every bit as self-centred as his mother, choosing to be a kingpin in the battle of the sexes, not a smitten courtier.

King Rat.

That's how Tess must have seen him.

'I'm sorry.' The apology spilled off his tongue, sincerely felt yet sounding too facile even to his ears.

What else could he say?

He gestured an appeal for forgiveness, realising that he'd put her in an impossible position. Pride alone would have dictated that no intimate bond be established with him. But for the letter from Brazil and his decision to use a marriage with Tess to get to his half-brothers, his son would have been brought up without knowing a father. Which proved Enrique more right than Nick cared to acknowledge, yet acknowledge it he must.

'I'm sorry,' he repeated, even more anguished by having done so much wrong to Tess whom he truly liked and wanted to keep in his life.

The boiling anger in her eyes cooled to a simmering scepticism, making Nick acutely aware that he'd given her no grounds for believing there was any real caring behind his apology. Words were not about to convince her otherwise. Instinctively he reached across the table and took her left hand in his, intent on reforging a physical link with her. The strong sexual connection between them had created this situation. Nick automatically employed that power now to move past the mental barriers Tess held against him.

'If I'd been you, I wouldn't have told me, either,' he confessed, offering a rueful smile in the hope of lessening the tension between them. With a gentle pressure on her soft palm, he fervently added, 'I'm glad you've told me now, Tess.'

Was he?

Her gaze dropped to the hand holding hers, feeling the tingling heat transmitted by his fingers, struggling to keep her mind above the wash of sexual desire that Nick Ramirez was so adept at setting in motion. She had to concentrate on the critical issues that had been raised between them, not let her thoughts get fuzzy with distracting feelings.

Nick had been proposing marriage for the purpose of having a child. It had clearly come as a huge shock to learn he already had one but he seemed to be accepting his fatherhood without any of the aggressive protest Tess had anticipated. He was even granting she had just cause for keeping it from him.

All in all, it was an incredibly *positive* reaction from him and she found it highly confusing since it contradicted what she knew of his attitude to relationships in general. Yet it did tie in with his stated reason for proposing marriage—wanting a child with her—and the seductively subtle pressure on her left hand suggested he was still pursuing that end.

'Where is he—the baby—our son?' he asked, his voice gruff as though furred with emotion he couldn't control.

Did having a child affect him so deeply? Or was this some act to push through an agenda he was determined on carrying out by using whatever means came to hand?

'In your suite here?' he prompted when she didn't reply.

'No.' Still wary of letting Nick too close when she didn't understand where he was coming from, Tess kept her tone carefully matter-of-fact as she explained, 'I left him at home in the care of his nurse.'

'Nurse?' Alarm flashed at her.

'A Karitane nurse who specialises in helping new mothers with new babies,' she quickly explained, her mouth twitching into an ironic smile. 'I needed her more than Zack did. He's perfectly healthy, Nick.'

Relief.

Natural enough, Tess told herself. Everyone wanted a healthy child. Though she couldn't help wondering how well fatherhood would have worn with Nick if there had been something wrong with Zack. He was used to having his life running as he dictated it. What didn't suit him was very quickly jettisoned.

'Zack. You called him Zack. Is that short for Zachary?' he asked.

'No. It's just Zack.' Her chin lifted in defiance of any opinion he might hold on her choice of name for their son. 'I liked it.'

'Zack Ramirez,' he said testingly. 'Not bad. Shouldn't invite any taunting variations at school. It's a name a boy can live with easily enough.'

His arrogant assumption goaded Tess into coolly correcting him. 'It's Zack Steele, not Ramirez.'

Instantly a blast of dark, dangerous energy surged into a heart-jolting challenge. 'I'm his father, Tess.'

'You'll have to convince me that fatherhood suits you, Nick,' she challenged right back, though she was rattled by his intensity.

'Then let's get started. I'll drive you home and you can introduce me to our son.'

'You want to meet him tonight?'

'Is there any reason why I shouldn't?'

She wasn't ready for it.

This wasn't what she had envisaged coming out of tonight's encounter with Nick Ramirez. Not only was he acting totally out of character but he was now set on invading her private life, having been given an inarguable reason for doing so.

Maybe it was simply curiosity about his child driving this move—curiosity that might be quickly satisfied. It was probably best to agree to a visit right now and watch Nick in action with their baby son. If he truly did want to embrace fatherhood, well…seeing was believing, she told herself. The big problem she had with Nick's credibility this evening certainly needed some sorting out.

'Tess…' he urged, impatient with her apparent indecisiveness. His eyes were snapping with the need for quick, aggressive action. They weren't simmering with sexual promise. It was painfully evident that she wasn't really a part of what was going on inside Nick Ramirez at this moment. It was his child who'd grabbed him, wholly and solely.

'Okay. Zack will most likely be asleep and I'd prefer him not to be disturbed, but if viewing him will satisfy you…'

'Whatever's best for him,' came the swift agreement.

Nick was out of the booth and on his feet, drawing Tess from her seat without any regard for the fact that her glass was not yet empty and her chocolate cake was largely uneaten. Given his intense eagerness to see their son, any protest on a point of polite consideration seemed overwhelmingly petty. He tucked her arm around his, and Tess found herself swept along by a powerful force-field of irresistible purpose.

As always, her body was acutely conscious of his, shaming her with its wilfully wayward sexual responses when she knew sex was the last thing on Nick's mind. It might have been a weapon in his battle to win his own way earlier tonight but it was now well and truly sheathed, his mind side-tracked by Zack, his will-power trained on getting to his son.

They started down the staircase to the foyer. Most of the people below looked up at them—the women focusing on Nick, the men on her. No doubt about it—the dress she was wearing was designed to get a rise out of any male. She'd wanted to at least match—no, surpass—Nick's other women in the glamour stakes, proving she could be *hot*, too. And he had reacted. She'd succeeded in being a sex object. Except it wasn't what she really wanted, and not what he wanted, either. So it had all been for nothing…this dress…

For whatever reason, Nick had decided he wanted a child and he'd chosen her to partner him in procreation—a pragmatic choice as she was conveniently free of gold-digging ambitions, young enough to be reasonably assured of problem-free reproduction, and *comfortably* compatible in her understanding of how *his* life worked. The huge irony was—if he'd made this decision a year ago, dumped this proposition in her lap a year ago, she would have been wildly happy about it, not feeling so horribly screwed up inside.

It was eleven months too late.

Eleven months of soul devastation and heartache.

Nick had stormed her defences, taken the ultimate gift of herself, demonstrated beyond any shadow of a doubt that it had no real value to him, and she'd hated him for it—hated him because she'd loved him and he hadn't cared enough to even recognise what she'd been giving him.

At least the eleven months had left her with no illusions about what she could expect from a marriage with him. Nick would probably give her respect and courtesy, as he'd done throughout their professional relationship, plus the dubious pleasure of his company on a daily basis. He'd make the sex good for her. After all, he was an expert at it. But Tess knew she could never attach real caring—love—to his love-making.

It wasn't there.

She'd fooled herself about that once.

Never again.

Yet as long as she understood how it was with Nick and didn't expect it to change...perhaps it might not be such a bad idea to marry him. It could have benefits, especially for Zack.

Their son would have his father married to his mother—both parents together—and that was good. Zack wouldn't care how it had come about. He wouldn't know anything else, remember anything else but having them both there for him. As it should be.

As long as Nick *did* turn into the kind of father who'd be good for him.

Was he capable of selfless loving?

Tess doubted a woman would ever draw it from him, but an innocent child might—a child whose life had not yet been stamped with life's harsher lessons—a child he could shield from them. Was this what had triggered Nick's sudden drive towards fatherhood—the yen to shape a different world for a child of his own?

They'd reached the concierge's desk and Nick was ordering his car to be brought up from the parking area to the hotel entrance. Tess thought of the suite she'd booked for the night, knowing she wouldn't return to it. The butler appointed to the suite could pack her things and send them home to her tomorrow. It was just baggage—unimportant possessions, nothing that would make one whit of difference to the outcome of her life.

There was only one possession of great importance tonight.

Zack.

And how Nick responded to him.

If he couldn't feel a bond with their child, a marriage between the two of them would have no foundation worth considering. Forget sexual attraction. Forget the fantasy of loving each other for the rest of their lives. Forget the dreams of the black prince turning into her shining white knight, guarding her happiness against any encroaching shadows. Any future they might have together hinged on how much fatherhood truly meant to Nick.

That was it—plain and simple—and Tess planted that truth in the forefront of her mind, knowing she had to hang onto some common sense or she could end up being badly hurt by wanting too much from Nick Ramirez. A father for Zack—that was what this was about. His real father. And Nick Ramirez had better prove himself worthy of that title!

'Here it is,' he murmured, obviously referring to the silver Lamborghini being driven up to where they stood waiting.

Tess couldn't help tensing. Fast car…fast man…fast life…she had to be mad to even think for one moment that a family future with Nick Ramirez was even remotely possible. And she was letting him invade her life, her home, her heart…

She didn't realise her fingers had curled into claws, digging into Nick's arm. He covered her clenching hand with his, warming it with a soothing caress as he used his soft velvet voice to reduce the sudden rush of fear.

'I promise you it will be all right, Tess.' A thread of ruthless determination crept into his tone. 'I'll make it right.'

She took a deep breath. It was impossible to turn back, anyway. Nick was not about to forget he had a child. She lifted her gaze to meet and challenge the green eyes their son had inherited from his father. 'Zack looks like you but I don't want him to turn out like you, Nick. I hope you're prepared to leave a lot behind before you walk into his life tonight.'

His jawline tightened, making the intriguing little cleft in his chin more prominent, giving rise to the teasing question of how much a divided man he was between the surface Nick and the deep-down Nick. A muscle in his cheek pulsed as though it couldn't hold steady against a wave of inner pain—pain that sapped the brilliance from his eyes, leaving them flat and more unfathomable than ever.

He sighed, forcibly relaxing himself, then offered a wry little smile and said, 'Brave new world...here we come.'

The hotel parking attendant had opened the passenger door of the Lamborghini. Nick put

Tess into his car, settled himself in the driver's seat, and took control of transporting them both to the central holding point of their brave new world—a nine-week-old baby who was probably fast asleep, blissfully unaware of becoming the peg on which his parents were about to hang a very different future to anything either of them had envisaged.

CHAPTER SIX

NICK barely restrained himself from flouting the speed limit. The enticing power of his Lamborghini screamed at him to put his foot down and burn up the kilometres to Tess's residence at Randwick. His son was waiting there.

But speeding didn't belong to this *brave new world* of fatherhood. Neither did a Lamborghini. The days of swinging bachelorhood were over. Tess was right. He'd better get his mind geared to leaving a lot of stuff behind.

Zack looks like you but I don't want him to be like you.

The hell of that biting statement was it echoed precisely Nick's position with his own father. He looked like Enrique but he didn't want to be like him.

Now was the time for change, for proving to himself—and Tess—that he could be a good family man, a good husband, too. She didn't believe it but she'd opened the door to him tonight—the door into a life he could share with her and their son—and Nick knew he had to keep his foot in that opening or he'd lose not only Enrique's challenge to him, but his own sense of worth as a person.

Tess had shut him out of any personal sharing all during her pregnancy, the birth, the first months of Zack's infancy. He didn't even know… 'Was he born in LA?' he shot at the mother of his child.

He heard her suck in a quick breath. He gripped the driving wheel with knuckle-white intensity, reminding himself not to resent any of the decisions Tess had made, to keep the tone of any questions within a zone of warm interest and approval.

'No. He was born here in Sydney. At a private hospital in Mona Vale.' She sighed. 'I didn't go to LA, Nick. My mother doesn't need me for anything. I am truly superfluous to Livvy's life. I was superfluous to yours, too. So I used the LA location to put enough distance between us to be...out of sight, out of mind.'

He hated that self-effacing statement. He could hear the hurt of rejection behind it—the rejection he had unwittingly hit her with. 'You've owned a piece of my mind ever since we met, Tess,' he strongly asserted. 'And the longer we've known each other, the more space you've claimed there.'

He felt the sharp dart of her eyes, sensed the turmoil of vulnerability driving the silent query—whether he could be believed or not.

'I did not enjoy dealing with your PA these past six months,' he ran on, determined on correcting her view of him. 'I missed you, Tess. I missed your personal take on what I was doing. I missed the zing I always get in your company. I missed...'

'The zing?'

He flashed her a quick grin. 'The sexual battle that laced every word we spoke to each other.'

'We talked business,' she hotly argued, looking apalled at his interpretation of their meetings.

'Oh, come on,' he scoffed. 'We were always screwing with each other's heads. It was the sex we had while not having sex—thrust, parry, attacking every which way, going for whatever hit we could get, the exhilaration of matching and marking each other…'

Her hands lifted from her lap in agitation, gesturing a protest. 'It was a platonic relationship…'

'No such thing between a woman and a man when the chemistry is crackling.'

Her voice gathered more heat as she recalled, 'It was what *you* insisted we had after…'

'After we drove it too far and made it unmanageable between us?'

'Unmanageable?'

'It wasn't going to be fun any more, was it, Tess? Not after that night. It went too far too fast and felt too damned serious.'

'Does sex *have* to be fun to you?' she flung at him irritably.

'Fun doesn't end up clawing at you,' he argued. 'It's froth and bubble. The high, without any of the lows. The minute sex gets serious, all the negative stuff starts happening… possessiveness, jealousy, slavish obsession, manic arguments. People make fools of themselves, victims of their own raging hormones. I didn't think that was a good place for us to progress to.'

'Because the sex felt…too serious?'

He could hear her thinking her way around what he was saying, beginning to feel less sexually diminished by his retreat from physical intimacy with her.

'I valued what we had too much to risk it on passion running wild, getting out of control in a big way,' he pressed on. 'I wanted to keep you in my life without the aggravation of feeling owned by you.'

A hysterical little laugh gurgled from her throat. 'Better get used to the sense of being *owned*, Nick…if you have the heart of a father.'

Another shafting challenge.

The sexual stand-off was still in place, as far as Tess was concerned. Tonight was not about fun and games between a man and a woman. Tonight was about how he responded to their son.

And the mind-crawling truth was…he was being judged.

The sense of King Rat's integrity being on the chopping block was strong from the moment he entered the old colonial-styled mansion Tess used as both her business premises and home.

The nurse who greeted them at the front door was instantly told, 'This is Nick Ramirez, Zack's father.'

The father who had been conspicuous by his absence since the birth of his son.

That knowledge was certainly in the nurse's measuring eyes as she escorted them to the nursery upstairs, answering Tess's questions about Zack's evening—no problems—hadn't woken for his night feed yet. She left them at the nursery door, retreating from what had to be huge private business. The judgement axe was sharpening up in Tess's eyes as she ushered him into a room lit by a soft night lamp and dominated by a white cane bassinette which stood under a host of mobile objects strung from the ceiling.

Nick's entire body was gripped with electric tension as he faced the piece of furniture holding the child he'd made with Tess. Suddenly he was racked with uncertainty over whether he was capable of passing the fatherhood test. Was he prepared to cede power over his life to another human being…to be *owned*?

He forced his feet forward, fiercely telling himself it was too late to be carrying out any self-examination. Besides, there was no decision to be made here. The baby in the bassinette was his flesh and blood, irrevocably linked to him. They owned each other—had owned each other from the moment Zack had been conceived, and would own each other for as long as life went on. It was the quality of the ownership that was on the line.

The turbulence churning through Nick miraculously calmed once he'd reached the bassinette and his gaze finally rested on the living breathing object of all his angst.

'So tiny…' The incredulous comment whispered from his lips on a wave of awe.

'Zack is actually big for his age,' Tess dryly informed him.

Big?

Nick shook his head.

This baby was shockingly tiny and all swaddled up like a miniature Egyptian mummy in a blue and white checked cloth. Only his face was on show—a fine little face with properly proportioned features, nothing too big or too small, ears nestled tightly to the side of his head—important for a boy.

He had lots of black hair in corkscrew ringlets which could be embarrassing—very girly—as were the crescents of long, thick eyelashes fanned out across his cheeks, but attitude was the key to stopping any teasing on that score. Nick figured he could teach his son attitude. A *pretty boy* tag wouldn't last long.

The slight dimple in the centre of his chin was like a magnet, drawing Nick's finger into touching the genetic blueprint that belonged to both of them. Unbelievably soft skin. Nick couldn't resist feeling more of it, finger-feathering the delicately drawn jawline from ear to ear, smiling as his son emitted a snuffling little sigh. Nick sent him a mental message—*Hi, Zack. This is your father standing by.*

It was like a trigger for action. The swathed bundle started squirming, feet kicking out for freedom, hands punching at the constricting cloth. The finely arched baby brows dipped into a surprisingly adult frown and the rosebud mouth gulped for air a couple of times, then poured forth a full-blooded scream, proving his lungs were working at top capacity.

It startled Nick into turning to Tess in alarm. 'I didn't hurt him.'

She shook her head, smiling as she explained, 'It's just Zack's stomach clock going off. Time for his night feed. Would you like to pick him up and soothe him while I heat up his bottle?'

'Pick him up,' Nick muttered, his hands diving under the miniature bundle, eager to gather it up for a much closer and more personal encounter. It moved. It made itself heard in no uncertain terms. It was not some passive doll-like creature. This was his son!

'Mind you support his head, Nick,' Tess quickly instructed. 'He's not strong enough yet to hold it up on his own.'

'Got it!'

The loud bawling stopped the minute the baby was airborne. In a very swift maneouvre Nick had him tucked safely against his chest, head resting in the crook of his arm. If rocking was required, action stations had been reached, but Zack had apparently decided he didn't need soothing, or the distraction of being handled by a stranger had put a hold on further complaint. He was well and truly awake now and weighing Nick up with highly alert eyes—green eyes!

Father? they seemed to be asking. *What the devil is a father and do I want him standing by?*

'Yes, you do,' Nick heard himself crooning. 'You can trust me on that, Zack.'

'What?' Tess queried, distracted from getting a bottle of milk out of a mini-fridge and putting it in a microwave oven.

Her voice ended the moment of peace. Zack was far more familiar with his mother and promptly yelled for her. Trust clearly had to be earned and as far as their son was concerned, Nick hadn't been hanging around long enough to earn it.

'You've had a head start on me at soothing, Tess,' he excused when rocking had no calming effect and she came over to take Zack from him.

'I'll change his nappy while the milk is warming up,' she said briskly, carrying him off to a highly functional trolley loaded with a comprehensive range of baby toiletries.

Nick followed on her heels, wanting to see his son unwrapped from the cloth cocoon. Besides which, he needed to conquer the mystery of nappy-changing so he couldn't be accused of being useless on the baby front. The urge to be a hands-on father who automatically commanded Zack's trust was powering through him. *Standing by* was not enough. Bonding obviously came from real involvement in his life. Nick had some fast catching up to do to match Tess in the parental stakes.

Once laid on the flat trolley surface, Zack fought free of the constricting cloth with very little help from Tess—arms and legs going like pistons, determination to be rid of this imprisonment clearly written on his little face. Tess had quite a job undoing the press-studs on the blue body-suit he wore, her hands darting around all the kicking and squirming. However, he did lie still while she whipped off his nappy—an easy matter of opening two contact tabs.

Before Nick could get a good look of his son's *male* equipment, Tess had placed a small towel over it.

'What's with the modesty?' he protested. 'Seems to me Zack likes to get naked.'

'Yes. And the first thing he does on getting naked is let fly with a fountain of pee. We're right in his firing range but if you want to risk it…'

Even as she spoke, the towel was developing a wet patch and Nick found himself grinning at the look of blissful pleasure on Zack's face. 'Mother knows best,' he told his son and didn't care that he sounded fatuous. Two sets of green eyes were telegraphing a very mutual understanding of male instinct at each other.

'You can check him out now,' Tess tersely invited as she removed the absorbent towel and dropped it in a bucket. 'I'm not qualified to comment on the size of a baby boy's private parts, but the paediatrician who delivered him observed that Zack was built like a bull, and from this admiring approval I assume that our son needn't be concerned about looking suitably virile.'

A bull certainly seemed an exaggeration, but Nick was pleased to see this special area was absolutely free of problems. 'Nothing worse for a guy than feeling inadequate about his masculinity,' he explained, glad of the paediatrician's opinion. *Everything* was so *tiny*!

Tess threw him a derisive look as she covered Zack up with a fresh nappy. 'Hardly a feeling you'd be familiar with.'

'It's not just men who care about size, Tess,' he sliced back at her.

'I'm sure all the women you've had were very satisfied, Nick. I just don't want Zack to think he has to sample every female passing by because he's well endowed.'

'I do not and never have sampled every woman passing by,' Nick protested. 'I hope you're not going to load Zack up with a neurotic mess of unnatural inhibitions.'

She'd done up the press-studs, completing Zack's dressing, and with the confidence of plenty of practice she scooped him up and planted him against her shoulder. 'Guess you might have to stick around and make sure I don't,' she slung at him, scarlet flags in her cheeks again as she headed back to the microwave oven for the bottle of milk.

Another challenge.

Plus the major point that she was in the box seat...the one in control over their son's life. Nick saw very clearly that it wasn't just a matter of getting married but *staying* married if he was to have serious input on all the decisions that would shape Zack's future. And Tess was in the box seat there, as well. She didn't have to marry him and she'd already proven he was expendable. He had to change her thinking on that, make himself valuable to her.

She settled onto a rocking chair with Zack already attached to the teat of the bottle. Anger at her implied criticism of his life choices spilled into the terse comment. 'I'm surprised you're not breast-feeding. Isn't mother's milk best for babies?'

'I couldn't breast-feed. There were…' She grimaced. '…complications.'

He frowned. Tess had great breasts. He couldn't believe they had failed their prime function. Nick knew his own mother scorned the practice of breast-feeding—*peasant women who want to be cows*—rattling on about the old aristocracy having had it right with employing wet-nurses for their children. Was Tess lying, making excuses for the vanity of not wanting sagging breasts in future?

'What complications?' he asked.

'You don't really want to know the gory details, Nick,' she said dismissively.

Alarm streaked through him as her comment triggered a flurry of fears. 'I most certainly do.'

She winced at his persistence. 'Zack was born perfectly healthy.'

His mind zapped to the other side of the equation. 'But you weren't so healthy, Tess?'

She sighed. 'He was just a big baby. I wanted a natural birth but he seemed to get stuck in the birth canal and I didn't want him to be pulled out by instruments so I elected to have a Caesarean operation instead.'

Sounded like one hell of a birth process to Nick.

'Anyhow, Zack came out of it fine, but I ended up with an infection from the operation and had to be given antibiotics…'

'Making you too sick to breast-feed.'

'For a while I was too sick to do anything for Zack.'

Hence the private nurse, specialising in baby-care. All the more understandable now, yet Tess could surely have done with personal support throughout these painful difficulties. 'I should have been there. You should not have gone through this on your own.'

'I wasn't on my own.'

'No doubt the medical staff at your private hospital was adequate but…'

'Dad sat with me.'

'No…' The word burst from an instant welling of violent protest. Before Nick could even begin to monitor what he was saying or why, his mind spewed out a furious bank of resentment. 'You put *your* father in *my* place? You let *my* child be born a bastard like me and had Brian Steele witness it all?'

He could not contain the outrage, his hands flying out in emphatic fury. 'My God, Tess! However you judge the way I've lived my life, to shame me like that, to choose the man who showed me his door because I wasn't his flesh-and-blood son, to choose him to sit by you when it was *my son* being born...*my son*...'

'He's my father,' she countered fiercely. 'And the only person I've ever been able to count on to give me support when I needed it.'

'You didn't ask me, dammit! You didn't tell me! You didn't give me the chance to be there for you! To be there for both of you!'

Their raised voices broke Zack's concentration on the contents of his bottle. He abandoned the teat to yell his displeasure in the bad vibrations swirling around him.

Tess lifted him to her shoulder again to rub his back soothingly, her eyes snapping an urgent plea at Nick. 'Can we leave this until I put him down to sleep again?'

Nick's entire body clenched as he forced it to contain the offence he felt. His mind seethed with the rejection she had slapped on him, never mind the rejection she'd suffered at his hands. It took every ounce of control he had to give her a grim-faced nod and turn away from the sight of her *owning* his child as though he didn't count for anything in their lives.

He was going to count all right!

He was going to count as Tess's partner in raising their son and he was going to count as Zack's father and that was going to start happening tonight!

CHAPTER SEVEN

TESS could not calm her fluttering heart. She felt as though she was in a cage with a wild animal prowling around—a dangerous animal holding fire until it was time to attack without causing collateral damage. As long as Zack was in her arms she was safe, but once he was put back in the bassinette for the night, Nick was set to erupt again, giving vent to the violent feelings he'd obviously been suppressing since he'd broken the glass at the hotel.

This passionately raging Nick bore no resemblance to the ultra-smooth sophisticated man she'd known—the charming user who cynically knew the value of everything, was amused by how those values worked, and let very little really touch him.

There was nothing at all civilised about the depth of caring that had just exploded from him. He certainly found no *fun* in this situation. It was clawing at him every which way, and the inescapable fact that she was Brian Steele's daughter was far from irrelevant.

The past was not in the past. Not tonight. Birth…marriage…they were cycles of life, spiralling back into previous events that invariably influenced the future, touching off connections that never went away even though they might be shunned. It was impossible to close those connections out and pretend they didn't exist, didn't carry any weight. Nick's past had just come screaming alive, and while Tess knew where it was coming from, it didn't make it any easier to face.

Zack snoozed off before completely emptying the bottle of milk, burping contentedly against her shoulder as she carried him over to the change table to wrap him up snugly again. She was acutely conscious of Nick standing by, watching her every move, his gaze trained exclusively on his son until Zack was laid in the bassinette, looking at peace with his small innocent world. No emotional scars for him yet. Tess hoped he would never have any bad baggage to carry.

Her skin literally prickled with nervous tension as she led Nick out of the nursery quarters and across the wide central corridor of the upper floor to her own private apartment. 'There are electronic monitors so that both I and the nurse can hear if Zack is disturbed, no matter where we are,' she explained as she closed the door, trying to maintain a matter-of-fact air.

'I'm sure you've been meticulous in setting up a safe environment.'

The clipped reply put an even tighter band around her chest. Nick's resentment at having been left out of everything was coming through loud and clear. She watched him taking in her personal living area, moving to open the door to her bedroom suite, casing that space, as well.

'We'd better start looking for a family home, Tess. This won't do for both of us with Zack, any more than my apartment at Woolloomooloo will,' he said, his green eyes shooting unassailable determination at her.

Tess felt her knees go weak. Apparently Nick was now intent on bulldozing her into marriage, mentally overriding objections from her before she'd even made them. He'd spoken fiercely of *his* rights, but he was just as blind to the concerns underlining her decisions as she'd been to his.

'Dad didn't know you were my baby's father, Nick,' she blurted out. 'I didn't tell him. I still haven't. He was by my side at the hospital because I wanted someone to watch over me in case…in case anything went wrong.'

Nick's chest visibly expanded. Tess didn't know if he was taking in much needed air or containing a volatile response. A frantic urge to set the record completely straight sent words tumbling out of her mouth, wanting to reach him before terrible mistakes were made.

'I wasn't going to tell you, either. I met you tonight because Dad made me see it would eventually be very wrong to keep hiding your identity from Zack. He recalled that your mother did that to you, Nick, keeping you in the dark as to who your real father was, and how much it had hurt you. He said Zack had the right to know. But for this very strongly stated advice, I might have denied you any knowledge of your son.'

'No. I would have come after you, Tess.' He moved back towards her, his powerful body emanating a ruthless air of confidence, his eyes burning with purpose. 'I was already in the process of coming after you.'

Her breath caught in her throat, rendering her speechless as his hands slid around her waist, drawing her lower body into contact with his. Her own hands, having been lifted in appeal for his understanding, landed automatically on his chest and were instantly tempted into sliding higher to his shoulders as her face tilted up to read the expression on his.

'And nothing would have stopped me,' he asserted with a wry twist of his mouth. One arm clamped her very securely to him as he raised the other and grazed soft fingertips down her cheek, his eyes engaging hers very intently in apologetic appeal. 'I'm sorry we arrived at this place in this way, Tess, but we're here, and *you* are the woman I want to be here with.'

Was she?

He had proposed marriage before he knew about Zack, so she was definitely the wife of his choice against all other comers. And since there'd been such a formidable list of stunningly beautiful and remarkably talented women in his life, she should probably feel flattered, even elated that he had chosen her, not torn by fears of being fooled and used.

As though he could see the emotional chaos consuming her, he thickly murmured, 'Right now I'm hauling you in from the months that have separated us…' His head was bending, his mouth coming closer and closer to hers, breathing words onto her lips. '…from the misunderstanding that drove you away from me. I didn't stop wanting you, Tess…'

He kissed her. He kissed her in a way that stole her heart all over again—a kiss that started with tender reassurance, slid into seductive persuasion, incited erotic excitement, then burst into a passionate claim on all she was. There was no resistance in Tess to the marauding power of his desire. She wanted to feel it, wanted to lose herself in it, wanted to wallow in the sense that Nick Ramirez was hers—hers to have and to hold until…

No, she wouldn't think beyond this moment.

Everything within her was pulsing with pleasure in the wild passion he emitted and evoked, so why not just let herself indulge in the dream of his loving her for as long he brought her to this brilliant pitch of vibrant life?

Yes was dancing through her mind.

Yes was humming through her bloodstream.

She didn't want to listen to anything else.

His mouth broke from hers to gulp in air. He was holding her so tightly now, her breasts lifted with his chest as he refilled his lungs. It was like riding the crest of a wave, exhilarating, an intimate connection with natural forces that swept her along without any decision-making being required.

His lips trailed hot little kisses across her cheek to her ear. The words he whispered were like heady wine, sweetly intoxicating. 'One taste of you and I'm drowning again, Tess. If I were an old-time sailor on a journey, I'd never get past your siren song to go anywhere.'

But he had gone elsewhere.

To another woman.

And if he did that again…

A sudden savage surge of primitive possessiveness had her reaching up, grabbing his head, pulling it back, her eyes targeting his with a blazing warning. 'You take the step of marrying me, you stay with me, Nick. If you stray…don't even try to come back. The door will be closed to you and it will stay closed.'

'The owning,' he drawled, his mouth twitching with mocking amusement, his eyes dancing with devilment. 'Understood, Tess, but in all fairness I get to own you, too.' His fingers raked through her hair. 'I fancy seeing this crowning glory of yours spread in fiery abandonment across black satin pillows. *My* pillows. Whenever I want it there.'

He meant very visibly naked, which instantly stirred up all Tess's physical insecurities. He'd been naked with a whole tribe of gym-toned, perfectly body-sculpted women. Her mind marched to defensive stations, commanding a dampening down of ardour.

'Bad luck! I've only got chocolate-brown cotton on my bed if you're thinking of using it tonight.'

He laughed. 'That's my Tess! But no way is the image in my mind deflated,' he said with relish, then swooped and swept her right off her feet, cradling her across his chest as easily as he'd cradled Zack. 'Must try it out. Black might be a bit stark. Chocolate-brown could be a warmer contrast, especially for the pearly gleam of your skin.'

Pearly gleam...

Nick had sampled so many carefully tanned women, she'd thought he'd see her as washed-out white, but *pearly gleam* sounded attractive. Even enticing. And there really was nothing *wrong* with her body. He'd simply made her feel it wasn't up to *his mark* when he'd dumped her after only one night.

She needed him to erase the long miserable hangover from that rejection.

She needed him to make her feel so intensely desirable, no other woman could ever lure him into being unfaithful.

This was probably stretching the dream too far but hope was taking wing and Tess had no heart for tethering it. Indeed, her heart was pumping so hard and fast, it felt like a highly fateful drum-roll, heralding in what had to be a brave new world with Nick.

He set her on her feet beside the bed, viewing it approvingly over her shoulder. The quilt was actually made of dark brown and taupe silk squares in a checked pattern. These colours were repeated in a pile of decorator cushions with some gold brocade and tassels thrown in for added richness.

'Very sensual, seductive and sumptuous,' Nick observed. 'Just like you, Tess.'

'It's cotton underneath,' she whipped back, then wished she could tear her tongue out. Why couldn't she just accept the compliment, take it as a fortunate reflection of how he saw her? What was she fighting against?

The answer flashed like a neon light across the churning mess in her mind.

The surface stuff!

She hated the surface stuff…all the glittering gorgeous women Nick had preferred to her, women like his *Miss Universe* mother, strutting through his life, the silk and satin women with all their gold accessories, gathering their status symbols, including Nick

Ramirez amongst them, the Latin lover to surpass all others.

She'd been instinctively fighting it ever since she'd met Nick and couldn't stop herself even now when she had him—fool that she was, dismissing what obviously grabbed his attention.

'I know it's cotton underneath and that's like you, too—sensible, practical, longer-lasting, wash and wear, easy and comfortable to live with,' Nick rolled out as though revelling in both sides of her, his eyes teasing her insistence on flouting his flattery, seeming to enjoy her perversity.

'Oh, great! That puts me in the same class as a pair of old underpants,' tripped straight off her wayward tongue.

'No, you're in a class of your own.' He withdrew his hand from her hair and pressed a light finger to her lips, the amusement in his eyes winking out as an emerald-fire intensity flared over it. 'You don't have to keep telling me you're different to all the other women who've peopled my life. I hear it, I see it, I feel it, I taste it, I smell it. Every sense I have is constantly pointing it out to me.'

Right! So keep your mouth shut, Tess!

'The whole problem was…' he ran on '…you didn't fit into my picture. So this time around, I'm beginning with you as the centrepiece and waiting and watching for the picture to develop around you. So let me focus on you, Tess. We will inevitably get to the cotton, but don't deny the pleasure there is in the sumptuous sexuality you personify tonight.'

Wicked pleasure.

Designed to impact on him and give her the secret thrill of knowing it did. The battle of the sexes…another piece of compelling strategy. Nick knew it but it didn't matter that he knew it because there *was* pleasure in it for both of them…pleasure in the simmering sensuality in his eyes as he stroked the silky red ringlets that shimmered with artificial gold, as he caressed the sensitive nape of her neck and slowly, slowly, slid the supporting straps of her body-flaunting dress from her shoulders, holding her in spellbound anticipation for more exquisite and intimate touches.

Nick knew how to kiss.

He knew how to touch.

The memory of their one previous night together was racing along her nerves, making them tremble with excitement. She closed her eyes as his gaze fell to the soft slopes of her breasts, the pads of his fingers grazing up and down, easing aside the filmy fabric, pushing closer and closer to the peaks.

'Just as well Zack didn't ever learn what he's missing out on or he'd be screaming with frustration every time you give him a bottle,' Nick murmured, cupping the full weight of one of her breasts and using his thumb to circle the now rock-hard aureole and nipple, making her ache for the maternal experience *she* was missing. 'You were built for babies, Tess. And nothing is more sexy to a man…lovely soft, full breasts…'

He bent to kiss them, to gently suck on them, making every muscle in her body contract and quiver from the shafts of deep pleasure arcing from his mouth. His hands found the zipper at the back of her bodice, opened it, and the sheer weight of the layered and beaded skirt—no longer fastened to her waist—pulled the whole dress down into a flurry of frills around her feet. Only her mauve silk-and-lace panties saved her from being totally naked in front of him.

And he was still fully dressed!

'Look at you…' he said as he straightened up and stepped back from her, his hands lightly hooked on the curve of her hips near the elastic band of her panties, making her acutely aware of where his thumbs would move next.

'I'd rather look at you,' croaked from her hopelessly dry throat. She was burning up from the sudden rush of almost complete exposure, from her helpless response to Nick's expertise in fuelling sexual excitement.

'But you're far more exotic. And erotic,' he declared, grinning with wicked delight. 'Fantastic fire and ice with those diamond earrings dangling against your hair and the pendant nestling where it is…' His gaze sizzled down to her cleavage. 'Not to mention…' He tugged the panties down, his voice thickening as her most private place was revealed. '…snow-white thighs divided by a flaming arrow of hair.'

Her mind simply blew under the pressure of being so nakedly on show. His words probably should have banished the sense of his having preferred other women, but somehow they triggered a tormenting storm of stomach-wrenching comparisons.

'I would have thought a Brazilian wax job was more to your taste,' she snapped.

He shook his head. 'It bares what should be a teasing mystery. You, Tess...' He swept her off her feet and onto the bed, placing a knee between her thighs, accelerating her pounding sense of utter vulnerability. '...you...' he growled emphatically, his eyes sizzling with satisfaction in the wild spill of her hair over the rich chocolate cushions. '...are the epitome of visual sexiness.'

True or not, Tess fiercely told herself to stop worrying about it. She could concentrate on him now. He was taking off his formal jacket, tossing it onto the floor. The black bowtie was swiftly pulled apart, the studs on his pristine pin-tucked shirt pushed open, cufflinks removed and dropped into a trouser pocket.

Her breath literally caught in her throat as he finally discarded the dress shirt. Photographs of beautiful men in the raw—even seeing them in action on movie or television screens—did not have the physical impact of the real thing.

Nick Ramirez was perfectly muscled where a man was supposed to be muscled and the shape of him was all in such elegant proportion it was positively awesome—the leashed power in his broad shoulders, the strong width of chest, his torso tapering with athletic precision to a flat stomach—but most stunning of all, the sudden expanse of satin-smooth skin, darkly gleaming with a kind of animal vitality that was totally mesmerising.

Even as her gaze gloated over his glorious masculinity, he was stripping off the rest of his clothes, adding to the magnetic enticement of power-packed manhood. She wanted to touch, wanted to taste, knew there couldn't be a woman on earth who wouldn't wish to have him available to her like this, wanting exactly what she wanted.

Nick was offering himself to *her* tonight.

Tess reached out and took, her hands gliding slowly, revelling in the silky heat of him, feeling it fire up the hectic and hungry desire already coursing through her blood, exciting her with the exhilarating knowledge that underneath this satin skin he was pumped up and hard with arousal.

Her mind filled with a wild wanton joy as she caressed him more intimately, provocatively, exulting in his desire for her, savagely wanting to drive it to blinding, deafening heights where he could see only her, hear only her, feel only her, know only her.

The groan from deep in his throat sounded anguished as he left the bed momentarily to rid himself of the last of his clothes. His eyes were like bolts of green lightning, zigzagging over her body, shooting electric tension into all the high spots, raising tremors in all her muscles, making her pulse race at the promise of intense stimulation to come.

He looked magnificent, smooth and dark and so sexually male, her heart quailed at the terrible soul-wrenching need to keep him to herself. The yearning to possess clutched at her stomach. Her breasts ached with it. A wild cry broke from her throat as he brought all his dynamic aggressive energy down to her, the full body contact making her arch into him and driving her arms and legs to wind shamelessly around him, demanding an instant appeasement of the fierce hunger inside her.

It came, hard and fast, a wild rocketing plunge that steamed straight through her moist heat, pounding its urgency to claim the innermost depths of her, not once, not twice, but a wild barrage of possession—a blisteringly primal coupling that drove them both to the edge of intolerable yet torturously exquisite tension.

His eyes blazed a highly dominant basic challenge at her—determined on holding control, maintaining the forceful rhythm until she broke it by shattering into climax. The dark strain on his face, the thin-lipped grimness of his mouth, the jut of his chin—all spoke of what it was costing him, but cost was no object when it came to winning for Nick. Most notably with women.

For Tess this was a soul-deep contest. She refused to be an easy lay for him. Let him wait. Let *his* limits be tested. Let his arrogant confidence in his sexual expertise take a knock for once. She revelled in the sense of teetering on the brink of orgasm, holding on as long as she could, working her inner muscles to squeeze him into surrendering to her first, fizzing around him with wickedly voluptuous provocation, gritting her teeth against the mounting waves of tumultuous sensation, hanging on because it bound him to her so intensely there was no room for thought of anything or anyone else.

He was hers.

All hers.

And with that ecstatic thought tap-dancing all over her tightly focused concentration, Tess lost the battle, her muscles rippling convulsively along the powerful length of his shaft, the out of control flutters swirling into a swamping tidal wave of pleasure that lifted her to an incredible crest of creaming bliss and spilled her into sweet heavenly contentment.

She heard him cry out and it sounded like the triumphant shout of a winner who'd completely spent himself in winning, making the victory more deeply prized, but she didn't feel beaten as she felt the erratic spasms of his release. Her nerve-endings tingled with an exultant awareness of their ultimate fusion, giving her the sense of a very exclusive sharing…a richer, deeper, mutual fulfilment than could ever be achieved with anyone else.

Tess clung to that belief as the physical intensity of their intimacy eased into a languidly comfortable nestling, Nick's arm around her shoulders, her head resting on his chest, their soft breathing attuned to a relaxed togetherness.

'I've heard it said that the secret to a successful marriage is lots of sex,' Nick murmured, the deep timbre of his voice rumbling up from his chest, resonating in her ear.

Other people might have said loving each other, Tess thought, the dreamy happiness in her heart fraying around the edges as his reality chewed on it.

Would a constant barrage of *making love* keep Nick satisfied with his commitment?

She hadn't yet consented to marry him but the temptation to give in and take what he was offering—if only for the pleasure no other man had ever given her—was very strong. She feathered her fingers over his tautly packed flesh and felt the faint quivers under his skin, knowing he was excitingly sensitised to her touch, revelling in the knowledge.

'I don't see myself as a wife who would have headaches,' she said whimsically.

As her hand drifted below his hip-bone, towards his groin, he plucked it off him and carried it to the pillow beside her head, rolling her onto her back, taking command of the situation.

'To have and to hold from this day forth,' he intoned, his eyes glittering purposeful satisfaction in his domination. 'No messing with that vow, Tess?'

'It goes both ways, Nick,' she reminded him, not conceding anything.

'Fine. As long as you're ready for it. It's a very powerful weapon—desire—and women like testing it, but don't ever stir it unless you're prepared to match what you stir. Understood?'

Power…the idea of having any sexual power over Nick hadn't entered Tess's head. It amazed her that he felt she did have it. She'd viewed her whole association with him as being entirely the other way.

'Tease…and I'll take it as an invitation,' he ran on, the glitter changing to a hard, ruthless gleam as he added, 'Try bartering with it and I'll walk.'

No bartering with sex.

Tess mentally wrote the rule in her mind although it seemed to run contrary to everything she thought Nick had stood for. Surely it was how his world worked—selling everything with sex.

'Understood, Tess?' he repeated, his eyes boring into hers so intensely, he left her in no doubt this was a prime requirement for a workable relationship between them.

'Yes,' she agreed.

He released her hand and moved his to trace her lips with feathering fingertips. 'Power is a fine balancing act,' he murmured.

He wanted it in his hands, Tess thought.

Then he bent his head and kissed her, and she didn't care if he always had sexual power over her.

As long as she remained desirable to him.

Uniquely desirable.

The one and only woman he wanted.

This might only be a dream—a foolish dream that couldn't possibly last—but Tess wanted to hang onto it as long as she could.

CHAPTER EIGHT

FROM the time Zack woke them the next morning, Nick started operating on the presumption that Tess would marry him, no question about whether it *was* actually settled between them. Watching him with their baby son—his pleasure in sharing this new life—Tess could not bring herself to disabuse him of the idea.

Let it ride for the moment, she decided.

See how long Nick's keenness for it lasted.

He did not leave until after breakfast, and only then with the declared intention of returning within an hour or two, once he'd collected the legal forms they had to fill out and have officially filed in order to get married.

Tess waved him off in his flash silver Lamborghini, wondering in a somewhat bemused fashion if he'd drive back in a sedate family sedan. The air seemed to be crackling with changes coming so fast, she was grateful for the respite from Nick's presence, needing some time and space to come to grips with a proposal she would have declared impossible yesterday.

As she turned to go inside, her gaze swept around the old white weatherboard colonial mansion she had transformed to suit herself and her business. It was perfectly sited here at Randwick; close to the inner city, close to Fox Studios, and close to the National Institute for Dramatic Art. Its semicircular driveway—previously a carriageway—provided off-street parking for clients, and the downstairs rooms housed not only her casting agency but also a top photographers' studio so that portfolios could be created under her guiding eye.

She had always liked the gracious style of the place, its wide verandahs with their ornate white iron-lace finish and the old-fashioned bullnose iron roof which was painted the same dark green as the Norfolk pines that stood in the grounds. Somehow it presented a statement of lasting quality, of class that was by no means diminished by the changing architectural styles demanded by modern society.

But Nick was right. While it would still have suited her as a single mother—the perfect set-up, in fact—being married to him and establishing a family unit would definitely mean moving.

Where to and to what?

Tess couldn't get her mind around that, either. The sense of still being in dreamworld was too strong for such down-to-earth decisions. All she knew with absolute certainty was she was not about to sell this place. It represented the life she'd made for herself—a life she trusted.

Trust was very much on her mind when Nick returned with the legal forms, intent on nailing their marriage down. Zack was having his mid-morning nap upstairs, so Tess was in her office, going over the list of new contracts her PA had organised. The moment Nick was ushered in, he was commandeering her desk, laying out the documents, handing her a pen, instructing what was needed and where, pouring out the energy that automatically swept people along with him, doing his will.

'Once I lodge these at the register office with the relevant documents—copies of our birth certificates—we have to wait a month,' he informed her, hitching himself onto the front of the desk, arrogantly taking up a position of dominant control.

A month, she thought. Was a month long enough for testing how genuine Nick's commitment was to both herself and Zack?

'Which means we'll be running into Christmas and New Year,' he ran on, 'making the best function places a difficult proposition. But I thought if we employed a top wedding planner, got the invitations out straight away...'

'Stop!'

He glowered at her suspiciously as she put the pen down and rolled her chair back from his overbearing and highly distracting vicinity. 'Stop what?' he demanded.

She clutched at the common sense she'd been working on before he'd returned. 'I've had some time to think about this, Nick.'

A thunderous tension instantly descended. 'Don't tell me you've changed your mind.'

'I haven't once said I would marry you,' she stated sharply, refusing to be intimidated by the pressure of his will. 'In fact, you've given me very little time to consider your proposal.'

'What's to consider? We have a duty of care to our son which is best served by the two of us getting married. Given your background and my own, how can there possibly be any argument between us over that?'

Flustered by his ruthless logic, Tess seized on her main uncertainty. 'What about us?'

'I thought we settled *us* last night. Did we or did we not lay down the rules for our marriage to work? *And* reach a mutual understanding over them.'

In the heat of the night, yes, but…

'What's the point of backtracking now, Tess? Just sign the papers and give it a chance.' His eyes glittered at her in hard, relentless challenge. 'Remember how it was for you as a kid—lost between Livvy's and your father's worlds. I sure as hell remember how it was for me—not wanted by anyone, shuttled aside to fend for myself. We have to make it different for Zack. For his sake, you must see our marriage as the best way.'

Give it a chance...

For Zack's sake...

Yes. Her mind seized on the cogent argument of their own wretched childhoods. It was the right thing—the only fair thing—to do for their son. To at least try a marriage with Nick.

She was probably putting her heart on the chopping block, but on the positive personal side, she wouldn't have a cold lonely bed for as long as Nick kept faith with his commitment. She might as well take the pleasure he was offering while she could.

'Okay!' she decided, rolling her chair back to the desk and proceeding to sign the forms with a sense of reckless determination. She was probably a fool, taking fool's gold, but until this marriage was proven worthless, she would give it a chance. For Zack's sake!

'But I don't want a big social wedding,' she said emphatically, putting the pen down and facing Nick with her decision.

'Why not?' His eyes narrowed in fiercely probing assessment. 'Neither of us is planning to do this again. It's a one-off, Tess. Why not do the big splash...the whole fairy-tale wedding that all women want?'

'For one thing, it wouldn't be a fairy-tale wedding.' Her own eyes mocked that impossible concept as she pressed the inescapable truth. 'More like a three-ring circus.'

He frowned.

'Think about it, Nick,' she invited derisively, her hands gesturing the grand scale of what would inevitably occur. 'It wouldn't be a wonderful personal occasion. It would be the gossipfest of the year—my father and his three wives in attendance—your mother and my mother competing for the limelight—the bride who *is* Brian Steele's daughter and the groom who turned out to be *not* his son...'

The dark frown lifted as his mouth twitched with sardonic humour. 'Could be quite amusing to have them all dancing to our tune.'

His cynical view of their family situation completely missed the point. 'Do you imagine anyone would actually be there to wish us well?' she threw at him in exasperation, thinking of all the bitchy A-list women who'd hate her for *roping in* the man they'd targeted.

She could hear them now—

The good old pregnancy trap...

The Steele billions behind her...

Nothing to do with love, darling...

Nick shrugged. 'Humanity is as it is. We swim in that stream, Tess, and so will our son. Hiding from it won't make it go away.'

'But we don't have to play to the gallery,' she protested, her innate sense of self-protection forbidding the taking of that road.

'What alternative do you have in mind?' he shot at her, his face hardening. 'Running away?'

'Yes...no...I mean...just choosing how I'd like our wedding to be, Nick,' she pleaded, still grasping at the chance that what he promised would work out. 'I was thinking very private...'

'You can't keep our marriage a permanent secret any more than you could have kept our son a secret, and putting off facing people with the truth only makes it harder,' he argued in harsh warning, then tempered his tone to a gentler note as he added, 'There's no shame in our situation, Tess. I'll be right at your side, protecting you from…'

'No!' She pushed up from her chair in agitation at feeling pressured to perform in the public eye. 'Whose voice are you listening to, Nick?' she flared at him in fiery challenge. 'What focus do you have on our wedding day?'

'My focus is on being completely upfront, not hiding anything about us, Tess,' he drilled back at her.

Heat burned her cheeks at the implied criticism of her less open stance. 'Oh? Funny how I thought this marriage was only about you and me and Zack!' she countered. 'When did it start developing other more public agendas?'

She flung the question at him as she rounded the desk and moved away, turning her back on *his focus*. It wasn't that she couldn't brave other people's opinions and attitudes. It wasn't that she couldn't defy them. She could and would face them when she had to…but not *before* her wedding to Nick Ramirez and not *at it*!

The *surface stuff* would count for too much.

The dream would be tarnished by it.

If they were married privately just before Christmas and completely missed the *social* festive season in Sydney, spending that time away on their honeymoon, maybe they could start off well, celebrating Zack's first Christmas together, feeling like a family.

She desperately wanted to hold onto her dream, believe in it…if only for a little while.

Nick did not move. His mind was locked in battle with his natural instincts. Yes, this marriage was about Tess and Zack but he wasn't into sneaking off to do anything. It went totally against his grain. To his mind, a man wasn't a man if he didn't stand up to be counted.

It was bad enough that Tess had hidden the fact of giving birth to his son, denying him the chance to stand by her. He wanted to ensure that everyone who had any contact with their lives was left in no doubt that he was proud to have Tess as his wife and the mother of his child.

A wedding was a public statement.

That was what it should be.

Yet Tess was acting so skittishly about it, Nick was forced to do a swift reappraisal of his priorities. She'd whirled herself over to the set of French doors which opened onto the side verandah, and she stood there looking out, her arms tightly folded, her back turned to him…clearly a stance of brick-wall revulsion to participating in what she foresaw as *a three-ring circus*.

In his mind's eye, he could see Tess as such a spectacular, incandescent bride, she would absolutely obliterate the stardom of their prima donna mothers. There would be no competition at all. From anyone. Nevertheless, argument on that point looked highly futile at the moment and getting married was the whole object of this exercise.

In fact, given this current display of fraught nerves, best he waste no time at all in getting Zack and Tess legally tied to him. 'We could get on a plane, fly to Las Vegas, come home married—*fait accompli*—if that's how you want it,' he put forward, testing her attitude.

Her head jerked in negation. 'Las Vegas is tacky. Besides…' Her shoulder blades sharpened, signalling a strong wave of inner tension. '…I think it best we wait the month required by Australian law. It is some safeguard against marrying in haste and repenting at leisure.'

Was she having second thoughts or thinking he might have them? 'I won't change my mind, Tess,' he asserted.

She threw him a hard, measuring glance over her shoulder. 'You've hardly been tested by baby demands yet. How do I know you won't run from them, Nick? How do I know you won't leave the major parenting to me once you find out it's not all fun and games?'

'You want the month to see how I stand up to it?'

'One night does not a father make,' she tossed at him.

'I am very personally aware of that,' he shot back. 'If I have one prime aim in life, it's to give my son everything *I* wanted from the father who wasn't there for me.'

'Good intentions don't always stick.'

'They're not intentions. They're vows I'll live by.'

Her eyes mocked his claim. 'My life has been littered with broken promises.'

'Is that why you want a private wedding, Tess? Easier to call it off? No loss of face if no one knows about it?'

'That works both ways. You might get bored with both of us.'

'No chance.'

He shifted off the desk and moved up behind her, hating the power she still had to limit his connection to her life and Zack's. He had to erase her doubts about his commitment, melt the staunchly held independence he sensed was gaining ground again, build up a need for him, stoke the desire that could override every other consideration.

He slid his arms around her waist and drew her back against him. She wore figure-hugging, sexy blue jeans and as he fitted her lushly curved bottom to his groin, her rigidity broke under a wave of little tremors. Even so, her arms remained defensively folded across the white singlet top, denying him easy access to her sensational breasts. He bent his head to nudge aside the rioting mass of red ringlets so he could play erotic games with the delicate shell of her ear, wanting to win back the soft, pliant, sensual woman who'd shared her bed with him last night.

'A month of nights won't even begin to satisfy all you stir in me, Tess,' he murmured, blowing softly into her ear.

Her whole body shuddered with pleasure, whipping him into instant arousal. Her arms loosened, dropping to her sides and moving backwards to claw her hands up and down his thighs, inciting an even more urgent desire, matching his erotic move with her own. Compelled to challenge her for dominant sexual power, Nick thrust his hands up beneath her singlet and took possession of her breasts, his own fingers seductively kneading, not clawing.

'We should save something special for our wedding night,' she said, lifting her shoulders back to raise her breasts in proud defiance of his ownership, though the husky edge of her voice betrayed her excitement in it.

'Tell me what would please you?' he urged, purring his own wicked pleasure in the double-edged question. 'How do you envisage our wedding day…and night?'

'Private…beautiful…'

The lilt in her voice started off her siren song again. The need—the desire—to have sex with *this* woman was totally obsessive. 'You want private, you'd better shut the French doors in front of you, Tess,' he said gruffly, dropping one hand down to unclip the waist-band of her jeans. 'As for beautiful, you'll make our wedding beautiful regardless of where we are and what ceremony you choose.'

'There's a place up in far north Queensland…'

'Fine! Book it!' Stud undone, zipper undone, heat uncontainable. 'Shut the doors, Tess!'

One month later Nick was looking at another set of closed doors, waiting for his bride to appear. He'd respected Tess's wish for a completely private wedding—not a whisper to the media about where or when—but she'd certainly stunned him with her choice of place.

He'd felt it wrong that she'd shunned the traditional fairy-tale wedding which should have been detailed with every last scrap of high society trimmings. In a way, it seemed she was cheated out of it by family that had taken a lot from both of them and should be made to go through a few days' pain for Tess's sake, acknowledging her right to be a princess bride.

Yet the moment he'd seen this chapel, Nick had understood that Tess did not feel short-changed by the wedding *she* had arranged. This was the ultimate in romantic fantasy and to Nick's mind, uniquely suited to her.

It was a beautiful little chapel, built in the grounds of a Great Barrier Reef Resort located near Cairns in far north Queensland. Three sides of it were virtually walls of glass; the end wall looking directly out on a white sand beach and a clear turquoise sea, the side walls giving a view of green lawns, palm trees and tropical gardens. Only the wall housing the arched entrance doors was solid, blocking out the sight of other buildings, ensuring that those inside the chapel had this glorious, pristine piece of the world to themselves.

There was no strip of red carpet bisecting the four rows of white pews. Unbelievably the aisle was the glass surface of an underground aquarium, artistically lit to highlight the fantastic shapes and colours of living coral with a horde of tiny tropical fish darting in and out of it. The effect was amazing, giving one the feeling of walking on the sea.

A professional wedding celebrant—a guy in his early fifties with a benevolent, fatherly look about him—stood with Nick, awaiting the bride. To their left were two women in sparkling aqua green dresses—one a pianist seated at a white baby grand piano, the other a singer standing beside her. To the right was a white table, holding a magnificent arrangement of flowers to one side and the official papers to be signed with individual gold pens on the other.

A bell was rung from somewhere outside, obviously the signal to start proceedings. Nick had been burning with impatience for this moment, wanting the waiting over. It had been a long month, carrying the acute sense of having to prove himself worthy of Tess's consideration as a husband for her, as well as a father for Zack. He wanted the chapel doors to open now, wanted the ceremony over and done with, the marriage certificate signed, sealed and delivered.

The pianist began playing the opening chords to Schubert's *Ave Maria* and as the chapel doors were finally opened, the singer gave full vibrant voice to the traditional hymn, heralding in the bride.

Ave, indeed, Nick thought, feeling completely blown away at the sight of Tess, magnificently gowned in white lace beaded with shimmering threads of tiny crystals. A frothy veil attached to a sparkling tiara adorned her glorious hair which shone with the golden-red fire of the sun, making her look like a goddess of the sea as she walked slowly down the amazing aisle towards him.

A goddess...bringing the gift of life to him...not carrying a bouquet of flowers, but the child they had created together, the living symbol of their union and the pivotal hope for a different life *for* him and *with* him…Zack!

And Nick realised in that moment how absolutely right this wedding was—just the three of them, an intimate entwinement of lives that were about to be legally joined. The only other people here were professionals performing a service run by a highly professional wedding company—outsiders who came cleanly into this hour that belonged solely to Tess and him and Zack, then went cleanly out of it, having contributed what was needed and wanted.

It was strange how deeply moved he was by this personal and private choice. His heart seemed to turn over as Tess reached him and offered Zack to him to hold while the marriage ceremony took place. Her lovely blue eyes seemed to be transmitting an intensely vulnerable hope that this bonding would prove good and true.

The words, 'Trust me,' spilled straight from Nick's mind and off his tongue as he took their son in his arms. It won a wobbly smile from Tess, a sheen of emotional tears making huge blue pools of her eyes. Nick wasn't sure this meant she accepted his word or only wished she could believe in it.

Zack had no doubts, giving a happy, confident gurgle at the exchange of parental control. He'd learnt to trust his father over the past month and Nick privately swore he'd never knowingly let his son down on anything important to him. Trust between adults was a far more complex equation and he hoped Tess accepted that he took today's formal commitment to each other very seriously.

It wasn't a paper marriage to him.

He might have thought of it like that before he'd known about Zack, but this baby in his arms made a world of difference, and Tess, having given birth to his son, took a far more special place in his life, as well. Because of this, instead of throwing up a cynical shield to the words being spoken by the marriage celebrant, Nick found himself listening to them, appreciating the truths behind them.

'This union then is most serious, because it will bind you together for life in a relationship so close and intimate, it will profoundly influence your whole future. That future with its hopes and disappointments, its successes and its failures, its pleasures and its pains, its joys and its sorrows, is hidden from your eyes. You know these elements are mingled in every life and are to be expected in your own…'

Except once married couples hit the bad side of the scales these days, most people didn't go the distance. It took real commitment to stick in there and work things through. The determination to do it welled up in Nick. No way was his child going to be a victim of divorce!

This father is going to play the game straight, Zack, he beamed at his son.

'And so,' the celebrant continued, 'not knowing what is before you, you take each other for better or for worse, for richer or for poorer, in sickness and in health, until death. Truly then, these words are most serious, and it is a beautiful tribute to your undoubted faith in each other, that recognising their full import, you are willing and ready to pronounce them.'

He bestowed an approving smile on the two of them and asked them to join hands, nodding to Nick first as he proceeded with the ceremony. 'Please repeat after me…'

* * *

Listening to Nick repeat the old marriage vows in a solemn tone—with no hesitation nor the slightest hint of cynical humour—was precisely what Tess needed to feed the hope that somehow this marriage would be held together.

The celebrant had shown her many modern variations of the marriage service, giving different versions of speeches that could be made by the bride and groom. They were prettily dressed up with pleasing promises, but what they boiled down to was signing up for a partnership contract that would only be kept as long as conditions remained agreeable.

Tess had deliberately chosen the traditional lifelong commitment vows, not consulting Nick over them since he'd given her free rein on making all the decisions about their wedding. They conveyed what *she* wanted, what *she* wished with all her heart, and she felt her heart swelling with a wild joy in Nick's sombre recitation of them.

While he could merely be giving an appropriate performance, the hand holding hers seemed to be transmitting genuine feeling, reinforcing the warm assurance pulsing through his voice. Rightly or wrongly, it imbued her with a happy confidence as she spoke herself, a confidence secretly bolstered by the knowledge she would never break these vows. To her they were very real, and if they weren't real for Nick…she didn't want to know.

When they were finally pronounced 'Husband and wife,' the kiss they shared felt like a kiss of love to Tess…tender, caring, the sweet caress of souls touching and entwining in recognition of belonging together. Whether it was her own deep need fuelling pure fantasy she couldn't tell, but as they moved on to the table to put their signatures to this marriage, the lyrics being sung by the wedding singer about always remembering these feelings and never letting them end found instant echoes in her mind.

CHAPTER NINE

'WHAT'S going on, Tessa?' her father demanded, his sharp blue gaze assessing her new home as she ushered him through it to the patio overlooking Sydney Harbour. 'I heard Nick Ramirez snapped this property up when it came on the market a month or so ago. Paid fifteen million for it.'

'Yes, he did,' she agreed, anxiously wondering if this get-together *here* for morning tea was the best lead-in to the news she had to impart.

'So how much did he take off you to sell it on?' Her father's tone was both belligerent and suspicious, hating the idea that Nick might have ripped off his daughter on a property deal. 'Not that it would be a bad buy in any event,' he added, not wanting to demean her business sense. 'Dress circle location at Point Piper. Can't go wrong with it. But it's a hell of a quick turnover from him to you.'

'It wasn't like that, Dad,' she stated quietly.

Shaggy white eyebrows beetled down. 'What are you saying? He was fronting for you in buying this place?'

'Well, yes. He bought it for me. And Zack. As a home for us.'

'Why use him?'

Tess's heart sank at the distaste and disapproval in his voice.

'If you wanted to employ an agent to buy you a new home…'

'Dad, please stop,' she begged. 'I just want to show you…'

'Okay…okay…' He held up a hand, halting himself from any further outpouring of prejudice from past personal circumstances. He swept his gaze around some more. 'It's a fine house, Tessa.'

At last they stepped out onto the patio facing a view that swept right down the wide expanse of middle harbour to the opera house at Bennelong Point and beyond, with Sydney's huge coathanger bridge forming a fabulous backdrop. It was a beautiful sunny morning, blue sky, sparkling water, and Tess desperately wanted her father to be warmly influenced by positive elements.

'Going to need quite a few staff to maintain all this for you,' he observed, gesturing to the grounds which had been terraced down to the foreshore; beautifully manicured lawns and perfectly planned gardens sweeping out from the patio, a swimming pool surrounded by a colonnaded pavilion on a lower level, a tennis court below that, and finally a boatshed and wharf.

'That's been taken care of, Dad,' she assured him, walking on to the entertainment bar under the side pergola, and waving to the table and chairs she'd set up for their use. 'Sit down and relax while I brew us a pot of tea.'

'Hard to get good reliable people,' he warned, following her to sit on a stool on the other side of the bar while she boiled water for the pot. 'Did you get their credentials vetted properly? Having made the decision to set up home here, you've got to think more about security, Tessa. It's not just you now, you know. There's my grandchild to think of. Not that kidnapping has been a common crime in

Australia, but…where is Zack?' He swung around on the stool to look for a pram or some other baby container. 'I was expecting to see him.'

Tess took a deep breath and feeling there really was no way to blunt the shock, simply said, 'Zack is with his father.'

'Father!' He swung back very sharply, eyes lasering Tess's for a lot more information than that.

'You advised telling him about his son and I did,' she hastily declared.

'I didn't advise giving up any custodial rights,' was snapped back at her. 'Just who is this guy, Tessa? I thought you said he wouldn't be interested.'

'I was wrong.'

'But Zack is still only a baby. How could you let him out of your care? My grandson…'

'He's not out of my care. We're…we're a family, Dad.' She screwed her courage to the sticking point and blurted out, 'I married Zack's father three weeks ago.'

His jaw dropped in shock.

'I didn't want a big fussy wedding,' she rattled out as quickly as she could. 'We flew up to Cairns and…'

Her father's hands crashed down on the bar counter as he stood up from the stool, his shoulders squaring, his barrel chest puffing out aggressively as he towered up to his full formidable height and thundered, 'You marry some bastard who got you pregnant without letting me get the lawyers onto him first! Where are your brains, Tessa? He took you once and walked away and he'll take you again. Big time!'

'No, he won't!' she retorted with absolute certainty. 'Nick would never take a cent of Steele money. He bought this place for us all by himself. He's paid for everything in it. He's employing the staff, paying their wages. This is all…'

'Nick!' The name exploded from her father's mouth. His neck and face went bright red. 'Are you telling me you've married Nick Ramirez? That *he's* Zack's father? Is this what you're telling me, Tessa?'

'Yes, I am.' Her chin came up in proud defiance of any criticism of her personal judgement.

He shook his head in rank incredulity. 'I don't believe it!' He turned his back on her as though confirmation would be too painful to confront. 'I can't believe it!'

'Nick is good with Zack, Dad,' Tess pleaded. 'Very good.'

He wheeled around, arms flying out, hands clenched to punch out his points. 'Marrying Nick Ramirez is setting yourself up for one humiliation after another,' he cried in anguished protest at her decision. 'He might not be a gigolo bleeding you of money, but I've heard he's into the pants of every beautiful woman who walks through his life. *Just like his father.*'

Hate-filled words, loaded with his own humiliation at the hands of Enrique Ramirez.

Tess frantically sought a way to counter them, her stomach churning over the very real possibility of a unbridgeable rift with her father opening up. She couldn't deny Nick's personal history and it was impossible to claim the future would be any different, yet she burned with the need to believe in the sense of unity she felt she had achieved with him in the past seven weeks.

'At least Zack will know I married his father,' she said fiercely. 'He'll know I tried to set up a family home and life for him. And if it fails, he'll still have—he'll always have—a mother who not only loves him but will always have time for him.'

Tears welled into her eyes and her throat choked up as memories of how deeply and frequently her own mother had failed in giving her either time or caring when it was sorely needed. There had been so many emotional *holes* in her life and maybe Nick wouldn't fill them. Maybe he'd leave them emptier than ever in the end. But right now…

The electric kettle started a shrill whistle and she reached blindly for the switch. In the few seconds it took to find it and click it off, her father had rounded the counter of the bar and she found herself wrapped in a tight hug, her back being patted as though she were a baby needing comfort. Which she did.

'It's okay…okay. You've got a father, Tessa,' he gruffly assured her. 'No matter what happens with Nick Ramirez, you just remember you've got a father to turn to.'

The knotted tension inside her started unravelling. Tess's whole body sagged in relief. Her father was not going to storm away. He cared enough to stay for her, and the proven magnitude of that caring caused the tears to flow unchecked.

'I'm sorry you had it so rough as a kid, Tessa.' His big chest rose and fell in a long, ragged sigh. 'Damned difficult situation. I tried to even it out. Didn't do too well, I guess.'

He hadn't done too badly, Tess thought, given Livvy's capricious temperament and his third wife's jealousy. She held no grudge against her father for his part in her life. 'You've always done good, Dad,' she managed to choke out.

'You should have let me give you a proper wedding,' he said, a touch of wounded pride coming to the fore. 'My only daughter…it should have been the biggest and best damned wedding money could buy.'

Tess sucked in a deep breath and lifted her head back to speak directly to him, gathering all her mental strength to keep her voice from wobbling. 'You can't buy people's feelings, Dad. *Damned wedding* says it in a nutshell. You would have hated handing me over to Nick and your three wives would have been at each other's throats…'

He grimaced at that undeniable truth.

'Much better to keep it small and private—just me and Nick and Zack.'

'Zack…' His mouth slowly twisted up into a wry smile. 'Guess I got stuck with my own advice.'

'It was the right advice, Dad. It turned out well.'

He searched her eyes worriedly. 'Did it, Tessa? Never mind Zack. I mean for you. God knows you've been short-changed of love all your life. Marrying for the sake of a child…'

'No!' She shook her head vehemently. 'Don't think that, Dad. Nick and I…we do have something good going together…'

Sex! Fantastic, addictive, incredibly wonderful sex! And lots of it! But she couldn't say that to her father and a self-conscious blush was heating up her cheeks even as she thought it.

'I wouldn't have married him if I hadn't...*wanted* him as my husband.'

'*Wanted...*' The tone of voice and the derisive flash in the blue eyes knew precisely what she was referring to in relation to Nick Ramirez.

It shamed Tess into revealing the truth in her heart. 'I love him, Dad. I have from the very beginning. And I'm going to take all I can have of him. Please...try to understand and go along with me?'

'Oh, I understand, Tessa.' He lifted a hand to her cheek and gently rubbed at the wet stain of tears as his eyes shared a moment of mocking reflection with her. 'We grab what we can of what feels good. That's what makes life worth living.'

Tess wasn't sure that was her philosophy, but she could see it was his...*take, but expect to pay a price, because nothing comes free.* It was part of the corruption that came with great wealth. Love was above that, she argued to herself. It was a gift that couldn't be bought. But it could be paid for in pain, a little voice in her mind warned.

'Let's get this kettle boiled again,' her father directed, releasing her from his embrace. 'We could both do with a cup of tea.'

It was a huge relief that their usual father/daughter harmony had been re-established and Tess was grateful for some normal activity to bridge the awkwardness of having released so much naked emotion. The tea was quickly made and she carried the pot over to the table where her father had finally seated himself.

'Have you told your mother about your marriage?' he asked.

'Not yet. She's off touring at the moment and we've only just returned from our honeymoon. Nick wants to hold a big celebration party once we've got this house in order. I'll break it to her before the invitations go out.'

'Bound to create a sensation the moment you go public on it.'

'Yes, but it shouldn't last long. And it's easier to ride with a *fait accompli*, don't you think?'

'What's done is done,' he intoned dryly. 'And since we've now had our private *tête-à-tête*, where is your husband with my grandson?'

She heard the belligerent note edging his voice again and sensed it heralded a demand for a face to face meeting with Nick who had insisted on the same thing, conceding her only half an hour alone with her father before he barged in on them. The image of two bulls locking horns agitated her mind as she glanced nervously towards the flight of steps leading down from the garden level to the pool terrace.

Her gaze was caught and held by Nick's head rising into view as he mounted the steps—his shoulders, then Zack in the carry pouch harnessed to his father's chest, little baby legs happily kicking, Nick smiling down at him, having the usual one-sided conversation he had with their son, which Zack adored, lapping up being the focus of loving vocal attention.

'He cares about his son,' came the gruff observation from her father.

'Very much.'

'And you, Tessa…' The tone sharpened. '…how much does he care about you?'

She hesitated, not wanting to sound negative, yet having no real knowledge of the answer. 'More than I expected,' she said. 'He keeps…surprising me.' Which was absolutely true.

But she was very much on tenterhooks again as Nick approached, the good humour on his face fading into a tense *on guard* look, green eyes watching and acutely assessing the body language of the man whose financial power and influential connections could become a force to be reckoned with in their lives.

Her father pushed back his chair, rose to his feet, and for her sake—Tess knew—moved to make peace, not war, thrusting out his hand for Nick to take if he was willing.

'You no longer carry my name,' he started, referring to the eighteen years before the surname of Steele was legally changed to Ramirez. 'I respect the integrity behind publicly correcting that lie and proclaiming your true bloodline. However, my daughter tells me you are now my son-in-law, the father of my grandson, and those two circumstances unquestionably makes you family. Right?'

'Right!' Nick affirmed, grasping the offered hand and eyeballing her father with a charge of dynamic energy that encompassed all of them as he added, 'And let it be clear we would have been family much sooner if Tess had told me she was pregnant with my child.'

Her father nodded an acknowledgement that truth was being spoken on that point, too, though he very deliberately posed the question—'Difficult situation when choices seem… forced…don't you think?'

The reply was instant. 'I don't blame Tess for the decisions she made. Given her viewpoint, she had just cause for them, though I would have told her differently, given the chance. I deeply regret that I wasn't at her side, sharing what should have been shared.'

'I'd like to think you were up for it,' her father said testingly. 'Don't know if she told you but Tessa had a real bad time giving birth. Damned doctors were slow to act on a Caesarean in my opinion. Put stress on Tessa and on Zack. Then getting an infection from the operation...'

'Dad, that's over,' Tess broke in insistently, seeing Nick's face tightening up and frightened of any threat to the rather fragile peace-making.

'Yes, she did tell me,' Nick bit out, ignoring her interruption as he concentrated unrelentingly on her father. 'You have my respect...and deep gratitude...for answering her needs, for ensuring Tess was not alone while she was giving birth to my child. You were there for her, supporting her, and I thank you for it very sincerely.'

'She's my daughter...'

'And now my wife,' Nick sliced back, his voice gathering a fierce vehemence as he went on. 'Believe me...you will not be required to sit in my place again.' He withdrew his hand from her father's clasp to curl it possessively around Zack. 'Nor will you be required to stand in for me any time in the future where my wife or son is concerned.'

Pride blazed from him and Tess held her breath as her father's eyes narrowed, denying pride any power whatsoever.

'Make good on those words, Nick Ramirez, and you'll never have a quarrel with me,' he punched out.

'I am not my father, Brian Steele. Don't make the mistake of dressing me with his character,' came the swift counter-stroke. 'I took his name because it belonged to me, but I am my own man and one thing you can be absolutely certain of…I will always fight for what belongs to me.'

'So will I. I wouldn't forget who your wife is, if I were you.'

'Dad…' Tess leapt to her feet, her hands begging her father to listen, to hear, to realise… 'Threats won't make good things happen. Don't do this. Please? It's my choice, my risk, my life…'

'*Our* life!' Nick sharply corrected, moving to put his free arm around her shoulders and tuck her right next to him. 'Tess and I are working it out together. We have a child.

We're going to make a good home, be a family. You can be part of it...'

'Please, Dad?' Tess leapt in, her heart hammering with a wild, joyful hope in the powerful flow of emotion pouring from Nick. 'Let it be good?'

Her father heaved a big sigh, visibly putting aside the suspicions and animosity. He gave Nick a challenging glare then dropped his gaze to the table. 'Cup of tea would have gone cold by now,' he growled. 'And I haven't even had a nurse of my grandson. Better start making good on that...both of you. I get invited over here and all you're giving me is aggravation.'

As fast as the tension had escalated between the two men, it eased. Her father slid into a conversation about acquiring property. Nick joined him in sitting down at the table, contributing to the neutral topic while gently lifting Zack out of the carry pouch and passing him over to his grandfather.

Intensely grateful for the truce, Tess left them to establishing a safe meeting ground while she retreated behind the bar to boil a fresh lot of water. After being caught up in a strong swirl of primitive male undercurrents—paternal protection and husband staking *his* claims—it was with a sense of almost hysterical relief that she now played her part in the highly civilised activity of serving morning tea.

Fortunately, both these important men in her life had the self-control and intelligence to avoid an irrepairable situation, though Tess was aware of considerable testing and weighing being carried on behind their seemingly innocuous exchange of ideas and opinions. Certainly, neither of them was about to withdraw from this engagement, giving ground to his opponent, and respect was eventually granted, though Tess sensed it was hedged around with a lot of provisions relating to how the future was handled.

Which, she readily conceded, was only reasonable. She had her own doubts about how far Nick's commitment to her would extend. Their marriage currently hinged on fatherhood and sex and both factors still had their novelty to Nick. While she did believe he would always be there for his son, his sexual affairs had never lasted long. To her knowledge, six months at most. After that…

She instantly put a mental block on looking too far ahead. As yet, Nick had given her no reason to fear any break up of their marriage and she wasn't about to present any hint of uncertainty about its future to her father. Today, at least, she wanted to present a solid front with Nick.

'Looking at Zack…and you…' Her father shot a sardonic look at Nick. '…couldn't have been any doubt in *your* mind that you're his father.'

'No. Though I would have believed Tess's word even if Zack had favoured her in looks,' Nick rolled back at him.

'As I did, your mother,' came the mocking remembrance.

Tess tensed, anticipating a swift return to crossing swords.

Nick shook his head. 'There is no comparison between my mother and Tess,' he said quietly. 'Their hearts are in very different places.'

Her father grunted a grudging approval. 'Good that you're aware of it.'

'And while I appreciate that Zack's birth was very difficult for her,' Nick ran on, 'should Tess ever feel up to going through with another pregnancy…'

'You *want* us to have another child?' she leapt in, elation whipping up a surge of happiness at this plan for their future.

'Neither your mother nor mine provided us with a brother or sister, Tess,' he pointed out. 'I think we were both lonely children.'

'Yes,' she quickly agreed.

Nick's mesmerisingly magnetic green eyes searched hers warily, not wanting to apply pressure yet unable to stop an eloquent appeal from shining through. 'I'd like us to do better for Zack.'

'We will.'

The promise tripped straight off her tongue, accompanied by a brilliantly joyous smile that instantly demolished any further note of discord from her father. Or if there was one during the rest of his visit, Tess didn't hear it. She heard only the hope singing in her heart.

Nick had just surprised her again.

Another child…proving a deep commitment to their marriage…ongoing partners in creating life and sharing in it.

Tess added this good feeling to all the other good feelings Nick had given her. It had to be getting close to love. Or maybe she was colouring *the surprises* with her own love.

Whatever…life with Nick was good.

And getting better every day.

CHAPTER TEN

THE invitation to breakfast with his mother *at home* meant she wanted something from him. The messages she'd been persistently leaving for him over the past three weeks had told Nick she had some issue on her mind that required his attention and ignoring it was not going to make it go away. Besides which, now that Brian Steele knew about his marriage to Tess, it was probably best to break the news privately to the new mother-in-law, as well.

One thing was certain. He didn't want Tess anywhere near his mother until he'd dealt with the initial reaction, which would inevitably shoot out a host of bad vibrations, making Tess feel even more vulnerable about their marriage. As it was, she didn't trust him to keep to his commitment.

My risk, she'd fired at her father.

And she'd looked stunned at the suggestion that they have another child—stunned but happy that he was planning so much of a future with her—which implied she thought of their relationship as a temporary one on *his* part, though clearly not on hers. She expected him to stray. After all, a long string of temporary relationships had been the pattern of his life—his whole life—and they hadn't been together long enough for her to believe this marriage would be any different.

Though it was.

Hugely different to anything Nick had known before.

He wasn't about to lose it or have it damaged by people who didn't understand where he was with Tess and what he felt with her and Zack. Tess had warded off any threat of damage by her father yesterday, standing firmly by her *choice* to marry him. It was up to him this morning to ensure damage didn't come their way from his mother.

Breakfast in the Condor residence was held in a brilliant sunny room, decorated in buttercup-yellow and white, the table situated to take full advantage of the view over Balmoral

Beach and the marina where Philip Condor kept his yacht.

The housekeeper ushered Nick into it. His mother, of course, was gracefully posed on a chair turned to half-face where he would enter, so he was given the full impact of the figure-hugging chartreuse slacks—the perfect curve of hip and thigh denying the slightest dimple of cellulite—matched with a tied at the waist floral blouse in chartreuse, white and lemon, showing off the top-end female ammunition.

'Darling!' She rose from her chair with a fluid sexiness that had probably been practised a million times, giving him pouty air kisses on both cheeks before tucking her arm around his in a cosy hug and leading him to the chair at the head of the table—*the man's* place. 'Where have you been?' she chided prettily, her fingers busily stroking to get under his skin.

It reminded Nick of what a very *straight* pleasure it was to live with Tess who never played these little power games. He could not recall her ever triggering the kind of cynical double thinking he did around his mother. Indeed, around all the women who'd paraded through his life. Except Tess. Who'd made a practice of always dealing directly, not attempting to oil her way anywhere.

Still, he had to concede Tess had never done without financially—an heiress to a fortune from the day she was born. Nadia Kilman had been the only child of very poor immigrants to Australia—people who'd striven hard to give their beautiful daughter every possible advantage in their new country, only to be cheated of revelling in her glory, both of them dying while trying to save their home on the outskirts of Sydney from a summer firestorm.

Of course, they'd ensured Nadia was safe first. Nadia, at sixteen, had already begun a shining future as a model. Her rags to riches background had served her well, too, drawing admiration and generating sympathetic chances for her to advance. And advance. And advance. No looking back for Nadia Kilman. Looking forward was much more to her liking.

'You've got me here now, Mother,' Nick stated dryly. 'What's on your mind?'

Probably best to play her game first, get her in a good mood.

'Juice? Coffee?' Ready to play serving maid, which undoubtedly meant she wanted a big favour from him! After all, he was only her son, not a billionaire marriage prospect.

'I'll help myself, thank you.'

A complete breakfast buffet was laid out. He poured himself a long glass of freshly squeezed orange juice and took a croissant to help pass the time in a civil manner. They both settled at the table, his mother projecting immense pleasure in his company.

'You bought the Upton place at Point Piper!' came the opening line, the gold-amber eyes sparkling delight in the acquisition.

'Yes. I heard it was to be put on the market and did a private deal,' he answered matter-of-factly.

'I've been to so many wonderful parties there! Though I must say, neither the Uptons nor the Farrells before them ever made the most of that marvellous house. Now what I'd like to suggest, Nick—and you know how good I am at this—instead of getting in some professional interior decorator…'

'No. Don't go there, Mother,' he warned. 'The position is already taken.'

'But I *need* a new project.' She pouted and smiled, playing all her appealing tricks. 'And I'd give you a brilliant result. I promise your new home will be the talk of the town. Let me pay off whatever contract you've signed…'

'No. This is not a negotiable situation.'

'Darling, *everything* is negotiable. It's just a matter of finding the right price.'

Nick shook his head, realising he would have made the same cynical generalisation only a few weeks ago, but he knew now that wasn't true. The love he felt towards his son wasn't negotiable. And the trust he wanted Tess to feel with him wasn't negotiable. In fact, nothing relating to either Zack or Tess was negotiable.

'I know you like to do things your own way,' his mother ran on, 'but you have to concede that I have huge expertise in…'

He waved a sharp dismissal of any persuasive tactics and stated bluntly, 'I've married since I saw you last. My wife will be choosing and overseeing whatever decoration she wants done in our home.'

'Married!' She stared at him in stunned disbelief. When he didn't repudiate his statement, disbelief moved to chagrin. 'Why haven't I heard of this?'

'Well, basically it's none of your business,' Nick answered evenly, shrugging away any criticism as he added, 'I don't recall you ever consulting me on any of your marriages. You just went ahead…'

'You knew *who* I was marrying,' she broke in, more angry at having her own plans frustrated than caring about his choice of wife.

'Irrelevant, Mother. The point is…'

'I want to know who,' she cut in petulantly. 'After all your cynical cracks about my marriages, I want to know who and what changed your mind about giving marriage a try yourself. It's so totally out of character…'

'You may have misjudged my character.'

The thought burned through his mind again… *I am not my father!*

She rolled her eyes. 'Just give me her name. I'll judge for myself where you're coming from, Nick.'

He felt a quiet sense of pride as he said, 'Tessa Steele is now my wife.'

'Tessa Steele?' His mother's voice climbed, gathering a shrill edge. 'Tessa Steele—Brian Steele's daughter?'

He nodded.

She broke into a wild peal of laughter. 'Oh, that's priceless! Absolutely priceless!' she spluttered, standing up and pirouetting around, clapping her hands in girlish glee. 'Brian gets rid of me as his wife and you get his one and only daughter to marry you! I love it!'

Nick sighed in sheer exasperation at her habit of turning everything back to herself. Just for once, he wished she could move beyond the centre of her own universe.

Her arms lifted, hands reaching out to gloatingly gather in and express what his marriage to Tess meant to her. 'It has such delicious symmetry! And all that lovely money is back in the family! What a glorious, fabulous coup!'

Money!

Nick's jaw clenched as he fought back a tumultuous wave of hatred for the values his mother had espoused all her life…the sheer meanness of it in human terms.

'Nothing on this earth would induce me to take one cent of the Steele family fortune,' he grated.

His mother was momentarily dumbfounded by this emphatic claim, but she quickly rallied, scoffing, 'Then why marry her? She's not even beautiful.'

'She is to me.' He stood up, too angry to remain seated. 'And more to the point, Tess has had my child—a son…'

'A child!' she spat, rolling her eyes at the supposed idiocy of his decisions. 'So, the boot is on the other foot and you fell for it. She used that trap to get you to marry her, just as I did, Brian.'

'No, Mother. Not as you did, Brian. I wasn't his son, whereas Zack is definitely mine.'

'You have proof of that?'

'Indisputable.'

'Well, it was damned clever of her, anyway. No doubt she guessed you had a thing about being rejected by your father. And having a boy-baby…perfect weapon to pull you in.'

Anger was pulsing from both of them and the conversation was fast escalating into a vicious row because his mother had decided her side wasn't winning any more and she had no understanding of the stakes in play and probably never would.

Nick took a deep breath to calm himself down and quietly corrected her view. 'Tess didn't use it to pull me in. In fact, she didn't even reveal our son's existence until *after* I'd proposed marriage to her.'

'What?'

'You heard me. I proposed marriage first.'

'Why?'

'Because I wanted to. Because I wanted exactly what Tess and Zack are now giving me.'

'And just when did you decide that, Nick? I know you were still playing the field when Enrique died and that wasn't even two months ago.'

The packet from Brazil…

Weird irony that he had barely given a thought to his father's letter since Tess had told him about Zack, yet what he'd read as his father's fantasy of an ideal life was now shaping up as his reality. Had Enrique got it right at the end? Certainly the carrot of meeting two half-brothers had pushed Nick into considering a marriage with Tess and subsequently acting on the idea, bringing him to where he was now.

'Did the news of your father's death suddenly awaken a sense of mortality in you?' his mother mocked, impatient for a definitive reply from him. 'Time to get married and beget children?' she ran on, determined on pinning him down to her satisfaction.

Which meant fitting his decisions and actions into her values and that was impossible. Nick shook his head, realising he'd moved too far from his mother's standpoint to establish any understanding between them.

'Just go on living your own life, Mother, and let me live mine,' he said dismissively, holding up a hand in farewell before heading out of her domain.

Far from acknowledging his exit line, her face lit up with the excitement of having seized an insight that answered everything on her terms. 'The inheritance! That's what this marriage is about, isn't it? You denied that Enrique had left you anything but why would he gift me the emerald necklace and not give you—his own son!—much more? Marrying Tessa Steele is your ticket to the Ramirez estate,' she declared triumphantly.

Nick's stomach contracted at the sickening equation.

Her golden eyes narrowed to a satisfied glitter. 'Yes, I can see him laughing as he wrote in the provision,' she ran on. 'A well-rounded joke on life…'

'No, Mother,' Nick bit out in grim fury. 'I won't touch a cent of the Ramirez fortune, either, and you could not be more wrong in linking Tess to a black joke on life by your Brazilian lover. She was not named in my father's letter to me.'

One perfectly plucked eyebrow arched in disbelief. 'Darling, you can trust me to keep a secret.'

It was futile trying to correct her.

She gave her feline smile. 'What exactly did Enrique write to you?'

'I told you,' he said with cold finality. 'He revealed I had two half-brothers—family I didn't know about.'

'And they'd get the inheritance if you didn't...'

'This is not about any inheritance!' he yelled, driven beyond any tolerance for her priorities. 'I came to tell you I had a family of my own now. Though I can see you're not the least bit interested in your grandson, any more than you were ever interested in me.'

'How can you say that?' she protested heatedly.

'Very easily!' He tipped her a savagely mocking salute. 'Good morning to you, Mother! Go ask Philip to buy you another house to decorate. Mine is off limits to you!'

'Off limits?' she screeched after him as he made his exit from the breakfast room, closing the door on *her scene*.

He didn't wait to be shown out of the *showcase* home. He strode out on his own steam, wishing he hadn't bothered coming. The only shared ground he had left with his mother was their past—the mother-son link that had tied them together whether they liked it or not. He'd thought it warranted courtesy but his mother's attitude towards Tess and their marriage precluded that.

This was the parting of the ways.

It was time to let go what had never been good, anyway.

The emptiness there'd always been in his relationship with his mother was being filled by Zack and Tess. He certainly didn't need to hang onto any maternal apron strings.

All this sound reasoning was running through Nick's mind as he drove away from Balmoral Beach. Unhappily, he was not taking into account the fact that his mother might not want to let him go, nor did he consider how frustrated she might be feeling about being thwarted by him on a number of issues.

In fact, Nadia Kilman/Steele/Manning/Hardwick/Condor was deciding on milking another source for the information she wanted—Nick's new convenient wife, who could hardly deny her the right to see her own grandson!

CHAPTER ELEVEN

BY THE time Nadia Condor finally took her leave, Tess felt the bottom had dropped out of her brave new world with Nick and she was free-falling into the most miserable darkness of her life. At least she'd cobbled enough pride together so that Nick's mother could not have realised how much pain she had delivered, but that was little solace for the total shattering of her private fantasy.

The whole black irony was…she'd believed Nick's word that this marriage would never involve them in *the property trap*. He didn't want or need any part of her wealth and she didn't want or need any part of his. It had never occurred to her there could be other property tied to their marriage. She knew nothing of the *fabulous Ramirez estate*. More to the point, Nick had not mentioned his father's death, nor the terms of inheritance.

A marriage of convenience—that was what he had proposed and what she had accepted, *for Zack's sake*, so their son would have a live-in father for as long as Nick was prepared to *live in.* What she had to do now was hold onto that reasoning and move forward as though nothing had changed, because in real terms, nothing had.

They were married.

Nick had bought them this magnificent family home.

He was not only living in, but proving to be a great father, even wanting them to have another child together—a brother or sister for Zack.

She had no complaints about him as a husband, either. He was caring, considerate, as generous with the time they spent together as though they truly were lovers, and the sex they shared had not lost one iota of its passionate heat. This was as good as she could have expected it to get…given that love had never been declared.

Promising it in his marriage vows didn't count. *She* had chosen the words to be spoken.

At the time, his tone of voice had actually persuaded her into thinking he meant them, but no doubt she'd been carried away by the emotional high of the ceremony, no feet on the ground at all.

It had taken Nadia Condor to bring her crashing down to earth today. Loving Nick Ramirez with all her heart did not mean he ever had to love her back. She had to stop feeding herself this fantasy. It was completely out of kilter with Nick's purpose in choosing her as his wife…the one woman he could count on not to demand a divorce settlement, which he'd told her upfront!

This terrible grief now ravaging her heart was grief she'd given to herself. Nick hadn't lied to her. He had withheld some highly personal and private motivation for his decision to marry, but he hadn't lied to her. Nor had he seduced her into marriage. He had laid out his plan very reasonably…not offering anything more than a partnership that could serve both of them well. He was fulfilling his part of their partnership.

It was absurd of her to feel deceived.

It was wrong to blame Nick for her own love affair with self-deception.

She would not let Nadia Condor destroy the solidly supportive relationship they had achieved together, starting from the night of revelation when Nick had learnt about their son. His love for Zack was real. And while their marriage might have been conceived for the sake of *financial* convenience—Tess hated that with a deep, dark, savage hatred—she kept telling herself it had progressed to something else.

Something good.

Too good to be messed up by foolish pride.

So when Nick came home from work, she tried not to show any difference inside her, tried to act naturally as they followed their normal evening routine, tried to stay relaxed in both behaviour and conversation. She didn't realise she was a dismal failure. She was trying so hard…

Something was wrong.

Nick couldn't pick up on precisely what it was, but Tess was definitely not her usual self.

During the hour before dinner, designated as playtime with Zack before he was put to bed with his bottle, her face did not light up with ready smiles and laughter. No amusing anecdotes of their son's daily activities were offered. She was quiet, seemingly preoccupied, only joining in the fun of playing with Zack when Nick drew her into it, and then he sensed it was an effort for her to take any real pleasure in what they were doing. Her mind seemed elsewhere, not clicking easily with his.

The Karitane nurse she had employed, Carol Tunny, was still with them. Although her expertise with new-born babies was not really required any more, it was good to have her on hand to take care of Zack when both of them were busy. Nick reasoned that it couldn't be any worry over their son that had Tess disturbed. They saw him settled happily for the night in his new cot, and there was no word to Carol about any concern.

Nick threw his arm around Tess's shoulders in a casual hug as they headed downstairs for dinner, wanting to project comforting support if she needed to unload some personal burden onto him. Her back muscles instantly stiffened as though his touch was unwelcome, even offensive!

'Tess?' he queried, frowning at her reaction.

An apologetic smile was flashed and her shoulders sagged loosely as she gave vent to a sigh. 'Long day with people coming and going, leaving me brochures on furniture and fabric samples for curtains and upholstery.'

'Tess, if decisions are stressing you out, just leave the whole interior decorating up to…'

'No, I want to choose. It's *our* home,' she said with passionate emphasis. 'If I leave it to *them*, we'll get the polished, professional, up to the minute trendy outcome that says nothing about us, apart from the fact we've got *the money* to do it.'

Nick suspected that an heiress sore point was burning. 'Has anyone been criticising your decisions? Making you feel…'

'No, no. It's just been a trying day. How was yours?' She shot him a guarded glance. 'You didn't let me know how breakfast with your mother went.'

Damn! That had probably been chewing up her mind! He should have telephoned and given her a report, ensuring she knew the meeting was totally inconsequential. Though Tess should realise that *his* mother's opinion of their marriage would be as irrelevant as *her* mother's opinion—both of them based on the way they lived their own lives.

'Predictably,' he drawled. 'She can't imagine I didn't marry you only for money, any more than I daresay Livvy Curtin can imagine you didn't marry me only for sex. Why else, darling?' he mimicked mockingly.

Tess flashed him an ironic smile. 'Why else, indeed?'

Nick relaxed, thinking how easy it was to communicate with Tess. The nuances from their family backgrounds were instantly recognised and appreciated. Sometimes words weren't even necessary. Just a look conveyed meaning and understanding. One of the best things about their relationship was this sense of togetherness, of so much being truly shared.

'No joy in being told she has a grandson,' he added. 'No doubt Zack is solid evidence of her aging. I don't foresee much social contact between us from now on.'

'You don't mind losing a mother?'

'Did I ever have one?'

'She has been…a central figure in your life, Nick.'

'Difficult not to be when she was the only blood relation who laid claim to me, which could hardly be evaded once I'd been used to snag your father into marriage. That was very public motherhood. Undeniable. So possession had to be maintained, didn't it?'

His mind drifted to his other blood relations—his unknown half-brothers—wondering what situations they had been born into—how their mothers had *explained* their pregnancies. If Enrique had claimed them as his sons at all, Nick had little doubt that it had been done after he was dead, not before.

They might have been adopted out, or led to believe other men were their fathers, as he had once believed Brian Steele was his. In which case, the news from Brazil could well be causing as much upheaval in their lives as had eventuated for him.

'Possessions can be important to people,' Tess commented wryly.

'They certainly are to my mother,' Nick answered with feeling, frowning over her avid fixation on the Ramirez estate. He didn't care if it went to his half-brothers. It might make a positive difference in their lives. A wonderful windfall. To him, it would always be tainted—a death-gift, not a life-gift. He had no need of it and he wanted no part of it.

'Well, Nadia did know what it was like to be without when she was a child, Nick,' Tess reminded him. 'You and I have never been *in that place*.'

True. Because of his mother's ambitious machinations he had been born to wealth and privilege, just like Tess. He didn't know what *need* was in any material sense so it was all too easy for him to overlook what was behind his mother's drive to acquire the riches of this world. Maybe to her, one could never have enough.

'She's always looking for more,' he muttered as they entered the dining-room. 'Even this morning she wanted to get her hands on this house, decorating it to give herself a buzz and get more admiration from people with her achievement. She doesn't understand the word, *home*. Everything is a showcase for her.'

'What does *home* mean to you?' Tess asked in a quiet, testing tone that struck another wrong note with Nick.

He swung her into a full embrace, one arm gathering her close as he lifted a hand to her face where the signs of inner tension were all too evident...her lovely blue eyes clouded, her gaze flickering from his, seeking evasion. He cupped her cheek to command her attention.

'The old adage is true, Tess. *Home is where the heart is.* And my heart is here with you and Zack,' he said, intently watching her response.

'Right!' She flashed a bright smile...all teeth, not reaching her eyes—and whirled out of his embrace, waving her arms at the dining-room suite which had been brought from his Woolloomooloo apartment. The table was glass, set on slabs of black marble and the black leather chairs from Italy were the latest modern style. 'Then you won't mind if I throw out this stark furniture and replace it with a lovely soft apple-green arrangement because my heart isn't into black. I don't want darkness. I don't want…'

'Apple-green sounds great!' he quickly assured her, hearing an almost frantic note in her voice. 'By all means, throw this furniture out. It was only meant as a stop-gap until we made other choices.'

Although the top end of the table where he stood was set for dinner, the far end was strewn with brochures and fabric samples, and Tess headed for them, snatching up some as she effectively put the whole length of the table between them.

'I'd like you to take a look at these. But open the bottle of chardonnay first.' She gestured to the ice-bucket—wine selected and ready for them. 'We're having a chicken-and-chorizo hot pot, cook tells me. She'll probably be serving it any minute now. Might as well pour the wine.'

Something was very wrong, Nick decided.

Evasive tactics were being employed, both verbal and physical, and he could feel Tess's emotional detachment from him. Barriers were being put up again. Nick didn't know why but he knew where they could best be smashed.

He was not about to tolerate any barriers in the bedroom.

Tess sat at the dressing-table in the master bedroom, brushing her hair, trying to calm her inner agitation with the steady, repetitive action. She had her own furniture around her here, having brought it from her home in Randwick. It didn't suit this house—this room—but at least it gave her the comfortable sense of familiarity.

She'd put on a wrap-around robe, a blue silk and lace negligee which was part of a lingerie set she'd bought for their honeymoon. It was designed to look alluring, but seduction was not on her agenda tonight. She'd felt too vulnerable for the uninhibited nakedness Nick had encouraged in their bedroom, though the robe was not so much to hide her nakedness but to take away the chill of it. It was mid-summer and the air-conditioning in the house was adapted to summer temperatures, yet goose-bumps kept shivering over her skin.

She wished she could feel the heat of desire building up in her, anticipating the intimacies to come in the bed Nick expected her to share with him tonight. For better or for worse, he was her husband, and as he'd said himself, great sex was the glue that made marriages stick and she desperately wanted their marriage to stick, regardless of why it had come about. He was her husband and she loved him so she should be able to respond to the sexual pleasure he was so good at giving.

Behind her the door to the *en suite* bathroom opened. She didn't turn around or stop brushing. The mirror in front of her reflected the sheer physical beauty of the naked man who emerged from the bathroom—a man any woman would be delighted to mate with—although the dark predatory look he shot at Tess instantly paralysed her lungs and sent a weird flutter of fear through her heart.

She'd thought she knew Nick.

But did she really?

Had he used sex to blind her to questions she should have asked before marrying him? But there was still Zack to consider. For their son's sake…

Although maybe her father was right and it was wrong to marry for the sake of a child. Wrong for her. Terribly, terribly wrong for her!

Her stomach contracted in waves of panic as Nick crossed the room to where she sat. Her chest felt as though it had steel bands around it, tightening with each step he took. She forgot to keep brushing her hair. Her mind spun with the torturous conflict of wanting this man, yet hating not being wanted for herself.

It was impossible to pretend nothing had changed.

It had changed where it counted most with Tess.

Nick was using her for financial gain.

He'd married her for financial gain.

There might be a million other reasons, as well, and all of them valid and meaningful, but Tess could not bring herself to ignore that one.

'Let me,' he said, taking the hairbrush from her motionless hand, a sensual little smile curving his sexy mouth, desire simmering in his eyes.

Let him, she told herself, hanging onto the safety of silence because maybe she could respond to his strong sexuality and be swept along by the flow of it. If she could just lose this wretched mental misery in physical sensation, drown it out…

'I swear you have the most erotic hair I've ever seen or touched,' Nick murmured, wielding the brush gently and following its bristles with his fingers.

Tess closed her eyes. Could she believe him? How much of what he said to her was true?

'And it looks best against your beautiful, bare skin,' he whispered, softly blowing the words into her ear while starting to slide the silk negligee from her shoulders.

There was no conscious decision to move. The reaction exploded from her so fast, Tess found herself on her feet, her whole body quivering as she wheeled to rebuff any further touch by Nick, the stool she'd been sitting on now standing between them, the back of her thighs pressed hard against the dressing-table, her hands clutching the edges of her robe throat-high, her eyes flaring fierce rejection.

Nick straightened up, emanating a flood of full male aggression that was not about to be turned away by anything. The muscles in his chest and arms became more sharply delineated with the tension of battle readiness. His face took on the ruthless cut of a warrior primed to beat any opposition and his eyes glittered with the determination to tear down anything that stood in the way of where he wanted to be.

'Spit it out, Tess!' he commanded, as though he'd sensed the build-up of the emotional mountain that was now separating them.

'November the fifteenth,' burst off her tongue.

'What about it?' was whipped back at her.

'That was the day you called me, wanting to set up a meeting. You said you'd been waiting for me to get back from LA. You said you'd missed me.'

'I did miss you but I didn't say I'd been waiting for you to get back from LA,' he sharply corrected. 'I said Livvy was in Sydney so it seemed logical to expect you to be home, as well.'

It jolted the swirling chaos in her mind into a sober reassessment. Nick's recollection was more accurate than hers. He hadn't lied to her. But he hadn't told her the truth, either!

'That was the day you decided to marry me, wasn't it?' she hurled at him.

'The day I started considering a marriage with you,' he admitted, not the least bit perturbed by the accusation. 'No decision was made at that point.'

'But what made you consider it, Nick? What got your mind thinking along lines it had never travelled before?' she mocked savagely. 'What was behind that call to me on November the fifteenth?'

She saw it in his eyes—the recognition of what she now knew—but he didn't come straight out with it. He challenged for her information instead.

'Why don't you tell me, Tess?'

The silky invitation in his voice did not ring any warning bells in her raging mind. She saw it as another evasion, whipping her into laying out the truth in irrefutable terms.

'That was the day your mother received a fabulous emerald necklace from your father, Enrique Ramirez,' she punched out. 'The day you received a packet from Brazil, informing you of your father's death and laying down conditions for...'

'Naming *you* as the woman I had to marry in order to gain an inheritance?' Nick cut in, fury sparking into his eyes, lashing from his voice. 'Did my mother go as far as that, Tess?'

Not quite.

Not quite but...the implication had been there because it neatly tied up loose ends in their family history.

Yet the violent turbulence emanating from Nick checked the fierce run of her own. She was no longer so sure of where he was coming from and belatedly her memory was murmuring that Nadia Condor came from a different place. In fact, there was only one safe place to be and she offered it to the man she still wanted to keep as her husband no matter how much grief he gave her.

'Tell me the truth, Nick.'

CHAPTER TWELVE

THE truth…

The words rocketed around Nick's brain, pounding out thoughts and feelings that hadn't formed any insightful pattern because there'd been no need to stand back and define where he was at with Tess. He'd been living with her on a deeply intimate basis—time blurred by how good it was. She was his wife, the mother of his son. They were a family.

'This is the truth,' he insisted, reaching out, grabbing her hand, holding it tight, moving to pull her with him, striding for the bed. She couldn't deny how they were in bed together.

'Nick…'

The anguish in her voice goaded him into more volatile action. He swung and scooped her off her feet, cradling her tightly across his chest, his eyes stabbing through the frantic fear in hers. 'This is the truth,' he declared passionately, knowing Tess had nothing to fear from him. Absolutely nothing!

He laid her on the spill of gold and brown satin cushions, imprisoning her legs with his, the need to hold onto her urging him to cover her every possible move. His hands captured hers, stilling their wild flutter. He poured his whole life-force into crushing the doubts feeding her fear, his eyes meeting and holding hers with relentless intensity.

'What you feel with me and what I feel with you...the owning...the deep sense of union...has it ever happened for you with anyone else, Tess?' he demanded.

She remained defiantly silent, not prepared to surrender her soul to him. Fiery Tess. Icy Tess. Fighting him because of his mother's bloody-minded interference.

'No,' he answered. 'Not for you and not for me because it can only happen if the feelings are mutual, tapping into something so powerful it has to be unique to us.'

He paused, gathering himself to deliver more truth.

She was listening. She wasn't straining against his hold. He could feel the whole focus of her being gathering its concentration on what he was saying, poised to sift every word for the worth of its meaning.

'The truth is...you let my mother come into our home and destroy your trust in what we have together. My mother, who wouldn't know truth if it hit her in the face!'

'She might not know the truth but she hit me in the face with that date, Nick,' came the fierce retaliation.

'I did not marry you for money,' he retorted just as fiercely.

'No. You married me because I was probably the one woman you could think of who wouldn't bother trying to get a slice of the fabulous Ramirez estate. The woman who already had so much money to burn...'

'Stop it! Stop this absurd belittling of yourself! I won't have it! You're my wife because you're the only woman I could envisage spending my life with. Having a child with. It has nothing to do with money!'

'November the fifteenth!' she hurled at him, her eyes flaring frustration with his refusal to attach any importance to that date.

'Was the day I decided I would not live my life as my father had,' he thundered back at her. 'He disowned me in life and by God, I disown him in death! I am *me*, the man you married, Tess. Not my mother, grasping for all she can get. Not my father who took his pleasure without caring about the lives he left in his wake. I care about you and I care about our son and our marriage is not about money. If you can't feel that…'

His eyes blazed into hers, intent on forcefully imprinting his truth. 'You *must* feel it…'

Tess lay very still, absorbing the passion pumping from Nick, deeply moved by it yet wretchedly unsure how much of his caring was actually aimed at *her*. When his mouth crashed down onto hers, ruthlessly bent on making her *feel* it, she didn't resist its wild marauding, letting her lips respond to every pressure he subjected them to, moving her tongue to the driving command of his, mentally registering every erotic sensation he incited and feeling the familiar bursts of desire building deep inside her body.

Just go with them, she told herself.

Nick might well have chosen to marry her to prove something about himself. If it wasn't for money, she could live with being the wife of his choice. As the situation stood—according to Nick—she and Zack were the beneficiaries of his personal mission to become *a family man* instead of a philanderer.

She wanted him to keep being *the family man*, and that meant keeping the sex good and giving it freely because he'd told her right at the beginning that was the glue which would make their marriage stick, and there was to be no stirring up desire without delivering, no bartering sex for other things. She had agreed and still did agree because she wanted a *have and hold* marriage with him.

'Say you feel it, Tess!' he demanded, heaving himself up to check the response in her eyes.

'Yes,' she said, because he couldn't look so fiercely determined unless the caring was there to drive such depth of feeling.

Their marriage *was* important to him. Besides, she reasoned it certainly wasn't the promise of an inheritance inspiring his love for Zack. The caring for their son was very, very real. And Tess did feel the caring for her in his next kiss.

It was much, much softer, tender, more wooing a response than compelling it. His grip on her hands loosened, the need to hold her captive to his will sliding into the desire for the mutual coming together that gave them both so much pleasure. There was no doubting the deep physical communion they invariably shared, which Nick had invoked in his argument and which Tess felt every time they made love.

Wanting to give herself up to it, wanting to forget Nadia Condor and the mercenary motives she had made so believable, wanting to make the date of November the fifteenth totally meaningless, Tess dragged her hands out from under Nick's, wound her arms around his neck and kissed him back with all the deep yearning for love in her heart.

'This is the truth,' he murmured against her lips. 'Taste it, Tess.'

'Yes,' she said.

It tasted good.

'Feel it!' he repeated, trailing slow-burn kisses down her throat, building the heat that would end up fusing them together.

It felt good.

Her fingers slithered into his hair as he shifted lower and she hugged his head to her breasts as he kissed them, making her feel voluptuously sexy, beautifully female and intensely desirable. The woman he chose as his wife, she thought. For this, not for money. She had to believe it. She did believe it.

He moved himself further down, caressing and kissing her stomach, her navel, exciting tremulous rivulets of pleasure, his tongue sliding erotically over the scar from the Caesarean operation…no, sliding reverently…projecting how much he valued the gift of his son. Their son. And for this he had married her, as well. Not for money.

She felt his truth with every sense she possessed as his mouth closed over her clitoris, driving waves of desperate delight through her body, her limbs, her every muscle. The intensity of feeling pummelled her heart. She groaned, cried out, her fingers clenching in his hair, tugging, needing, and he lifted himself to answer her need, answer it as only he ever had, giving himself into her possession, wildly, wholly, every plunge a promise of exquisite fulfilment to come.

And it ended as it always did with him possessing her, holding her to a fantastic pinnacle of pleasure as she melted around him, then fiercely concentrating on his own climax while Tess revelled in feeling his entire body straining to join his life-force with hers, exulted in feeling the tumultuous joy of it when it happened.

And, of course, this could have nothing to do with money! It had a truth all its own…impossible to buy, impossible to simulate, impossible to deny. It was a truth that kept her warmly content within Nick's embrace afterwards, her head resting on his shoulder, her arm flung across his chest, her legs sprawled over his.

She didn't want to move.

She was with her husband, her lover, and in the secret fantasy she still nursed in her heart, her soulmate.

Nick didn't want to talk. His body was relaxed. Tess's silky hair was spread carelessly over his shoulder. Her warm breath caressed his skin. The sense of physical harmony between them did not invite any thought of conflict, yet he could not quite rid his mind of the distress his mother had inflicted on Tess.

The date—November the fifteenth—had been significant, and there *was* a link between the packet from Brazil and his decision to pursue the idea of a marriage with Tess. His denial that the link was to an inheritance from the Ramirez estate was absolutely true because nothing would ever persuade him to accept any part of his father's property. It would always feel like thirty pieces of silver to him—blood money.

But he hadn't been entirely honest with Tess. Remembering how he'd been thinking that day…it hadn't been the need to prove Enrique's opinion of him wrong that had swayed him into picking up his father's challenge. At that point in time he had arrogantly dismissed the view that his life was following the same pattern as his father's. There wasn't anything *to correct*. What had influenced his decisions and actions was the promise of a meeting with the two half-brothers he hadn't known about.

His only blood-related family.

Except that wasn't true any more. It hadn't been true from the moment Tess had told him about Zack and blown him onto a different path again. Immediate fatherhood. And fatherhood took precedence over brotherhood any day. He was living the reality of his own family right now with Tess and their son and it was so good, Nick knew he'd do everything within his power to protect it from any damage.

The weird irony was he'd barely given a thought to Enrique's challenge since Tess had presented him with Zack, yet two months down the track, Nick was beginning to feel the Brazilian playboy he'd so bitterly scorned, had finally seen the light on what was the good life. He'd written in his letter—*Find a woman you'd be happy to spend your life with, a woman you'd be happy to have children with...*

A father's advice.

Nick had mentally mocked it.

Yet he wondered now if the letter—the challenge—might not have been motivated by genuine caring...the regrets of a lifetime piling up to produce a perception Enrique had wanted to pass on to a son, a last act meant to do good at the end, hopefully redressing the harm.

Tess heaved a sigh.

Nick's arm instantly cuddled her closer to him. He dropped a kiss on the top of her head. 'Are you okay with me now, Tess?' he asked, hoping there was no poison left from his mother's visit.

'Mmmh...' It sounded like a happy hum.

'Feeling good?' He smiled confidently.

'Good sex,' she said on another sigh.

His smile faltered and died. Yet there was nothing wrong with the comment. The sex had been good. It was always good with Tess. He had just more or less defined their relationship as great because it was never anything but good.

So why did he feel dissatisfied, frustrated, gutted because she thought that what he'd put out tonight was only *good sex*? He found himself savagely wishing she'd said something else.

But what?

What more did he want from her?

He was being unreasonable. He'd achieved what he'd set out to achieve. Tess had forgotten about his mother's rotten suppositions and they'd ended the day on a good note.

Together.

As they should be.

CHAPTER THIRTEEN

TESS was in the dining-room, watching the apple-green silk curtains being put up, feeling a warm, tingly excitement in her choice. This house was slowly turning into their home—not a showcase of intimidating possessions but a place which would soon become pleasing and harmonious and comfortable.

She was not expecting any visitors. It was Saturday morning, not a time for people to call, especially not without an appointment. It surprised her when their newly acquired housekeeper, Betty Parker, came into the dining-room to hand her a business card and announce, 'I've put the gentleman in the sitting-room, Mrs Ramirez.'

The gentleman. The rather old-fashioned term and the respectful tone in the housekeeper's voice instantly piqued Tess's curiosity. The extremely efficient Betty Parker was only in her late forties with a very modern outlook on life. Clearly she was highly impressed by the visitor.

Tess glanced at the card for identification. Shock punched her heart and chilled her skin.

Javier Estes…an attorney…a Rio de Janeiro address.

There could be only one connection—the Ramirez estate in Brazil. And why would a lawyer fly all the way to Sydney if there wasn't an inheritance to administer?

It had to be about money.

And if there was money…Nick had lied to her!

'Mr Estes asked to see Mr Ramirez,' Betty informed her, 'but since he's down at the pool terrace with the baby…'

Teaching Zack to swim in the heated spa pool and Zack was taking to the water like a little tadpole…their son…with his father…who loved him. Did it matter so much that Nick didn't love her? That he'd married her for…

For what?

Tess's teeth clenched.

She didn't know yet but she was going to find out!

'You were right to come and tell me before fetching Nick, Betty,' she quickly assured the housekeeper, handing back the card. 'Take this down to him now while I go and greet Mr Estes and keep him company.'

Betty smiled and nodded, confiding, 'I thought he had to be a very important gentleman, not to be kept waiting too long, and with Mr Ramirez in the pool...'

'Absolutely right. Thank you.'

It would be fifteen minutes, at least, before Nick could appear respectably dressed, as he'd undoubtedly want to be for this visitor. Tess had no qualms whatsoever about greeting the Brazilian as she was, her fawn slacks and the striped shirt in fawn, sky-blue and white, being definitely in the class of smart casual at home.

The sitting-room was one of the few rooms Tess had finished furnishing to her satisfaction. Amazingly she had picked up all the pieces at auction and she loved how right the arrangement looked to her eyes; the three chesterfields upholstered in shades of cream and peach and a very pastel apple-green, the marble coffee tables with their subtle swirls of peach, the complementary pattern in the main floor rug…but the lawyer from Brazil was not admiring any of this. He was not seated, either. He stood by the full-length windows, gazing out at the view of Sydney Harbour.

'Mr Estes…'

He swung around and Tess had an instant appreciation of the impact he'd had on the housekeeper. He was tall and the fine head of perfectly groomed white hair framing the dark olive-skinned patrician face gave him a look of commanding authority. His shoulders did not have the stoop of age yet Tess judged the man to be in his seventies from the deeply carved lines in his cheeks and the sag of what had once been a formidable jawline.

He was beautifully dressed in a grey silk suit—accessorised to sartorial perfection. He looked like big money and he most certainly represented big money, and if she hadn't been around big money all her life, Tess might well have felt intimidated by Javier Estes. As it was, the sight of him sickened her and she found herself bristling with aggression, wanting to fight whatever he was bringing into her home.

For several moments it appeared he stared sharply at her, the set of faintly tinted rimless glasses he wore making her unsure of his expression. But then his mouth curved into a disarming smile and he spoke her name as though he found it charming to attach it to her.

'Tessa Steele...'

'Tessa Steele Ramirez,' she clipped out, establishing her marital status to Nick as she moved forward to offer her hand.

'Of course.' *His* hands formed a quick, graceful gesture, appealing for sympathetic understanding. 'A curiosity for me that Enrique's son chose his wife from the Steele family since there had been...shall we say...a scandalous connection?'

'That wasn't of Nick's making. Nor of mine,' she stated dismissively, relieved to hear confirmation that she had been Nick's choice..a surprising one to this man.

'Which makes you both strongly individual people,' he remarked, his gaze roving over her hair before he added admiringly, 'And you are strikingly beautiful.' He enfolded her hand in both of his, pressing lightly as his eyes definitely glinted with male appreciation, despite his age. 'I can see why many things might be overlooked, given a woman such as yourself.'

'Likewise, many things might be overlooked because Nick is the man he is, Mr Estes,' Tess dryly retorted. 'But let's move on from surface judgements and get to whatever purpose has brought you all the way from Brazil.' She extracted her hand and waved towards the sofa grouping. 'Shall we sit down?'

'I was waiting for your husband.'

'He will be here shortly. In the meantime…'

She moved to seat herself, expecting him to follow but he didn't. He remained standing by the windows, watching her settle herself. Tess had the feeling he was keenly observing everything about her, fitting answers to questions he had in his mind. It seemed to validate Nadia Condor's contention that Nick's marrying her *was* linked to an inheritance from his father, which put Tess even more on edge about Nick's lying to her about it.

'Being a lawyer and coming from Rio de Janeiro, I assume you have something to do with executing the will of Enrique Ramirez, Mr Estes,' she put forward, probing for information.

'I am the sole executor,' he conceded. Then with an air of considerable pride, he added, 'Enrique entrusted me with judging if each mission was fulfilled in spirit as well as on paper.'

'Each *mission*?' Tess quizzed, finding the term rather odd.

One eyebrow arched, challenging her ignorance. 'You are unaware of the conditions attached to your husband's inheritance from his father?'

There it was—the link to Nick's marriage proposal!

'Since I don't know of any inheritance, I can hardly be aware of conditions,' she shot back at the lawyer, her chin lifting with considerable pride of her own as she added, 'I did not marry my husband for money, Mr Estes.'

His mouth twitched in ironic amusement. 'I did not imagine it would be a factor to you, given the wealth of your own family. But there is most certainly an inheritance at stake here…'

'Like hell there is!'

The furious words cracked across the room as Nick charged into it, barely clothed in one of the white towelling robes kept in the dressing rooms at the pool. It hung loosely from his shoulders, gaping at the front because he clearly hadn't stopped long enough to drag its edges together and do up the tie-belt. The brief black swimsuit he wore underneath it was clearly visible.

Zack, probably still as naked as he'd been in the pool, was wrapped in a towel and riding in the crook of Nick's arm, his little face looking brilliantly alert to the fascination of his father in steaming attack mode, his gaze following Nick's other arm as it stabbed out at Javier Estes then swept back, pointing to the door.

'Get out of our home!'

'Nick!' The shocked gasp literally exploded from Tess's lips as she leapt to her feet, the urge to intervene driven by his appalling lack of civility.

His eyes were like green shards of ice, determined on freezing any further action from her. 'Keep out of this, Tess! This man has no business here with us. He came uninvited. He is not welcome. He goes with the same nothing Enrique Ramirez granted me when I was eighteen.'

'I came to give,' Javier Estes argued.

'I don't want what you came to give. I didn't want any part of what my father denied me while he was alive, and I certainly don't want it after he's dead. If you assumed I would take it, you could not be more wrong.'

'You fulfilled the conditions.'

'Not to benefit from the Ramirez estate,' was whipped back so fast, there was no leeway granted for argument.

'I can still award a third of it…'

'No!'

The old man gestured urgently to Zack. 'You have a son…Enrique's grandson…'

'Leave my boy out of this.'

'Why would you deny him his heritage?'

'Because the only heritage that counts is right here with his mother and me.' Nick strode over to Tess, his free arm gathering her close to him to present a united family to Javier Estes. 'Tess and I will bring up our son *our* way. To value what *we* value. And that's about loving him, caring about the person he is and always being there for him. Zack doesn't need anything from Enrique Ramirez.'

Tess stood in the secure circle of his arm, feeling the fiercely proud independence pumping from Nick and encompassing her as an essential part of what he wanted in his life. Partners, she thought in deep relief, finally dismissing the painful conflict stirred by the arrival of Javier Estes.

A partnership was what Nick had proposed in the beginning. It had nothing to do with gaining an inheritance. It was about sharing what they believed was important for children. And happily sharing a bed, as well. It wasn't *all* she wanted, but…the sick anxiety she had carried into this room was draining away.

Nick had not lied to her.

The lawyer from Brazil did not appear at all perturbed by Nick's violent and vehement outburst. He seemed to look approvingly on the family grouping which was being flaunted at him. After a few moments of silently weighing what he'd just been told, he calmly asked, 'You think Enrique didn't care about you?'

'I remember my meeting with him in Rio de Janeiro very well,' Nick retorted with bitter derision. 'One could say everything about it was indelibly imprinted on my brain.'

'As it was on Enrique's,' came the soberly paced reply. 'Why do you imagine he paid to get reports on your life for the past sixteen years?'

Reports? Did Nick know he'd been under surveillance? It made Tess feel creepy even thinking about it, but Nick did not seem surprised by the claim. He glared at Javier Estes in grim-faced silence as the lawyer put forward another argument.

'Why do you imagine he constructed the letter he did for you before he died—the task he set you in the hope of changing what he knew to be a life of hollow pleasures...' His gaze moved, pointedly encompassing Zack and Tess before adding, '...into what you have now?'

Tess's mind instantly seized on *the letter*.

Received on November the fifteenth with the packet from Brazil?

Was getting married and starting a family part of the task—the mission he had to carry out before…but why do it when he didn't want the inheritance? Why rush into proposing to her if there was no other agenda on the line? It made no sense.

Nick's arm around her tightened as he growled, 'What I have now is due to Tess—the person she is and what *she* has given me.'

She silently savoured those words. They weren't hollow. They were loaded with meaning, making her feel truly important to Nick.

The old man nodded and smiled. 'I can see that your commitment to each other is genuine. Enrique would be pleased.'

Nick's hand knifed the air in disgust. 'I did not marry Tess to please my father.'

An eyebrow arched in challenge. 'Can you deny that his letter prompted you into thinking about marriage? There is…considerable serendipity…in the timing.'

There certainly is, Tess thought.

As Nadia Condor had observed to extremely hurtful effect.

'Serendipity, yes,' Nick bitingly conceded, 'but my marriage to Tess still has nothing to do with the conditions Enrique laid down for inheriting whatever he'd decided was my share of his estate.'

'The inheritance...' The lawyer flip-flopped his hand, indicating that it was an ambivalent factor. 'Enrique simply used it as a power tool to drive you into reappraising your life. It worked, did it not?'

Breath hissed out from between Nick's clenched teeth. He was steaming over this manipulation from the grave, yet Tess reasoned it had done him no harm. Even if it was rebellion against his father's appraisal of his life that had spurred him into proposing marriage to her, it had led to what they shared now. And Nick certainly valued it enough to come charging in to protect it.

'You actually sowed the seeds of caring by confronting Enrique when you were eighteen,' the lawyer went on. 'He could not acknowledge your existence without destroying the powerful connections that had become the fabric of his life, but his wife had not borne him sons—only two sickly daughters—and she could not give him any more children. It hurt him to turn you away.'

'Tough!' Nick mocked. 'Forgive me but I'm not impressed with my value rising because my father couldn't have legitimate sons.'

'It was coming face to face with you that made him care,' the lawyer shot back, his long elegant hands making a comprehensive gesture at Nick as he explained further. 'The boy—the young man—you were at eighteen. You made him want to know you. As the years went on and his wife died of leukaemia and both daughters passed away from other ailments, Enrique became more and more obsessed with your life.'

'I'm not impressed with having my life spied upon, either,' Nick said in savage rejection of his father's obsession. 'If that's still happening, call off the watchdogs, Estes, because...'

'He also watched over the lives of your two half-brothers whom he searched out after he'd sent you away.'

Half-brothers?

Tess's mind boggled over the shockingly broadened picture the lawyer had just drawn.

Words exploded from Nick, seemingly shot from an eruption of jealous fury. 'He met *them*? Acknowledged *them* as his sons?'

The deep poison of rejection was spilling out.

'No.' Javier Estes shook his head with a rueful air. 'The structure of their lives was such that Enrique judged it wiser for him to remain unknown.'

'Oh, come on!' Nick tersely challenged, his disbelief in any sensitivity from his father pouring into scorn. 'They would have interfered with his life, just as I would have. Much safer to leave any contact until after he was dead.'

'Perhaps that is true. But he cared enough about all three of you to give you to each other...*if* that was what you wanted.'

'Give? A gift comes free, Estes. A gift is not attached to conditions.'

'Each mission was designed for the good of each son.'

'*Each* mission?' Nick's voice climbed with outrage. *'Each...mission?'*

Zack decided he should match his father's outburst with a full-blooded scream. Even a four-month-old baby was not immune to the tensions running riot in this room, Tess thought, taking him in her arms as Nick thrust him at her in distracted agitation, beyond the task of soothing their son when all his own testosterone was fired up to blast the executor of Enrique Ramirez's will right back to the world he came from—a world Nick clearly rejected with every atom of his being.

'Best take Zack out of here, Tess,' he muttered, his eyes flickering with barely controllable fury.

'No.' She quickly tucked Zack's head into the curve of her neck and shoulder—his favourite comforter place—bringing down the volume of his distress to a snuffling whimper as she rubbed her cheek over the soft springy curls on his head. 'Whatever's going on here we stand together,' she insisted, her own eyes flashing unshakable determination.

No way was she going to miss out on information which would answer so much about how Nick thought and felt!

He sucked in a deep breath, his chest expanding to muscle-bristling tension as he faced the lawyer again. In a dangerously low voice throbbing with all manner of threats, he posed the question, 'Are you telling me that any meeting with my half-brothers is conditional upon *their* performing missions set by *our father* before he died?'

'That is correct, yes.'

'There never was any guarantee of a meeting with them even if I did *my part* in fulfilling my father's fantasy?'

'You each had to earn the right to...'

'The right!' Nick completely lost it. 'Don't you see how obscene this is? How absolutely, grotesquely obscene? We're not his sons. We're his performing monkeys!'

He threw out his hands in furious disgust as he advanced on Javier Estes. 'And you...

you're the director of his circus. Having fun, are you? Seeing how well the outcast bastards are coming into Enrique's fold and toeing his line, handing out rewards to them for being good little monkeys…'

Javier Estes stiffened in the face of oncoming attack. 'I assure you, sir, it was not meant to be like that. There were lifestyle issues…'

'They're my brothers!' Nick shouted him down. 'They belong to me by blood! Let them reject me as they might, but Enrique did not have the right to give out knowledge of our existence, then keep us apart. We're men with the right to choose for ourselves.'

'Do you not think your brotherhood would naturally become more meaningful if you each had a mission to complete in order to meet at all?' Estes argued earnestly.

'Twist it any way you like…' Nick hurled at him from a bare metre away, then forced himself to come to a halt, his hands clenched, his chin jutting aggressively as he emphatically declared, '…it is still an obscene misuse of power and I will not be party to it. Not to any of it. I do not *need* what Enrique could have given me. I now have my own family.'

He backed off, raising a warning hand to the lawyer who was opening his mouth to speak again. 'Enough! Call off the watchdogs. Go back to Brazil. We have no business together. It's over. Finished.' His hands scissored the air with violent decisiveness. 'Gone!'

Nick turned his back on Javier Estes and strode straight over to Tess, plucked Zack out of her hold and nestled their son against his shoulder. 'I'm taking him back to the swimming pool, Tess. If you want to see this guy out, do so. Or get Betty to do it. I'm all out of being polite to circus directors.'

Tess nodded, acutely aware of major turbulence driving him. She was vividly reminded of when she'd told him her father had sat with her during Zack's birth. Nick's sense of rightness had been hugely, deeply violated. It was again now.

Blood ties…his son's birth being kept from him…his brothers being kept from him…

She watched him carry their child out of the room. Their departure was followed by a silence loaded with far too much painful family history to be easily bridged. Javier Estes did not move to take his leave, didn't even suggest it. He seemed rooted to the spot, perhaps shocked into a reassessment of his role as executor of a will that viewed people as puppets to be manipulated into play.

'This is a sad business,' he finally murmured, grimacing over his failure to win Nick's co-operation with the master plan.

'A gift might have been good, Mr Estes,' Tess said quietly. 'Something freely given…'

'When has something freely given ever been valued?' he tossed at her derisively, then shook his head. 'It seemed he was complying with the conditions…'

'What were the conditions?' Tess asked, determined on knowing the full truth now.

'To find a woman he loved, marry her, have a child, set up a family life…stop flitting aimlessly from woman to woman in empty relationships.' The lawyer gestured an appeal. 'Is that not good advice? Does it not suggest a father's caring to you?'

A woman he loved…

The watchdogs had apparently missed the point that she'd already had Nick's child and their marriage was based on love for their son, not love for each other.

'I came because he had not contacted me,' the lawyer said in frustration. 'The other two had. It was the natural thing to do.'

'The other brothers?'

'Yes. And the meeting date has been set.'

'They have completed their missions?'

He frowned. 'I'm not at liberty to say.'

'But the meeting date has been set,' Tess pressed, thinking how pointless it was to set a date if no one was going to turn up.

'February the fourteenth. Four o'clock in the afternoon. In my office,' he reeled off.

'In Rio de Janeiro?'

'Of course. There is the matter of settling the estate.'

'Nick is not about to change his mind on the inheritance, Mr Estes,' Tess said, mocking that purpose.

He winced. 'The face to face rejection when he was eighteen...it is not forgotten, nor forgiven. It is a rather bleak irony, do you not think, that it was he who impressed Enrique so much…' He sighed. '…and he who gains nothing from it?'

'Perhaps the other brothers did not have such a *displaced* life. For Nick and for me…having to pay a price for what should be our natural rights as human beings…it eats at our souls, Mr Estes. And we have to save ourselves from that, or at least limit the damage.'

A musing little smile curled his lips and his eyes seemed to glint with respectful admiration. 'You understand him.'

'I love him,' she stated simply.

A slow nod of acknowledgement. 'I regret that I cannot break the terms of the will. I cannot *give* him his brothers. If you love him, Tessa Steele Ramirez, you will not leave him displaced. You know the date and time for the meeting…'

But I didn't say Nick loved me back, Mr Estes.

She escorted the lawyer from Brazil to the front door, watched him leave, then wandered back through the beautiful family home Nick had bought for them, reviewing in her mind every step made to where they were now.

Their marriage had nothing to do with an inheritance. Nadia Condor had been very wrong about that. But had Nick started on this journey with her to get to his brothers?

Had the destination of the journey changed?

If so…when and why?

Tess kept seeing the image of a set of scales being loaded with her and Zack on one side and Nick's two half-brothers on the other. The weight had been dramatically tipped this morning with the brothers being discarded. Nevertheless, this did not leave Tess with any sense of winning. She knew Nick was losing and there was no way of forgetting the pain of his loss.

It had to be addressed.

CHAPTER FOURTEEN

NICK felt too raw, too angry, too *exposed*, to be anywhere near Tess. Nor was he in a fit frame of mind to be looking after their son. It was wrong to use his own fatherhood as a blind to the churning hatred stirred by *his* father's attitude towards himself and his brothers—owing them nothing except their lives, giving them nothing, not even each other. He had to deal with this alone, get past it, move on into his future.

He sought out Carol Tunny, the Karitane nurse who was now an integral part of their household, finding her in the nursery quarters where Zack was due to have his morning nap. Having left his son in her care, he decided what he needed was some hard, mindless, physical task to get rid of this sickening inner turbulence.

He headed for the boatshed beside the wharf, discarding the white bathrobe at the pool terrace on his way down to the harbour foreshore. His small racing yacht was up on the slips, ready for the hull to be scraped clean of barnacles—precisely the kind of job that should work him back in control of himself.

He'd been at it for a good hour when Tess walked in. He stopped scraping and stared at her, realising she probably had some issues rising out of the Brazilian lawyer's visit, though he'd gone all out to refute the inheritance shadow on their marriage. She couldn't believe that any more.

Yet he sensed the barriers were up again.

She looked as cool, calm and collected as she'd always been when they'd worked together, discussing the casting of the right people for particular projects. Her clothes were neatly co-ordinated, smart but not sexy, her make-up minimal, her glorious red-gold hair pulled back into a pony-tail because of the summer heat, although quite a few provocative little ringlets escaped confinement.

To Nick's intense chagrin, it wasn't just her appearance reminding him of former times. It was the *on guard* expression on her face, the wariness sharpening the clear blue of her lovely eyes. The intimacy of their marriage should have changed this. The violent feelings he'd been working hard at setting aside, boiled up into frustration that Tess still didn't trust him.

'Hot work,' she remarked, shooting a glance over his sweaty, grime-streaked chest and arms. Her gaze didn't fall as low as the brief swimming costume he was still wearing. In fact, it quickly diverted to the small bar-fridge in the corner of the boatshed. 'Can I get you a cold drink, Nick?' she asked, already moving to supply it.

She was nervous of him.

He hated that, too.

'Yes. Thanks,' he said, trying to sound civilised, conscious that he probably looked as though he'd walked out of a primitive jungle. He strode over to the sink to wash up. 'I take it you've sent Javier Estes packing.'

'He's gone,' she stated simply.

'And you want to talk about it,' he slung at her as he turned on the taps.

'Yes.' She opened the door of the small refrigerator and studied what was stocked on its shelves.

At least she was being direct this time, Nick told himself, not silently bottling up her concerns as she had after the visit of his mother. He grabbed the soap and a washing sponge, splashed water over his face, arms and chest, then worked at presenting a cleaner, cooler aspect of himself. He was towelling himself dry as Tess placed a cold can of flavoured mineral water on the sink. He reached out to grab her wrist, to hold her beside him.

'I never wanted the inheritance, Tess,' he stated, his eyes blazing into hers, fiercely intent on burning that fact into her brain so it couldn't ever be in dispute again.

Her gaze dropped to the strong encirclement of his hand. 'But you did have another agenda, Nick,' she said quietly. 'When you proposed marriage to me, you were thinking of getting to your brothers.'

'Was I?'

It forced her gaze to lift again, to meet his in challenge. He challenged right back.

'Maybe I used the idea of them as an excuse to go after what I really wanted with you, Tess.'

She frowned, then gave him an aching look that begged the truth, no fancy side-steps, no dressing up what had moved him to change the status quo of their *work only* relationship. 'November the fifteenth,' she reminded him.

The truth…

Strange how hard it was to surrender it, even to instil the trust which he knew was vital to the life he now had. But there was no alternative, no diversionary tactic that would leave him less exposed to her, no shield to hide the poverty which had plagued his life, despite all the material riches that had been there for the taking. Only the truth would serve what he most needed in their relationship.

Nick set down the towel and drew Tess into a loose embrace as he focused his mind on seeking the best path towards understanding. He rested his forehead lightly on hers, needing their minds to meet. 'You have a family,' he started. 'It may be dysfunctional but you've met every member of it. You know what they're like, you know where they come from, and you can mix freely with them, both on your mother's side and your father's.'

Her shoulders pulled back, muscles tensing, whether in impatience or resistance he couldn't tell, but she was not in tune with this talk about her family.

'That's not to say you weren't alone, Tess, and were very lonely most of the time,' he pushed on. 'I know this.'

A soft sigh whispered from her lips, relaxing the stiffness, but she said nothing, waiting for more from him.

'The packet from Brazil…learning I have two half-brothers, illegitimate sons like me, one in the USA and one in Britain…and being told I don't get to meet them or even know who they are unless the lawyer handling the Ramirez estate is convinced I've met my father's challenge…suddenly *I* had a family, Tess. I wasn't alone. There were two other guys out there connected to me by blood.'

'I do realise that had to be important to you, Nick,' she murmured.

A derisive little laugh gravelled from his throat. 'I felt like a long distance runner who'd been forced to run his race alone, not knowing he had brothers running parallel to himself. It made me think…that bastard who was our father kept them from me while he was alive, but be damned if I was going to let him keep them from me in death!'

'Nor should you.' She tipped her head back to look directly at him. 'That's what I came down here to say.'

'No, Tess. I don't want Enrique Ramirez living on in me. I don't want to see him living on in my brothers, still pulling our strings. Nor do I want the shadow of his influence on any part of our life together.'

'But…'

He quickly placed a silencing finger on her lips, hating the painful protest in her eyes. 'No. Listen to me.' He cupped her face, softly caressing the anxiety lines from the corners of her eyes, feeling an urgent tenderness that had to be expressed. 'You think I began this journey with you because of the packet from Brazil. And yes, it was the trigger that got me moving, but even as I read my father's challenge, I thought...Tess. As I stoked the desire to meet my brothers, I thought...Tess. There was never the slightest question in my mind as to whom I might ask to marry me.'

'You gave me many logical reasons,' she reminded him.

'Being reasonable was more acceptable to my long-held cynical view of life, love and marriage, but there was no reason whatsoever in the powerful feelings you stirred in me, Tess, and you must know reason flew completely out the door once you told me about Zack.'

She looked at him wonderingly, not quite convinced by what he was telling her.

'Surely you understand everything changed that night when I was confronted by you—already the mother of my child—and our son. It gave me the most intimate connections I could have, and I'm not like my father, Tess. I will not walk away. I will *never* walk away from what we have together and what we can give our children together.'

* * *

Tess felt the pain behind Nick's outpouring, the emptiness of a life that had known far more about rejection than connection. The realisation hit her that the one connection he had lived with—his mother—had never inspired trust in him. The reverse, in fact. Which explained much of how he had dealt with women.

He didn't trust.

Yet to fulfil his father's challenge he'd had to trust one woman enough to have a child by her—a woman who wouldn't cheat him of what was his. He'd chosen her without a moment's thought to any of the other women who'd streamed through his life. An intuitive choice or not, it was undoubtedly the biggest compliment he could ever give a woman and he'd given it to her.

She'd been standing in the circle of his embrace with her hands curled into fists against his chest, intent on holding off the sexual magnetism he could use to deflect her purpose in coming down here. It was impossible now to stop her fingers from uncurling, spreading across the vital strength of the man, over his heart, her own heart swelling with love for him—for the boy who'd been as lonely as she had been, more so since she had never been cruelly rejected by her father—for the man who'd broken his proudly guarded isolation to take *her* hand in a marriage aimed at making his own family.

'Thank you for trusting me, Nick,' she said softly, her fingers stroking the taut muscles supporting the pride which would still have him stand alone if he had to. 'Thank you for explaining the truth of how it was. It matters a lot to me.'

She knew intuitively he would retreat from her if she didn't show her belief in him. Now was the moment to capture an intimacy they hadn't reached before. 'I'm sorry I listened to your mother. She conjured up things that have plagued my life and although I tried to look past them, I needed you to set them aside for me, to make me feel right with you again.'

'Have I done that?' he asked with urgent intensity.

'Yes,' she answered emphatically. 'Yes, you have.'

A fierce triumph blazed from his eyes. 'Good! Because *you* are right for me, Tess. So very right in every way there is.'

It would be easy now just to revel in the rightness he felt with her, to hold him to herself and let no one else into their private little world, but Tess knew she would never feel right with herself if she did that. Love was about giving, not taking. Nick wanted his brothers. He might well have come to her and Zack eventually, but the thought of his brothers had brought him much sooner, giving Zack his father, giving her her husband…*until death*.

Nick had meant the vows.

There would be no walking away.

Ever.

She totally believed that now.

She took a deep breath and lifted a hand to his face, her eyes begging a stay in judgement. 'Do you think it's right to shut out your brothers when they've done whatever your father demanded of them in order to meet you, Nick? All these months, wanting a connection with you…'

'More likely wanting the inheritance,' he cut in with harsh cynicism.

'What if they're like you and don't care about the inheritance?' she swiftly argued. 'What if they've made their own way in life and been just as successful as you in their chosen careers, yet they've always felt alone and disconnected with the rest of the human race?'

He grimaced over her description, his eyes flashing a savage irony as he said, 'They may not be like me at all, Tess. I may have absolutely nothing in common with them.'

'But you do, Nick. You share a father who didn't care enough to make himself known to you in life, but who challenged the caring in all three of his sons after he died. It seems to me he was saying to each one of you...how much caring do you have in your hearts?'

'More than *he* ever had.'

'But you're letting that lack in him block your path to your brothers, Nick, and you'll be on the losing end again if you do that. This is your chance to break free of the blight your father cast over your life. It's the way to move past it.'

He frowned as though he wasn't grasping the logic of her argument, or grasping its significance all too strongly.

'You have a choice here,' Tess plunged on. 'You can hold out your hand to your brothers or turn your back on them. If you turn your back, Nick, if you reject the chance of meeting them and getting to know them…' She lifted her other hand to cup his face and plead earnestly with the heart and soul behind his eyes. *'…you will be just like your father.'*

'No!' His head jerked out of her hold in emphatic negation. He stepped back, his hands moving to close around her upper arms, maybe wanting to shake her out of a contention which was so violently offensive to him.

'Yes!' she pressed, reckless in her determination to resolve this issue. 'It's what he did to you. What he did to them. And they're going to Rio de Janeiro to meet you. Your blood brothers, Nick. The other two outcast illegitimate sons. They'll be there in Javier Estes' office at four o'clock in the afternoon of February the fourteenth…'

'How do you know this?

'I asked.'

'Why?' His fingers dug into the soft flesh below her shoulders. 'Why would you care whether I meet them or not?'

'Because *you* care...' She took a deep breath, and riding the wave of wildly heightened emotion that swirled from him, gave up her most secret truth. '...and I love you.' Her mouth twisted into a wry little smile at her own helplessly stated confession. 'Quite simply, Nick, I want the best for you.'

'You love me.' He repeated the words as though he was amazed by them. The pressure of his fingers on her arms eased. His eyes searched hers with an incredulous expression that moved slowly into a wondrous joy, spilling into a smile that caused her heart to pitter-patter all around her chest. 'You love me,' he intoned again, obviously relishing the sound of it and the sense of it.

'Don't start thinking you can take advantage of that,' she warned, reacting to a spurt of panic. 'I've got a highly developed sense of what's fair, Nick Ramirez.'

'And fair's fair,' he agreed. 'I'd like to have that absolutely established before I admit I love you, my beautiful Tess.'

It sucked the air right out of her lungs. She had to gasp for breath just to weakly repeat, 'You love me?'

'Hmmm…' His eyes narrowed in consideration. 'Maybe a mutual enslavement can work. It's the love factor being out of balance that causes misery and mayhem.'

She slammed her hand against his chest to force his focus back onto her. 'You actually do love me?'

'To distraction,' he answered in mock exasperation. 'Terrible distraction. I suspected it would happen if I let you get really close to me and here I've been, fighting like crazy to get you to trust me, desperate to convince you that you're at the centre of the world I truly care about, ready to do anything…'

'Anything?' she inserted giddily, her mind swimming in a cocktail of happiness.

He looked edgy. 'Almost anything.'

She slid her hands up around his neck and stepped closer. His eyes glinted with suspicion and some swiftly developing wicked plans of his own. Tess thought how amazing it was that he could so quickly excite a build-up of sexual awareness, of desire for fast and flagrant physical intimacy.

'So are you going to Rio for the fourteenth of February?' she quickly slipped in.

'If you come with me,' he decided without any trouble at all.

'I'll be with you,' she promised.

He nodded. 'I've come to the conclusion that it's not sex that glues a marriage together. What really makes it stick is loving each other.'

'I do love you, Nick,' she said for the sheer joy of revelling in the freedom to say it.

'Let's see how much.'

He kissed her.

And she showed him how much, which inspired him to show her a lot more.

Even in a boatshed, the sex was good.

But it wasn't the only good thing in their marriage.

CHAPTER FIFTEEN

NICK had wanted to give this party before they left for Rio de Janeiro, its purpose to publicly celebrate their marriage which he still felt was important to do. Their happiness together, he declared, would confound everyone and make it a scintillating affair, all the guests glittering madly around them, trying to shine light on cracks in their relationship and forced to concede failure because there were none.

And that was certainly happening tonight, Tess thought, secretly amused by some of the outrageous questions tossed at both her and Nick as they stood arm in arm, greeting and chatting to guests who were rolling up despite the short notice. The whole A-list of Sydney society was agog to assess the newly married couple and see what they'd done to the much envied dress circle residence at Point Piper.

The funny part was, Tess knew that only a short while ago she would have hated this kind of scene. The secure knowledge that Nick loved her made a world of difference. It simply didn't matter how they were viewed as a couple or what anyone said to them, the happiness in her heart could not be diminished or soured or poisoned.

Besides, generally people did wish them well, and even the envy seemed reasonably good-natured. Perhaps genuine happiness was infectious. Whatever…it was easy to smile and keep on smiling, even in the face of Nadia Condor's flaunting of the fabulous emerald necklace—her gift from Enrique Ramirez for producing such an outstanding son. Naturally she had chosen a classic black gown to show off the jewellery.

'So you're both travelling to Rio to collect,' she said with smug confidence in *her* reading of the situation. Nadia's beautiful golden eyes shimmered with pleasure. 'I knew you'd take the inheritance.'

'Actually we're just going to meet my brothers,' Nick drawled. 'Should have a fun time. And while we're there I'll sign my share of the inheritance over to an orphanage.'

The pleasure jolted into shock. 'An orphanage?'

'Yes. Tess and I think that would be very appropriate, don't we, darling?'

'There are so many children who are alone in this world,' she inserted, adding sympathetically, 'You must remember losing everything yourself when you were sixteen, Nadia.'

Her head lifted in haughty disdain. 'I've come a long way since I was sixteen.'

A long way…but to Tess's mind, Nadia had never arrived where she and Nick were now and probably never would. Which was sad. Impulsively she said, 'I was wondering—with all your experience of decorating houses, Nadia—if I could ask your advice on a few things when Nick and I get back.'

The disdain was instantly replaced by delighted anticipation. 'My dear, I'm sure we could have a lovely girls' time together. Just call me.'

'I will,' Tess promised.

Nadia sailed off with the sublimely confident air of a queen about to inspect her domain and order improvements on it in the very near future.

'She'll try to take over,' Nick muttered in warning.

'A bit of giving won't hurt.' Tess raised an eloquently knowing gaze to his. 'She needs us in her life, Nick. We're the only family she's got.'

His mouth tilted into a wry smile as he nodded. 'Okay, but you need to know my mother always aims to get her own way. Don't hesitate to yell for help when she moves the line beyond what's acceptable.'

She grinned. 'I'll yell.'

'And remember you come first with me. You are not and never will be in competition with my mother.'

She laughed, blissfully sure of his support.

He lowered his head to whisper in her ear, 'If you keep looking at me like that, I'm going to have to race you off to bed and...'

'Can't! Here comes *my* mother.'

He gave a mock groan and resumed the role of party host.

While Nadia Condor's style was regal, expecting everyone to worship at her court, admiring her unique and outstanding beauty, Livvy Curtin's style was totally flamboyant, expecting everyone to be dazzled into courting her for her magnificent theatrical value.

Tonight she was wearing a gown in dark red and purple satin—amazing with her now strawberry-blonde hair topping it off and jet-black jewellery to provide dramatic contrast. Of course, her main accessory was the thirty-something gym-toned gorgeous hunk on her arm, and Tess had to concede her mother didn't look much older, due to the many little surgical procedures she'd had done over the years.

Of course, she was late arriving. Livvy was always late arriving anywhere. It increased her own sense of worth to have people waiting for her—the power of a star. She descended upon Tess and Nick now as though she was bestowing a favour on them with her presence.

'Married! With child! And home! How very domestic, darlings!' she trumpeted at them, moving into her air-kiss routine. 'Though I must say this house does have a brilliant setting.'

'Nice to know something meets with your approval,' Tess couldn't help drawling.

'You're always so literal, Tessa. Actually you're looking better tonight than I've ever seen you. Positively blooming.' She batted her long false eyelashes at Nick in flirtatious appreciation of his obvious virility. 'You must be taking good care of my baby's needs.'

Baby!

Tess rolled her eyes. Of course taking years off her daughter's age took years off Livvy's own.

'Well, she's certainly taking good care of mine,' Nick replied, his voice rich with warm satisfaction.

'Really? I always thought Tessa took more after Brian than me—so uptight and inhibited and straight.' She actually reached out and patted Tess's cheek. 'I'm delighted to hear you have some of my heart and soul, darling.'

Tess gritted her teeth in exasperation over her mother's view on life and love. 'There's more to marriage than good sex, Mother,' she bit out.

It was the unforgiveable sin, calling Livvy Mother, and it instantly provoked a withdrawal from family intimacy. 'If you're going to talk in such boring platitudes, Tessa…'

'I've always been boring,' Tess waved her mother and her current toy-boy on. 'I'm sure you'll find more exciting company amongst our guests.'

'I do hope so, dear,' she huffed and sailed off to command adoring attention elsewhere.

'That was not your usual gracious self, Tess,' Nick commented, arching a quizzical eyebrow at her.

She heaved a sigh to rid herself of tension. 'Sorry! I find my mother endlessly embarrassing. I guess I am just as uptight and inhibited and straight as my father.'

'Not so I've noticed.'

'I felt she was reducing you to beefcake. Which is what she does to all men,' Tess added in rueful explanation.

'The Hollywood Dream runs on desirability,' Nick said seriously. 'You have to understand Livvy is obsessed with that and everything she does and says is probably aimed at bolstering her sense of desirability.'

'Including the toy-boy?'

'It has a currency.' He slanted her a sardonic little smile. 'It's all about counting her worth, Tess, just as my mother tots up possessions to count hers. Neither of them is about to change these ingrained habits. We just have to accept them as they are. And occasionally, we can even enjoy who they are.'

Tess thought about it, deciding it was probably fair comment. Sad comment. So okay, before the party ended she would make peace with Livvy and keep the doors open. Maybe somewhere down the line of the future, her mother might want to be a mother. And a grandmother.

Much later in the evening her father drew her aside from the discussion Nick was having with a film producer whose work he admired. 'Fine party, Tessa,' he remarked.

'I'm glad you're enjoying it, Dad.'

He gave a dry chuckle. 'A bit like the three-ring circus you reckoned a wedding would be, though for me it's been quite amusing observing the prima donnas staking out their own centre stages.' His shaggy white eyebrows lifted in query. 'No distress for you in it?'

She shook her head. 'They can't touch what Nick and I have together.'

'So it's working out fine for you.'

'As fine as it could be, Dad.'

Her father put his arm around her shoulders to give them a warm hug. 'I just wanted to tell you how proud I am of you. I married three beautiful women but you outshine all of them tonight. And you know why?'

'Because you like my blue dress best?' she teased, knowing blue was his favourite colour.

He laughed, hugging her closer. 'Because you've got it all together, Tessa,' he confided. 'You're not just beautiful. You shine with happiness. And let me tell you it does a father's heart good to see that shining from his daughter.' He dropped a kiss on the curls tumbling over the top of her head. 'Now go on back to your husband. And you can tell him I'm proud of him, too.'

'Because he's made me happy?'

His brows lowered for a thoughtful moment. 'Nick was a good kid. While I thought he was my son he gave me a great deal of pleasure. Whatever has gone on in his life between then and now…I think he's become a good man.' His face cleared into a smile. 'He couldn't have made you happy otherwise.'

A good man…

The phrase lingered in her mind.

It was true of Nick. No doubt about it. But she wondered and worried a little about his two unknown brothers. Were they good men? How would the meeting turn out for Nick? She had argued for it so strongly, but people were always the sum of their lives and the lives of the other two illegitimate sons of Enrique Ramirez could have been very bad.

What did they value?

What did they want?

The party ended. The guests departed. Nick finally did race Tess off to bed where they made love long into the night, idly discussing the party when they felt like talking. Naturally family members eventually featured in the conversation, which led to Tess bringing up her thoughts about their imminent trip to Brazil.

'You know your brothers might be in it just for their inheritance, Nick.'

She was very aware that hopes could end up hurting badly. There might be more rejections in store for the man she loved.

'It could be an end. It could be a beginning,' he mused, rolling her onto her back and leaning over her to trace her lips with a gently teasing finger. 'They can link their life journeys to ours or not, Tess, and part of that choice will be if we want to link to theirs, as well.' There was no concern in his eyes. 'We simply go. And what will be will be. All right?'

She nodded.

They had dealt with so much.

Of course they could deal with whatever else came up.

Together.

His kiss promised her that.

To have and to hold, from this day forth, for better or for worse…